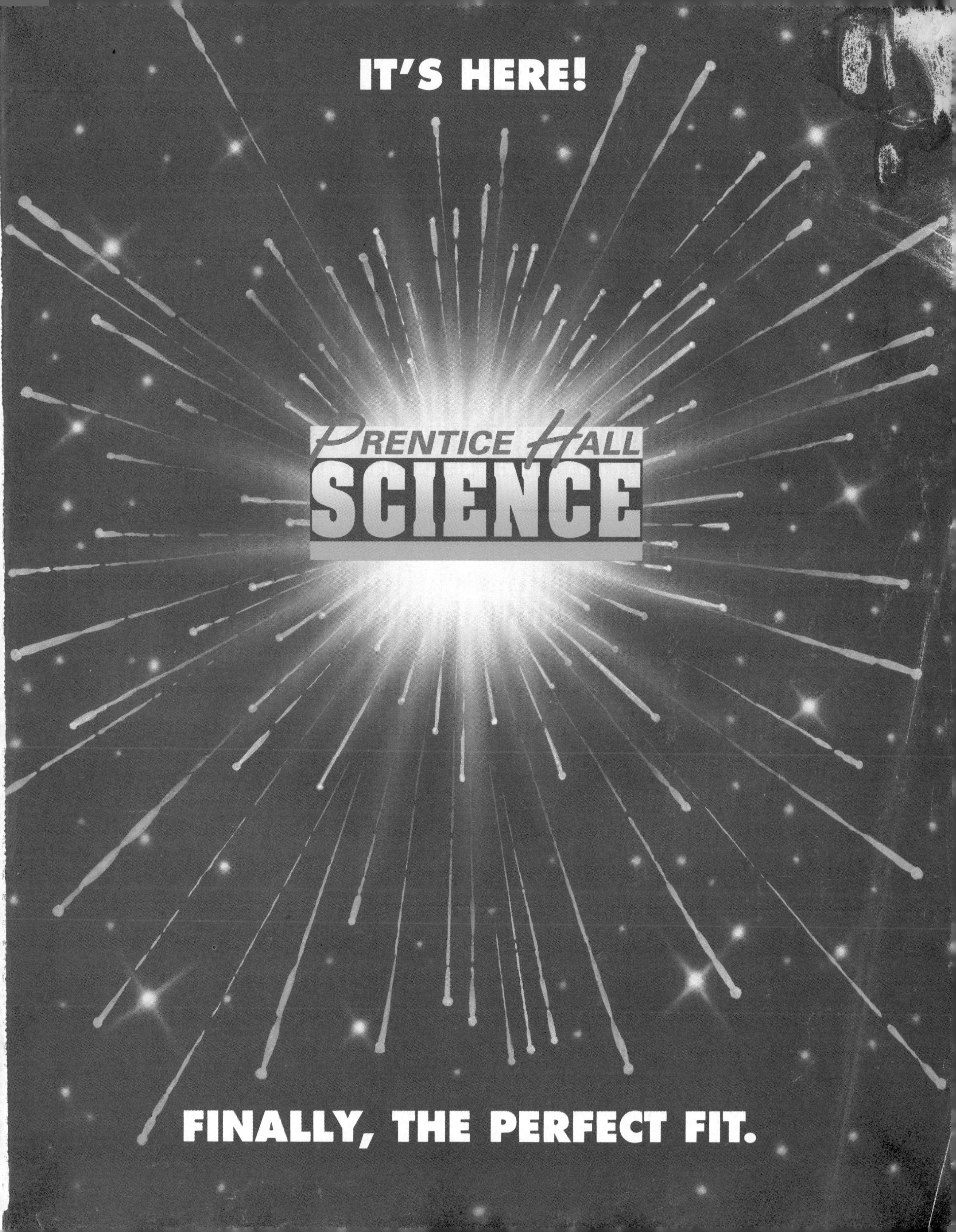
IT'S HERE!
PRENTICE HALL
SCIENCE
FINALLY, THE PERFECT FIT.

NOW YOU CAN CHOOSE THE PERFECT FIT FOR ALL YOUR CURRICULUM NEEDS.

The new Prentice Hall Science program consists of 19 hardcover books, each of which covers a particular area of science. All of the sciences are represented in the program so you can choose the perfect fit to *your* particular curriculum needs.

The flexibility of this program will allow you to teach those topics you want to teach, and to teach them *in-depth*. Virtually any approach to science—general, integrated, coordinated, thematic, etc.—is possible with Prentice Hall Science.

Above all, the program is designed to make your teaching experience easier and more fun.

ELECTRICITY AND MAGNETISM

Ch. 1. Electric Charges and Currents
Ch. 2. Magnetism
Ch. 3. Electromagnetism
Ch. 4. Electronics and Computers

HEREDITY: THE CODE OF LIFE

Ch. 1. What is Genetics?
Ch. 2. How Chromosomes Work
Ch. 3. Human Genetics
Ch. 4. Applied Genetics

ECOLOGY: EARTH'S LIVING RESOURCES

Ch. 1. Interactions Among Living Things
Ch. 2. Cycles in Nature
Ch. 3. Exploring Earth's Biomes
Ch. 4. Wildlife Conservation

PARADE OF LIFE: MONERANS, PROTISTS, FUNGI, AND PLANTS

Ch. 1. Classification of Living Things
Ch. 2. Viruses and Monerans
Ch. 3. Protists
Ch. 4. Fungi
Ch. 5. Plants Without Seeds
Ch. 6. Plants With Seeds

EXPLORING THE UNIVERSE

Ch. 1. Stars and Galaxies
Ch. 2. The Solar System
Ch. 3. Earth and Its Moon

EVOLUTION: CHANGE OVER TIME

Ch. 1. Earth's History in Fossils
Ch. 2. Changes in Living Things Over Time
Ch. 3. The Path to Modern Humans

EXPLORING EARTH'S WEATHER

Ch. 1. What Is Weather?
Ch. 2. What Is Climate?
Ch. 3. Climate in the United States

THE NATURE OF SCIENCE

Ch. 1. What is Science?
Ch. 2. Measurement and the Sciences
Ch. 3. Tools and the Sciences

ECOLOGY: EARTH'S NATURAL RESOURCES
Ch. 1. Energy Resources
Ch. 2. Earth's Nonliving Resources
Ch. 3. Pollution
Ch. 4. Conserving Earth's Resources

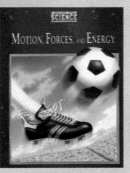

MOTION, FORCES, AND ENERGY
Ch. 1. What Is Motion?
Ch. 2. The Nature of Forces
Ch. 3. Forces in Fluids
Ch. 4. Work, Power, and Simple Machines
Ch. 5. Energy: Forms and Changes

PARADE OF LIFE: ANIMALS
Ch. 1. Sponges, Cnidarians, Worms, and Mollusks
Ch. 2. Arthropods and Echinoderms
Ch. 3. Fish and Amphibians
Ch. 4. Reptiles and Birds
Ch. 5. Mammals

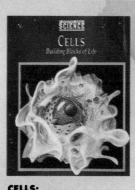

CELLS: BUILDING BLOCKS OF LIFE
Ch. 1. The Nature of LIfe
Ch. 2. Cell Structure and Function
Ch. 3. Cell Processes
Ch. 4. Cell Energy

DYNAMIC EARTH
Ch. 1. Movement of the Earth's Crust
Ch. 2. Earthquakes and Volcanoes
Ch. 3. Plate Tectonics
Ch. 4. Rocks and Minerals
Ch. 5. Weathering and Soil Formation
Ch. 6. Erosion and Deposition

MATTER: BUILDING BLOCK OF THE UNIVERSE
Ch. 1. General Properties of Matter
Ch. 2. Physical and Chemical Changes
Ch. 3. Mixtures, Elements, and Compounds
Ch. 4. Atoms: Building Blocks of Matter
Ch. 5. Classification of Elements: The Periodic Table

CHEMISTRY OF MATTER
Ch. 1. Atoms and Bonding
Ch. 2. Chemical Reactions
Ch. 3. Families of Chemical Compounds
Ch. 4. Chemical Technology
Ch. 5. Radioactive Elements

HUMAN BIOLOGY AND HEALTH
Ch. 1. The Human Body
Ch. 2. Skeletal and Muscular Systems
Ch. 3. Digestive System
Ch. 4. Circulatory System
Ch. 5. Respiratory and Excretory Systems
Ch. 6. Nervous and Endocrine Systems
Ch. 7. Reproduction and Development
Ch. 8. Immune System
Ch. 9. Alcohol, Tobacco, and Drugs

EXPLORING PLANET EARTH
Ch. 1. Earth's Atmosphere
Ch. 2. Earth's Oceans
Ch. 3. Earth's Fresh Water
Ch. 4. Earth's Landmasses
Ch. 5. Earth's Interior

HEAT ENERGY
Ch. 1. What Is Heat?
Ch. 2. Uses of Heat

SOUND AND LIGHT
Ch. 1. Characteristics of Waves
Ch. 2. Sound and Its Uses
Ch. 3. Light and the Electromagnetic Spectrum
Ch. 4. Light and Its Uses

A COMPLETELY INTEGRATED LEARNING SYSTEM...

The Prentice Hall Science program is an *integrated* learning system with a variety of print materials and multimedia components. All are designed to meet the needs of diverse learning styles and your technology needs.

THE STUDENT BOOK

Each book is a model of **excellent writing and dynamic visuals**—designed to be exciting and motivating to the student *and* the teacher, with relevant examples integrated throughout, and more opportunities for many different activities which apply to everyday life.

Problem-solving activities emphasize the thinking process, so problems may be more open-ended.

"Discovery Activities" throughout the book foster active learning.

Different sciences, and other disciplines, are integrated throughout the text and reinforced in the "Connections" features (the connections between computers and viruses is one example).

TEACHER'S RESOURCE PACKAGE

In addition to the student book, the complete teaching package contains:

ANNOTATED TEACHER'S EDITION

Designed to provide **"teacher-friendly"** support regardless of instructional approach:

- **Help is readily available** if you choose to teach thematically, to integrate the sciences, and/or to integrate the sciences with other curriculum areas.

- **Activity-based learning** is easy to implement through the use of Discovery Strategies, Activity Suggestions, and Teacher Demonstrations.

- Integration of all components is part of the teaching strategies.

- For instant accessibility, all of the teaching suggestions are wrapped around the student pages to which they refer.

ACTIVITY BOOK

Includes a **discovery activity for each chapter**, plus other activities including problem-solving and cooperative-learning activities.

THE REVIEW AND REINFORCEMENT GUIDE

Addresses **students' different learning styles** in a clear and comprehensive format:

- **Highly visual** for visual learners

TEACHER'S RESOURCE PACKAGE

CHAPTER 1

Interactions Among Living Things

*ENERGY	• In general, food and energy in an ecosystem flow from the producers to the consumers, and finally to the decomposers. • Producers capture light energy, which cannot be used by consumers, and change it into food energy, which can be used by all living things. • Energy is lost from the chain at each feeding level in an ecosystem.
*EVOLUTION	• Species evolve in response to the challenges of their environment. • Interactions among organisms can affect the directions in which organisms evolve.
*PATTERNS OF CHANGE	• Each time a change occurs in an ecosystem, an adjustment in the ecosystem's balance is required. • Organisms change and are changed by their environment. • Changes in the environment may be slow or rapid and may involve individuals, species, or entire communities.
SCALE AND STRUCTURE	• The world can be divided into ecosystems, which in turn consist of smaller components. The world itself can be described as an ecosystem.
*SYSTEMS AND INTERACTIONS	• All of the living and nonliving things in an environment are interconnected. • The populations in a community interact in many different ways.
*UNITY AND DIVERSITY	• Although the Earth's ecosystems vary greatly, they all contain the same basic kinds of interactions.
STABILITY	• Ecosystems adjust in response to changes. • The interactions within an ecosystem are in a state of dynamic balance.

CHAPTER 2

Cycles in Nature

*ENERGY	• Unlike energy, matter in an ecosystem can be recycled.
*EVOLUTION	• The types of organisms found in a particular place may change over time because of succession.
*PATTERNS OF CHANGE	• Ecosystems may undergo daily, lunar, and annual cycles of change. • Chemicals undergo a series of transformations as they cycle between the living and nonliving parts of ecosystems. • Over time, the community in a particular place may be gradually replaced by another community.
SCALE AND STRUCTURE	• Cycles of matter are an important part of ecosystems. • Biological clocks keep track of cycles of time that range in length from a few minutes to many years.
*SYSTEMS AND INTERACTIONS	• Biological clocks work with environmental factors to produce rhythmic changes in the appearance and behavior of organisms. • The moon and sun control the rise and fall of the tides. • Some events may change the rate of succession or reset cycles of succession.
*UNITY AND DIVERSITY	• Different kinds of organisms experience daily, lunar, and annual rhythms. • Organisms have different ways of escaping unfavorable environmental conditions. • The many different cycles involve the flow of matter from the nonliving part of the environment to living things and back again.
STABILITY	• Because of biological clocks, organisms continue to undergo rhythmic changes, even in the absence of environmental cues. • Matter is recycled in ecosystems.

CHAPTER 3

Exploring Earth's Biomes

*ENERGY	• Tube worms and other organisms living around deep-sea vents rely on heat energy from the Earth's interior rather than on energy from the sun.
*EVOLUTION	• Animals and plants that live in a desert biome have adaptations that allow them to survive on little water.
*PATTERNS OF CHANGE	• Plants and animals disperse, or spread out into new areas, often with help from wind, water, animals, and humans.
SCALE AND STRUCTURE	• The marine, or ocean, biome is the largest biome on Earth.
*SYSTEMS AND INTERACTIONS	• Most animals in the ocean depend either directly or indirectly on phytoplankton for food.
*UNITY AND DIVERSITY	• Tropical rain forest biomes have a greater diversity of plants and animals than any other biome.
STABILITY	• Land biomes are areas with similar climates, plants, and animals.

CHAPTER 4

Wildlife Conservation

*ENERGY	
*EVOLUTION	• Extinction is a natural part of Earth's history. • Human activities can change environments faster than organisms can adapt to these changes.
*PATTERNS OF CHANGE	• Human activities can cause organisms to become endangered or extinct. • Human activities have greatly increased the rate of extinction. • As their habitats are destroyed, certain species become rarer.
SCALE AND STRUCTURE	• Habitat destruction may affect the environment on local, regional, and global levels.
*SYSTEMS AND INTERACTIONS	• Exotic species interfere with the interactions of native communities. • Wildlife is necessary for the continued survival of the human species.
*UNITY AND DIVERSITY	• Humans harm wildlife and wildlife habitats through many activities that are motivated by many different things. • There are various methods for conserving wildlife.
STABILITY	• Wildlife conservation helps to preserve genetic diversity. • Conservation preserves resources for future use.

Comprehensive List of Laboratory Materials

Item	Quantities per Group	Chapter
Bottle cap	1	2
Bran flakes	20 mL	2
Cotton ball	1	2
Gauze, 25 cm-square	1	2
Gravel, clean	16 oz	4
Guppies	2	4
Houseflies	10	2
Index card	1	3
Jars, glass	1	2
large with cover	1	4
2-L, wide-mouthed	2	1
Lamp	1	3, 4
Lawn fertilizer	1/2 tsp	1
(or housplant food)		
Magnifying glass	1	2
Milk, canned	10 mL	2
Milk carton	1	3
Paper towel	1 sheet	2
Plants, aquatic (*Elodea*)	4	4
	8	1
Plastic wrap, clear	1 small roll (per class)	3
Pond snails, small	8	4
Pond water	3 L	1
Rubber band	1	2
Scissors	1	3
Seeds		
impatiens	10	3
lima bean	5	3
rye grass	30	3
Soil, sandy or potting	1 small bag	3
Stapler	1	3
Teaspoon	1	1

ECOLOGY
Earth's Living Resources

Anthea Maton
Former NSTA National Coordinator
Project Scope, Sequence, Coordination
Washington, DC

Jean Hopkins
Science Instructor and Department Chairperson
John H. Wood Middle School
San Antonio, Texas

Susan Johnson
Professor of Biology
Ball State University
Muncie, Indiana

David LaHart
Senior Instructor
Florida Solar Energy Center
Cape Canaveral, Florida

Maryanna Quon Warner
Science Instructor
Del Dios Middle School
Escondido, California

Jill D. Wright
Professor of Science Education
Director of International Field Programs
University of Pittsburgh
Pittsburgh, Pennsylvania

PRENTICE HALL
Upper Saddle River, New Jersey
Needham, Massachusetts

Prentice Hall Science

Ecology: Earth's Living Resources

Student Text	**Study Guide**
Annotated Teacher's Edition	**Integrated Science Activity Book**
Teacher's Resource Package	**Integrated Science Activity Book II**
Laboratory Manual	**Computer Test Bank**
Activity Book	**Transparency Binder**
Test Book	**Teacher's Desk Reference**
Review and Reinforcement	**Product Testing Activities**
Guide	**Prentice Hall Science Integrated Media**

The illustration on the cover, rendered by Joseph Cellini, shows humpbacked whales, one of many whale species that are endangered.

Credits begin on page 160.

THIRD EDITION

ISBN 0-13-423443-X

1 2 3 4 5 6 7 8 9 10   00 99 98 97 96

PRENTICE HALL
Simon & Schuster Education Group
A Viacom Company

STAFF CREDITS

Editorial:	Lorraine Smith-Phelan, Maureen Grassi, Christine Caputo, Joseph Berman, Rekha Sheorey, Matthew Hart, Kathleen Ventura
Technology Development:	Ted Tolles
Design:	AnnMarie Roselli, Laura Bird, Gerry Schrenk, Monduane Harris
Production:	Christina Burghard, Gertrude Szyferblatt, Elizabeth Torjussen, Gregory Myers, Cleasta Wilburn
Media Resources:	Libby Forsyth, Emily Rose, Martha Conway, Vickie Menanteaux, Suzi Myers
Marketing:	Andrew Socha, Jane Walker Neff, Victoria Willows
Pre-Press Production:	Kathryn Dix, Carol Barbara, Marie McNamara
Manufacturing:	Loretta Moe, Matt McCabe
National Science Consultants:	Kathy French, Jeannie Dennard, Patricia M. Cominsky, Charles Balko, Brenda Underwood

Contributing Writers

Linda Densman
Science Instructor
Hurst, TX

Linda Grant
Former Science Instructor
Weatherford, TX

Heather Hirschfeld
Science Writer
Durham, NC

Marcia Mungenast
Science Writer
Upper Montclair, NJ

Michael Ross
Science Writer
New York City, NY

Content Reviewers

Dan Anthony
Science Mentor
Rialto, CA

John Barrow
Science Instructor
Pomona, CA

Leslie Bettencourt
Science Instructor
Harrisville, RI

Stuart Birnbaum
Geologist
Helotes, TX

Carol Bishop
Science Instructor
Palm Desert, CA

Dan Bohan
Science Instructor
Palm Desert, CA

Steve M. Carlson
Science Instructor
Milwaukie, OR

Larry Flammer
Science Instructor
San Jose, CA

Steve Ferguson
Science Instructor
Lee's Summit, MO

Robin Lee Harris Freedman
Science Instructor
Fort Bragg, CA

Edith H. Gladden
Former Science Instructor
Philadelphia, PA

Vernita Marie Graves
Science Instructor
Tenafly, NJ

Jack Grube
Science Instructor
San Jose, CA

Emiel Hamberlin
Science Instructor
Chicago, IL

Dwight Kertzman
Science Instructor
Tulsa, OK

Judy Kirschbaum
Science/Computer Instructor
Tenafly, NJ

John F. Koser
Physics/Astronomy Instructor
Plymouth, MN

Kenneth L. Krause
Science Instructor
Milwaukie, OR

Ernest W. Kuehl, Jr.
Science Instructor
Bayside, NY

Mary Grace Lopez
Science Instructor
Corpus Christi, TX

Philip M. Lurie
Former Research Chemist
Paramus, NJ

Warren Maggard
Science Instructor
PeWee Valley, KY

Della M. McCaughan
Science Instructor
Biloxi, MS

Stanley J. Mulak
Former Science Instructor
Jensen Beach, FL

Richard Myers
Science Instructor
Portland, OR

Carol Nathanson
Science Mentor
Riverside, CA

Sylvia Neivert
Former Science Instructor
San Diego, CA

Jarvis VNC Pahl
Science Instructor
Rialto, CA

Kevin Reel
Science Department
Chairperson
Ojai, CA

Arlene Sackman
Science Instructor
Tulare, CA

Christine Schumacher
Science Instructor
Pikesville, MD

Suzanne Steinke
Science Instructor
Towson, MD

Len Svinth
Science Instructor/
Chairperson
Petaluma, CA

Elaine M. Tadros
Science Instructor
Palm Desert, CA

Susan J. Thomas
Science Instructor
Haverhill, MA

Joyce K. Walsh
Science Instructor
Midlothian, VA

Steve Weinberg
Science Instructor
West Hartford, CT

Charlene West, PhD
Director of Curriculum
Rialto, CA

John Westwater
Science Instructor
Medford, MA

Glenna Wilkoff
Science Instructor
Chesterfield, OH

Edee Norman Wiziecki
Science Instructor
Urbana, IL

Teacher Advisory Panel

Beverly Brown
Science Instructor
Livonia, MI

James Burg
Science Instructor
Cincinnati, OH

Karen M. Cannon
Science Instructor
San Diego, CA

John Eby
Science Instructor
Richmond, CA

Elsie M. Jones
Science Instructor
Marietta, GA

Michael Pierre McKereghan
Science Instructor
Denver, CO

Donald D. Pace, Sr.
Science Instructor
Reisterstown, MD

Carlos Francisco Sainz
Science Instructor
National City, CA

William Reed
Science Instructor
Indianapolis, IN

Multicultural Consultant

Steven J. Rakow
Associate Professor
University of Houston—
* Clear Lake*
Houston, TX

English as a Second Language (ESL) Consultants

Jaime Morales
Bilingual Coordinator
Huntington Park, CA

Pat Hollis Smith
Former ESL Instructor
Beaumont, TX

Reading Consultant

Larry Swinburne
Director
Swinburne Readability
Laboratory

CONTENTS

ECOLOGY: EARTH'S LIVING RESOURCES

Activity Bank/Reference Section

Features

CONCEPT MAPPING

Throughout your study of science, you will learn a variety of terms, facts, figures, and concepts. Each new topic you encounter will provide its own collection of words and ideas—which, at times, you may think seem endless. But each of the ideas within a particular topic is related in some way to the others. No concept in science is isolated. Thus it will help you to understand the topic if you see the whole picture; that is, the interconnectedness of all the individual terms and ideas. This is a much more effective and satisfying way of learning than memorizing separate facts.

Actually, this should be a rather familiar process for you. Although you may not think about it in this way, you analyze many of the elements in your daily life by looking for relationships or connections. For example, when you look at a collection of flowers, you may divide them into groups: roses, carnations, and daisies. You may then associate colors with these flowers: red, pink, and white. The general topic is flowers. The subtopic is types of flowers. And the colors are specific terms that describe flowers. A topic makes more sense and is more easily understood if you understand how it is broken down into individual ideas and how these ideas are related to one another and to the entire topic.

It is often helpful to organize information visually so that you can see how it all fits together. One technique for describing related ideas is called a **concept map**. In a concept map, an idea is represented by a word or phrase enclosed in a box. There are several ideas in any concept map. A connection between two ideas is made with a line. A word or two that describes the connection is written on or near the line. The general topic is located at the top of the map. That topic is then broken down into subtopics, or more specific ideas, by branching lines. The most specific topics are located at the bottom of the map.

To construct a concept map, first identify the important ideas or key terms in the chapter or section. Do not try to include too much information. Use your judgment as to what is really important. Write the general topic at the top of your map. Let's use an example to help illustrate this process. Suppose you decide that the key terms in a section you are reading are School, Living Things, Language Arts, Subtraction, Grammar, Mathematics, Experiments, Papers, Science, Addition, Novels. The general topic is School. Write and enclose this word in a box at the top of your map.

SCHOOL

Now choose the subtopics—Language Arts, Science, Mathematics. Figure out how they are related to the topic. Add these words to your map. Continue this procedure until you have included all the important ideas and terms. Then use lines to make the appropriate connections between ideas and terms. Don't forget to write a word or two on or near the connecting line to describe the nature of the connection.

Do not be concerned if you have to redraw your map (perhaps several times!) before you show all the important connections clearly. If, for example, you write papers for Science as well as for Language Arts, you may want to place these two subjects next to each other so that the lines do not overlap.

One more thing you should know about concept mapping: Concepts can be correctly mapped in many different ways. In fact, it is unlikely that any two people will draw identical concept maps for a complex topic. Thus there is no one correct concept map for any topic! Even

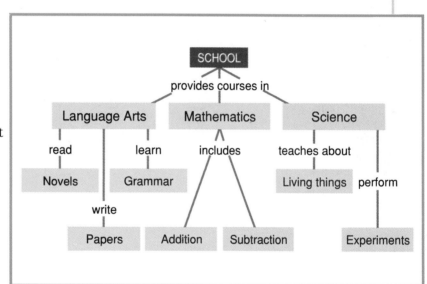

though your concept map may not match those of your classmates, it will be correct as long as it shows the most important concepts and the clear relationships among them. Your concept map will also be correct if it has meaning to you and if it helps you understand the material you are reading. A concept map should be so clear that if some of the terms are erased, the missing terms could easily be filled in by following the logic of the concept map.

Ecology: Earth's Living Resources

TEXT OVERVIEW

Ecology teaches that everything is connected to everything else. In this textbook students are introduced to the interactions and connections among living things. Students will gain an understanding of the interactions among living things as they study ecosystems, populations, competition, and symbiosis.

Next, students will discover the effects of daily, lunar, and annual rhythms on living things. They also will explore chemical cycles and the concept of ecological succession. Students are then introduced to the various biomes of the world. They will study the characteristics of the six land biomes and the two water biomes.

Finally, students will investigate wildlife conservation. They will learn about extinct and endangered species, causes of endangerment, and methods for wildlife conservation.

TEXT OBJECTIVES

1. Describe the basic interactions and relationships among living things.
2. Describe the effects of rhythms on organisms.
3. Explain the role of chemical cycles in nature.
4. Describe the process of ecological succession.
5. Identify the characteristics of the six land biomes and the two water biomes.
6. Discuss the reasons for the extinction of organisms and explain why people should try to save endangered species.

ECOLOGY
Earth's Living Resources

The red-cockaded woodpecker has an amazing way of protecting its young from the red rat snake.

The rat snake's tongue flickers in and out of its mouth, tasting the air. Food is nearby—warm, fat baby birds! The snake slithers up an old, diseased pine tree in search of its prey. But before it can reach the cavity in the tree trunk where the nest is hidden, the snake slithers into an unexpected patch of sticky pine sap. The sap gums up the snake's scales so that it loses its grip and falls off the tree.

A few minutes later, a red-cockaded woodpecker flies into the cavity in the old pine tree. After feeding its babies, the woodpecker does some housekeeping. Clinging to the trunk of the tree, the woodpecker pecks several holes

Many different kinds of places are home to Earth's living things. This forest of pink rhododendrons, Douglas firs, and redwoods is located in California's Redwoods State Park.

INTRODUCING ECOLOGY: EARTH'S LIVING RESOURCES

USING THE TEXTBOOK

Begin your introduction of the textbook by having students examine the textbook-opening photographs and captions. Before they read the textbook introduction, ask the following questions.

• **What does the caption tell you about the snake and the bird?** (That the snake will eat baby birds, but the bird has a way to protect its babies.)
• **How do you think the adult bird protects its babies from the snake?** (Accept all logical answers. Encourage students to think of things that a tree has that the bird could use to fight the snake.)
• **What is the relationship between the snake and the bird?** (Accept variations of the idea that the snake is a predator and the bird is prey.)

Now have students examine the photograph of the forest at the bottom of the page.
• **What does the photograph and the caption tell you about living things?** (That living things live in many different places and that different living things live together in the same place.)

Now have students study the photograph on the right.

into the bark surrounding the cavity. Sap runs out of the holes and oozes slowly down the tree. Then the woodpecker flies off to gather more food for its hungry babies.

The pine tree, snake, and woodpeckers you have just read about interact in an interesting way. In this textbook, you will first learn about the different kinds of interactions that occur among living things and between living things and their nonliving surroundings. Next, you will read about life cycles and other patterns of change in nature. You will then learn about the basic kinds of places that are home to Earth's living things. Finally, you will explore the reasons why organisms such as the red-cockaded woodpecker are in danger of disappearing forever from the Earth.

▲ Living things interact in many different ways. Locking horns to establish who's the boss, these two bull moose are battling in Alaska's Denali National Park.

CHAPTER DESCRIPTIONS

1 Interactions Among Living Things Chapter 1 focuses on living things in terms of their environment and relationships. Ecosystems, communities, populations, habitats, and niches are explained, as are food chains, food webs, and energy pyramids. Competition and predation, together with the symbiotic relationships of commensalism, mutualism, and parasitism, are also described.

2 Cycles in Nature In Chapter 2 the effects of daily, lunar, and annual rhythms on living things are discussed. Then the importance of chemical recycling in nature is explained. Finally, the ecological succession of a pond to a forest is described.

3 Exploring Earth's Biomes Chapter 3 discusses the major land biomes. These include tundra, coniferous forest, deciduous forest, tropical rain forest, grassland, and desert. The chapter also investigates the two water biomes, marine and freshwater biomes.

4 Wildlife Conservation Chapter 4 treats the subject of wildlife conservation. Extinct and endangered species are identified, and causes for their situations are discussed. Extinctions caused by human activities are described in detail. Finally, conservation methods are proposed.

Discovery *Activity*

Seeds of Change

1. Collect as many different kinds of uncooked seeds as you can from the foods you eat.
   - What kinds of foods contain or are made up of seeds?
   - Where are these foods grown?
2. Obtain a paper towel and a small glass jar with a lid. Fold the paper towel so that it can line the sides of the jar. Moisten the paper towel with water. Then place some of the seeds in the jar so that they are sandwiched between the glass and the paper towel. Cover the jar.
3. Observe the seeds daily.
   - How do the seeds change over time?
   - How might new kinds of plants appear in an area?
   - What sorts of things might affect what happens to the seeds?

G ■ 9

• **Why are the moose fighting with each other?** (Lead students to the concept of competition. In a given area, there is only enough food, water, and space for one bull moose.)

Now have students read the textbook introduction; then ask the following questions.

• **What does the example of the tree, the snake, and the bird tell you about living things?** (That they interact in many different and sometimes in unusual ways.)

• **What is ecology?** (Encourage students to experiment with a definition—the science that deals with the relationships and interactions of living things with each other and with their environment.)

DISCOVERY ACTIVITY

Seeds of Change

You may want to begin your introduction to the textbook by having students perform the Discovery Activity. Students might want to use index cards to label their seeds and to collect information about the foods that their seeds came from. After students have prepared their jars, suggest that they label each seed with tape on the outside of the jar. Encourage students to record their daily observations. As a group, discuss how the seeds change, how they might appear in an area, and what things could affect their growth. Ask students to hypothesize about the interaction between the seeds and their environment. Tell them they will discover the answers to their questions in the chapters that follow.

Chapter 1   INTERACTIONS AMONG LIVING THINGS

SECTION	HANDS-ON ACTIVITIES
1–1 Living Things and Their Environment pages G12–G17 Multicultural Opportunity 1–1, p. G12 ESL Strategy 1–1, p. G13	**Student Edition** ACTIVITY (Doing): Identifying Interactions, p. G15 ACTIVITY (Discovering): Home Sweet Home, p. G17 **Laboratory Manual** Examining an Unknown Community, p. G7 **Teacher Edition** Observing Environments, p. G10d
1–2 Food and Energy in the Environment pages G18–G23 Multicultural Opportunity 1–2, p. G18 ESL Strategy 1–2, p. G18	**Student Edition** ACTIVITY (Doing): Diet Delights, p. G19 ACTIVITY (Doing): Your Place in Line, p. G20 ACTIVITY BANK: Garbage in the Garden, p. G138 **Laboratory Manual** Investigating Relationships in an Ecosystem, p. G13 **Activity Book** ACTIVITY: Observing Decay, p. G21 **Teacher Edition** Interconnections in a Food Web, p. G10d
1–3 Interactions and Evolution pages G23–G35 Multicultural Opportunity 1–3, p. G23 ESL Strategy 1–3, p. G23	**Student Edition** ACTIVITY (Doing): Eat or Be Eaten, p. G23 ACTIVITY BANK: On Your Mark, Get Set, Grow! p. G141 **Laboratory Manual** Observing Schooling Behavior in Fishes, p. G17
1–4 Life in the Balance pages G35–G39 Multicultural Opportunity 1–4, p. G35 ESL Strategy 1–4, p. G35	**Student Edition** LABORATORY INVESTIGATION: A Little Off Balance, p. G40
Chapter Review pages G40–G43	

OUTSIDE TEACHER RESOURCES
Books

Boughey, A. S. *Ecology and Population,* Macmillan.

Hughey, Pat. *Scavengers and Decomposers: The Cleaning Crew,* Atheneum.

James, Robert. *Big Friend, Little Friend: A Book About Symbiosis,* Houghton.

Jezer, Marty. *Rachel Carson: Biologist and Author,* Chelsea House.

Street, P. *Animal Partners and Parasites,* Taplinger.

OTHER ACTIVITIES	MEDIA AND TECHNOLOGY
Activity Book CHAPTER DISCOVERY: Exploring Relationships Among Living Things, p. G9 ACTIVITY: Populations in Your Community, p. G17 ACTIVITY: Carrying Capacity, p. G33 **Review and Reinforcement Guide** Section 1–1, p. G5	**Prentice Hall Science Integrated Media** The Wonder of Ngorongoro **English/Spanish Audiotapes** Section 1–1
Activity Book ACTIVITY: Find the Food Chain, p. G19 ACTIVITY: A Food Web, p. G23 **Review and Reinforcement Guide** Section 1–2, p. G7	**Prentice Hall Science Integrated Media** The Wonder of Ngorongoro **Transparency Binder** Food Web Energy Pyramid **English/Spanish Audiotapes** Section 1–2
Student Edition ACTIVITY (Calculating): Shady Survival, p. G24 ACTIVITY (Reading): "Avenues of Delight and Discovery," p. G25 **Activity Book** ACTIVITY: Competition, p. G27 ACTIVITY: What Goes Up Must Come Down, p. G29 **Review and Reinforcement Guide** Section 1–3, p. G9	**Prentice Hall Science Integrated Media** A Question of Balance **English/Spanish Audiotapes** Section 1–3
Student Edition ACTIVITY (Writing): Who Missed the Moose? p. G38 **Activity Book** ACTIVITY: Analyzing Relationships Among Organisms, p. G25 **Review and Reinforcement Guide** Section 1–4, p. G11	**Prentice Hall Science Integrated Media** A Question of Balance **English/Spanish Audiotapes** Section 1–4
Test Book Chapter Test, p. G9 Performance-Based Tests, p. G91	**Test Book** Computer Test Bank Test, p. G17

*All materials in the Chapter Planning Guide Grid are available as part of the Prentice Hall Science Learning System.

Audiovisuals

Ants: Backyard Science, film, BFA
An Ecosystem: A Struggle for Survival, video, National Geographic

Interrelationships of Living Things, filmstrip, Eye Gate

Nature's Half Acre, film, Walt Disney
Predators of North America, video, National Geographic

CHAPTER OVERVIEW

Ecology teaches that everything is connected to everything else. It is the study of the interactions of organisms with one another and with their physical surroundings. In this chapter students will learn about these interconnections beginning with the concepts of environment and ecosystem. The first section includes the structure of ecosystems and the roles of organisms in populations and communities. Students will learn that a population is a group of organisms that all belong to the same species and live in a given area. A community consists of all the various populations of organisms living in a given area.

Energy flow through ecosystems includes concrete references to food chains and food webs, providing a network of feeding relationships for plants and animals. The functional classification of producers, consumers, and decomposers is introduced, and examples are provided. An energy pyramid is used to illustrate energy losses at successive feeding levels.

The third section covers relationships among organisms. The factors that limit population growth are discussed. Among these are competition, predation, and parasitism.

Finally, the last section emphasizes human impacts on ecosystems using Mono Lake as an example.

1–1 LIVING THINGS AND THEIR ENVIRONMENT
THEMATIC FOCUS

The purpose of this section is to introduce students to the interconnections among the living and nonliving things in an environment. Basic concepts studied by ecologists are discussed, and key vocabulary is defined. Students explore the connections that occur within ecosystems, communities, and populations. Through various examples, both in text and in photographs, students are shown that an organism is found in a particular habitat because that habitat provides the resources necessary for its survival.

The themes that can be focused on in this section are scale and structure and systems and interactions. The themes are interconnected in that ecosystems, regardless of scale, contain the same basic kinds of interactions.

Scale and structure: As ecologists try to understand the natural world, they divide it into ecosystems. An ecosystem can be as small as a drop of water or as large as the entire Earth. And one ecosystem often contains other smaller ecosystems within it. Stress that both the living organisms and the nonliving things are partners in keeping an ecosystem in balance.

*Systems and interactions: All the living and nonliving parts of an ecosystem are interconnected. Stress the fact that rocks, soil, air, and other nonliving things are as important—and sometimes as fragile—as the more obvious living plants and animals.

PERFORMANCE OBJECTIVES 1–1

1. Define environment.
2. Relate ecology to the relationships of living things with their environment.
3. Distinguish between living and nonliving things in an environment.
4. Compare ecosystems, communities, and populations.
5. Define habitat.

SCIENCE TERMS 1–1

environment p. G12
ecology p. G14
ecosystems p. G14
community p. G15
population p. G16
habitat p. G17

1–2 FOOD AND ENERGY IN THE ENVIRONMENT
THEMATIC FOCUS

The purpose of this section is to introduce students to the path that energy travels through an ecosystem. Organisms are classified by how they obtain food. Producers can make their own food using the energy of sunlight and nutrients in the soil. Consumers depend on the producers (or on other consumers) for their source of energy.

The themes that can be focused on in this section are energy and unity and diversity.

*Energy: In general, the food and energy in an ecosystem flow from the producers to the consumers and then to the decomposers. The process, however, is more of a circle than a straight line. The decomposers return nutrients to the soil so they can be used again by the producers. The producers capture light energy, which cannot be used by consumers, and change it into food energy. At each level of the feeding cycle, however, some of the energy is lost.

*Unity and diversity: Although the Earth's ecosystems vary greatly in both size and composition, the same kind of energy path is followed in all of them.

PERFORMANCE OBJECTIVES 1–2

1. Distinguish among producers, consumers, and decomposers.
2. Describe food chains and food webs.
3. Trace the path of solar energy through a simple food chain that includes humans.
4. Relate feeding levels to the available amount of energy.

SCIENCE TERMS 1–2

producer p. G18
consumer p. G18
decomposer p. G18
food chain p. G20
food web p. G20

1–3 INTERACTION AND EVOLUTION
THEMATIC FOCUS

The purpose of this section is to introduce students to the factors that can limit the growth of a population. Different relationships (competition, predation, and symbiosis) are defined and discussed. Central to the section is the idea that an ecosystem must remain in balance: The limits to its population are not negative factors, but rather are key processes needed to guarantee the survival of the system.

The themes that can be focused on in this section are evolution, patterns of change, and unity and diversity.

*Evolution: The interactions that are part of these limiting factors also affect the way organisms change over time. Organisms change and are changed by their environment. Each time a change occurs in an ecosystem, an adjustment in the ecosystem's balance is required.

*Patterns of change: The changes in the environment may be slow or rapid. They may involve individuals, species, or entire communities. But because all ecosystems are subject to the same types of change, these can be studied and sometimes controlled.

*Unity and diversity: All ecosystems adjust in response to change in an attempt to maintain a state of dynamic balance.

PERFORMANCE OBJECTIVES 1–3

1. **Describe how competition can serve as a limiting factor.**
2. **Describe how predation can have a positive impact on prey.**
3. **Define a symbiotic relationship.**
4. **Distinguish among commensalism, mutualism, and parasitism.**
5. **Describe how organisms adapt to their environment.**

SCIENCE TERMS 1–3

niche p. G23
competition p. G24
predator p. G26
prey p. G26
symbiosis p. G28
commensalism p. G28
mutualism p. G29
parasitism p. G30
parasite p. G31
host p. G31

1–4 LIFE IN THE BALANCE
THEMATIC FOCUS

The purpose of this section is to demonstrate to students that human activities can have a dramatic impact on an ecosystem. Using the example of Mono Lake in California, students see how a change in the level of water in the lake has had a widespread effect on the entire ecosystem.

The themes that can be focused on in this section are patterns of change, systems and interactions, and stability.

*Patterns of change: Stress the fact that although all ecosystems are always changing, an ecosystem is not indestructible. If the fundamental balance is destroyed, it may be impossible for the system to recover.

*Systems and interactions: The events described at Mono Lake illustrate how many—and often hidden—interconnections there are among the living and nonliving parts of an ecosystem. A change in one small part of the system can endanger the entire balance.

Stability: The interactions in any ecosystem, although amazingly diverse, must maintain a state of dynamic balance for the system to continue functioning. In most cases, the system can self-correct. It is only in the case of drastic assaults from outside forces that the stability of the system is threatened.

PERFORMANCE OBJECTIVES 1–4

1. **Explain why balance is important in an ecosystem.**
2. **Describe how human activities can change the balance of an ecosystem.**

Discovery *Learning*

TEACHER DEMONSTRATIONS MODELING

Observing Environments

Take students on a five-minute field trip on the grounds of the school or in a nearby park. Instruct students that they will be asked to take notes on the kinds of organisms they observe (both plant and animal) and the areas in which these organisms live (on the ground, in trees).

• **What organisms did you observe?** (Answers will vary. Compile a class list of all organisms noted.)
• **Where in the environment did each organism live?** (Add a column to your list of organisms detailing where they were seen.)
• **What was the energy source for these organisms?** (Students should reply that the sun is the energy source for green plants. They should be able to note that some of the animals eat green plants while other animals eat the plant-eaters. Lead students to the idea that in either case the sun is the original source of energy for most living things.)
• **In what ways were the organisms dependent on one another for survival?** (The most obvious instances will be those where organisms eat other organisms. Lead students to the idea that a robin depends on a tree for its nest, etc.)
• **In what ways were the organisms dependent on the nonliving environment for their survival?** (Possible answers are shelter, living space, air to breathe, soil to grow.)

Point out that in this chapter students will be looking into the ways living things interact with one another and with their environment.

Interconnections in a Food Web

A food web can be constructed by using a long piece of string and running it back and forth among students "named" for animals and plants. Be sure to include the sun in the web. After a dozen or so "organisms" are included in the web, have one drop out, releasing the string. Everyone who is connected to the loose piece must then drop his or her part of the string. Continue until the entire web collapses.
• **Was everything connected to everything else?** (yes)

CHAPTER 1
Interactions Among Living Things

INTEGRATING SCIENCE

This life science chapter provides you with numerous opportunities to integrate other areas of science, as well as other disciplines, into your curriculum. Blue-numbered annotations on the student page and integration notes on the teacher wraparound pages alert you to areas of possible integration.

In this chapter you can integrate meteorology (p. 15), physical education (p. 18), language arts (pp. 19, 25), nutrition (p. 20), art (p. 23), mathematics (p. 24), and geology (p. 36).

SCIENCE, TECHNOLOGY, AND SOCIETY/COOPERATIVE LEARNING

Since its discovery in the late eighteenth century by Captain Cook, the fragile interactions of the Antarctic ecosystem have been impacted by people. Captain Cook's diaries telling of southern seas full of life brought sealers and whalers who decimated the populations of seals and whales for their fur, blubber, and baleen used for stays for women's corsets.

Antarctica gained worldwide public attention in 1958 when it was targeted for cooperative scientific research during the International Geophysical Year. Shortly afterward, the Antarctic Treaty was signed. The treaty barred military activity and allowed signing nations to set up bases for scientific research. No provisions were

INTRODUCING CHAPTER 1

DISCOVERY LEARNING

▶ *Activity Book*

You may want to begin your teaching of the chapter by using the Chapter 1 Discovery Activity. Using this activity, students will discover ways in which organisms living in the same environment interact.

USING THE TEXTBOOK

Have students examine the photograph on page G10. Explain that the photograph shows some relationships among plants, animals, and nonliving things. The two insects in the photo are ants and aphids.
• **What do you think is shown in the picture?** (Possible answers are ants eating aphids, ants fighting with aphids, ants and aphids eating the leaves.)

Have students read the chapter introduction.
• **Ask students to describe what each of these organisms uses for food: aphids, ants, ladybugs, plants.** (Leaves, honeydew, aphids, sunlight and nutrients in the soil.)
• **In what way might the plant benefit from the aphids or the ants?** (Possible answer: The ants might be pollinators.)

Interactions Among Living Things

As sunlight falls on the leaves of a plant, substances in the leaves capture the sunlight's energy and use it to make food. But even as the leaves are making food, a tiny thief is stealing some of it. A small aphid (an insect) pokes its strawlike mouthparts into the leaf and begins to suck up food-rich sap.

Suddenly, a hungry ant scurries along the leaf toward the aphid. Is the aphid doomed to end up as the ant's lunch? No. Upon reaching the aphid, the ant begins to stroke the smaller insect with its feelers. The aphid responds by releasing a drop of a sugary substance called honeydew. The ant eagerly licks up the honeydew. Then the ant gently picks up the aphid in its jaws and carries it to another leaf. There the aphid is added to a "herd" being tended by ants. The ants take care of the aphids in exchange for meals of honeydew. The ants move the aphids to fresh leaves when the old ones wither. When it rains, the ants carry the aphids to more sheltered leaves. The ants also defend their herd from ladybugs and other aphid-devouring animals.

The interactions among aphids, ants, ladybugs, sunlight, and plants are just a few of the countless relationships that link living things to one another and to their surroundings. Read on to discover more about interactions among living things.

Journal *Activity*

You and Your World In your journal, explore the thoughts and feelings you have about environmental issues.

◄ *These orange-colored ants are busily tending a large "herd" of dark gray aphids.*

- **How is the plant different from the aphids, ants, and ladybugs?** (Possible answers: It can make its food from sunlight and nutrients in the soil; it cannot move from one place to another.)
- **Describe what might happen if the plants eaten by the aphids were all destroyed in a fire or volcanic eruption?** (The populations of aphids, ants, ladybugs, and many other organisms would decrease.)
- **Describe other disturbances in the environment shown in the picture that might have a dramatic effect on the organisms.** (Possible answers are sudden change in temperature, spraying of pesticides, land being cleared for farming.)
- **What are some other examples of one type of organism having an impact on another organism in its environment?** (Accept all logical responses.)

---

made for enforcement of the articles of the treaty or for control of commercial exploitation of mineral resources, if any were found.

As noble as the sentiments behind the treaty were, it is ironic that the very scientific bases set up to study and preserve this ecosystem have had the greatest impact on it. Competition between the scientists and the Antarctic wildlife for the few open ice areas displaced many animals and birds from their nesting grounds. The scientific bases were also the source of much organic, chemical, and biological pollution.

At present, members of the Antarctic Treaty are negotiating the future of Antarctica, while environmental groups and an increasingly environmentally aware public are nervously awaiting the outcome.

Cooperative learning: Using preassigned lab groups or randomly selected teams, have groups complete one of the following assignments.
- As members of the United States delegation to the conference debating the Antarctic Treaty, each group should formulate the policy that they plan to present to the convention. Group policies should address the following issues: mineral exploitation, tourism, declaration of Antarctica as a world park, enforcement policies, and scientific research. The groups should decide if each of these endeavors should be allowed and what, if any, restrictions will be placed on each activity.
- Draw a mural illustrating Antarctica before and after people began impacting the ecosystem. The mural should depict the history of people's impact on Antarctica starting with Captain Cook and ending with each group's prediction for the future.

See Cooperative Learning in the *Teacher's Desk Reference.*

JOURNAL ACTIVITY

You may wish to begin the Journal Activity with a class brainstorming session to compile a list of environmental issues that are specific to your local community, to state, and to worldwide concerns. Students may use the list to select topics for their writing activity. Students should be instructed to keep their journal activity in their portfolios.

1-1 Living Things and Their Environments

MULTICULTURAL OPPORTUNITY 1-1

In order to provide students with a meaningful analogy, have them think about their family environments. Family environments are functional units, as are ecosystems, and are composed of living elements (family members, pets, and so on) and nonliving elements (home, furnishings, and so on). Stress that just as there is variety in the environment, there are also many different types of families. Ask students to identify some of the living and nonliving elements of their family environments and describe how these elements interact to help the family function effectively.

Include students from different cultural backgrounds in the discussion. For example, Hispanic students may speak about the extended family that, although undergoing changes, is typical of Hispanic cultures. In addition to parents and children, it often includes grandparents, aunts, uncles, cousins, and even close family friends (compadres) living in the same house or neighborhood. You may also want to mention that pets play different roles in different cultures and that the animals chosen as pets vary in different countries. For instance, in China, cats are especially popular; the Japanese favor birds and crickets, while the Inuits (Eskimos) keep bear cubs and baby seals as pets.

1-1 Living Things and Their Environment

A thousand meters below the ocean's surface, the last traces of sunlight fade into nothingness. The water temperature is only a few degrees above freezing. There is very little food or oxygen. Yet the harsh, dark world of the deep sea is home to many organisms (living things). Nightmarish fishes with huge teeth and eyes glow with ghostly lights made by their own bodies. Octopuses and squids with webbed arms pulse through the water or float like falling parachutes. Strange spiky sea cucumbers sift through the muddy ocean floor for the bits of food that drift down from the sunlit world above.

On land, in a lush tropical rain forest, tall trees with clinging vines thrive in the warmth and sunlight. In the treetops, brightly colored parrots munch on seeds while monkeys chatter to one another. Snakes and lizards climb up and down the tree trunks in search of food. And piglike tapirs calmly make their way along the ground.

The deep sea and a rain forest are only two of the many different **environments** found on Earth. An

Figure 1–1 *The huge jaws and enormous teeth of this deep-sea fish enable it to catch and eat animals that are larger than itself. The eyelash viper and the Heliconia flowers on which it is coiled live in the same kind of environment as the blue-and-gold and scarlet macaws. What kind of environment is home to these organisms?* ❶

12 ■ G

TEACHING STRATEGY 1-1

FOCUS/MOTIVATION

Ask students to describe their environment twenty years from now. What kinds of efforts are they willing to make today to ensure their dreams come true?

CONTENT DEVELOPMENT

Begin this section by reviewing the important terms and being certain that students understand their meanings. The term *ecology* comes from the Greek word *oikos* meaning house or place to live. Ecol-

ogy is the study of organisms in their surroundings or homes. Point out that groups of similar organisms make up populations; groups of populations make up communities; and communities plus nonliving things make up ecosystems.

Emphasize the idea of interdependence throughout this chapter and especially in this lesson. Ask how all the organisms in your community are related. Have students describe how various organisms in the community function together while they share the same habitat. Ask them to

describe similar relationships in forest or beach habitats.

• **What are some ways living and nonliving factors affect each other?** (Rocks weather and produce soil. When plants get established in the soil they reduce erosions and hold the soil in place. When the plants die, their bodies add organic matter and nutrients to the soil. Thus the soil helps the plant and vice versa.)

Point out that humans, like other organisms, change in response to their environment.

environment consists of all the living and nonliving things with which an organism may interact.

Organisms obtain the food, water, and other resources they need to live and grow from their environment. Consider for a moment some of the things a parrot gets from its rain-forest environment. The parrot feeds on seeds and fruits from plants. It drinks water from puddles and streams. It has trees in which to perch and build its nest. It has air to breathe and to fly through. The parrot can live in a rain forest because this environment contains all the things a parrot needs to survive. Why wouldn't a parrot be able to live in an environment that is quite different from the rain forest, such as the deep sea or a desert? Can you explain why different environments contain different kinds of organisms? ③

Living things do not simply exist in their environment like photos in a frame. They constantly interact with their environment. Organisms can change in response to conditions in the environment. These changes can often be quite rapid. For example, within a few seconds, the fish known as a flounder can change its colors and spots to match the sand and pebbles on a new patch of ocean floor. Or the changes can be much slower. On windswept mountains, for example, trees grow so that they bend in the direction of the wind. Some slow changes involve entire groups of organisms, not just individual organisms. In Section 1–3, you will read about some of the ways organisms have evolved (changed over time) in response to their environment.

In addition to changing in response to their environment, living things also cause change in their environment. Earthworms and other burrowing animals dig tunnels in the soil. Woodpeckers drill holes in trees. Tree roots break up sidewalks. Beavers build dams that block flowing streams and thus create ponds. Can you identify some ways in which humans change their environment? ④

All of the living and nonliving things in an environment are interconnected. You can think of an environment as being like a giant spider web. However, the threads of this web are not spun from silk. The threads of an environment's web are the relationships among its plants, animals, soil, water, temperature, light, and other living and nonliving things.

Figure 1–2 *A few moments ago, the chameleon's environment was changed by the appearance of a juicy cricket. How does the chameleon respond to such short-term changes in its environment?* ②

Figure 1–3 *The relationships among the living and nonliving parts of the environment can be thought of as being like a giant spider web. But an environmental web is more complex—and perhaps more fragile—than the delicate web of a spider.*

G ■ 13

ESL STRATEGY 1–1

So that students may better understand the terminology in this section, have them answer the following questions according to their own world.
• **What kind of ecosystem do you live in?**
• **Where is your community?**
• **What kinds of living things are found in your community?**
• **Where is your habitat?**

ANNOTATION KEY

Answers
① Fish: deep sea. Viper, flowers, macaws: rain forest. (Applying concepts)
② The chameleon responds to the insect's appearance by snapping out its tongue to catch the insect. (Making inferences)
③ These environments do not contain the things the parrot needs to survive. The organisms in an environment depend on the resources available. As the resources change, so will the organisms. (Relating cause and effect)
④ Answers will vary. Possible answers are clearing forests for farms, building cities, making dams to provide electricity. (Applying concepts)

• **How do you change in response to your environment?** (Possible answers: Wear different clothing depending on the weather; tan when exposed to sunlight; stay inside when it is very cold or very hot; use a loud or soft voice depending on the situation.)

GUIDED PRACTICE

Skills Development
Skill: Making a Model

Have students develop a model of their school as an ecosystem. They will need to identify the living and nonliving parts of the system and decide how they interact.
• **Where do the energy, water, and food come from?** (Accept all logical responses.)

• **What are the habitats of the students, teachers, parents, administrators, and support people?** (Accept all logical responses.)

FOCUS/MOTIVATION

Have students describe the environment in which they live versus the environment that they would consider perfect to live in.

Think for a moment about what happens when an insect gets caught in a spider's web. As one thread of the web is disturbed, the shaking motion is transferred to all the threads that are part of the web. In an environmental web, changes in one thread may also be transmitted to other threads and have an effect on them. For example, cutting down the trees in a forest may affect the rainfall in a distant city. And when a thread is broken, the entire web is weakened.

To understand the changes that can occur in an environment and how they can affect the environment, you can study the science called **ecology.** Ecology is the study of the relationships and interactions of living things with one another and with their environment. Scientists who study these interactions are called ecologists.

Ecosystems

Living things inhabit many environments on Earth. From the polar ice caps to the forests and plains of the equator, living things can be found under ground, in air, in water, and on land. Organisms have been found at the bottom of ocean trenches kilometers deep and floating in the air more than eight kilometers above the Earth's surface.

To make sense of the number and variety of interactions among Earth's living things and their environment, ecologists find it useful to divide the world up into separate units known as **ecosystems.** An ecosystem consists of all the living and nonliving things in a given area that interact with one another. A forest ecosystem, for example, includes birds and squirrels in the trees, foxes and rabbits in the bushes, the trees and bushes themselves, insects and spiders, shade-loving wildflowers, ferns, mushrooms and other fungi, microorganisms (microscopic organisms) such as bacteria and protists, dead leaves, chemicals in the soil, rocks, sunlight, rain water, and many other living and nonliving things. How do the trees in a forest ecosystem interact with squirrels? With the soil? ❷

An ecosystem can be as tiny as a drop of pond water or a square meter of a garden. Or it can be as large as an ocean, a forest, or a planet. The size of

Figure 1–4 *A forest of broad-leaved trees is just one of the many kinds of ecosystems on Earth. What kinds of organisms would you find in this ecosystem?* ❶

an ecosystem is defined by the ecologist who is studying it. What ecosystem would you expect an ecologist interested in the interactions of freshwater swimming microorganisms to study? Would an ecologist studying the wildlife in and around Lake Tahoe, California, use a similar ecosystem? Why or why not? ④

It is useful to talk about ecosystems as if they were separate, self-contained units. However, it is important to keep in mind that ecosystems are not isolated. Ecosystems overlap and affect one another. The grizzly bears of a forest ecosystem may feed on the salmon of a stream ecosystem. Chemicals from aerosol cans, air conditioners, and refrigerators in the United States and elsewhere are carried great distances by the wind and eventually break down the protective ozone layer in the air above the poles. The "holes" thus created in the ozone layer allow extra radiation from the sun to reach the ecosystems near the poles, damaging them. Damage to these ecosystems may, in turn, result in damage to other ecosystems—including ones in which you live! So it is important that you realize all the living and nonliving things on Earth are ultimately connected to one another.

Communities

The living part of any ecosystem—all the different organisms that live together in that area—is called a **community.** The community of a pond, for example, might include fishes, frogs, snails, microorganisms, and water lilies. The members of a community interact with one another in many different ways. Lily pads provide a resting place for frogs. Large fishes

Figure 1–5 *A tide-pool ecosystem (inset) is a small part of the Pacific Northwest coast ecosystem. What larger ecosystem would encompass the Pacific coast ecosystem? Why do ecosystems come in all sizes?* ③

ACTIVITY DOING

Identifying Interactions

Ecosystems are all around you. Choose one particular ecosystem—an aquarium, swamp, lake, park, or city block, for example—and study the interactions that occur among the living and nonliving parts of the ecosystem. Include drawings and diagrams in your observations.

G ■ 15

INTEGRATION
SOCIAL STUDIES

Human civilization has flourished more in temperate deciduous forest than in any other environment. As a result, the land in these regions has been greatly altered by human activities, and many species of organisms have become endangered or extinct. Areas where this impact has been particularly great include North America, Europe, Japan, and Australia.

ACTIVITY DOING
IDENTIFYING INTERACTIONS

Skills: Classifying, diagramming, observing, comparing, relating, applying

Encourage students to make on-site observations of the ecosystem they choose. Remind them that, as in all field trips, they should not go alone and they should inform an adult of their whereabouts. Explain that their observations should be analyzed and presented in terms of the ecological concepts covered in this chapter. Ask them to share their drawings and diagrams with the class. Use their drawings to illustrate some of the points you will make while teaching the chapter.

GUIDED PRACTICE

▶ *Laboratory Manual*

At this point you may want to have students complete the Chapter 1 Laboratory Investigation, Examining an Unknown Community, in the *Laboratory Manual.* Through this investigation, students will gain insights into the way field ecologists study a community.

CONTENT DEVELOPMENT

The hole in the ozone layer allows more ultraviolet radiation to reach the ecosystems of Antarctica than in past years. Some recent data suggest that the excess radiation is reducing the rate of photosynthesis in the Antarctic phytoplankton. If this is the case, the amount of food available in the system is also being reduced. In addition, oxygen production and carbon dioxide uptake are reduced. This leads to an increase in the amount of

greenhouse gases in the atmosphere.

● ● ● ● **Integration** ● ● ● ●

Use the discussion of the ozone layer to integrate concepts of weather in your lesson.

INDEPENDENT PRACTICE

▶ *Activity Book*

Students who need help understanding the concepts of community and population should be provided with the Chapter 1 activity, Populations in Your Community.

WHAT, IF ANYTHING, IS A SPECIES?

The standard working definition of species does not apply to organisms that reproduce asexually. Microbiologists examine both the external and internal characteristics of bacteria and protists to help determine whether particular organisms belong in the same species. A useful, if not particularly informative, definition of species that works for these organisms is: A group of similar organisms that is given a two-part scientific name.

BIOTIC POTENTIAL

The *biotic potential* of a species is defined as the size that a population would reach if all offspring were to survive and produce young. For example, two elephants, under ideal conditions, would produce 19 million descendants after 750 years. In actuality, no population ever reaches its biotic potential. The factors that prevent its ideal growth are called *limiting factors* or *environmental resistance*.

Figure 1–6 *The plains of Africa are home to many different kinds of living things. What members of the African plains community can you identify here?* ❶

Figure 1–7 *Some populations— such as that of the flamingoes in Botswana, Africa—are enormous. Others—such as that of the treehoppers on a twig in Costa Rica—are quite small.*

eat frogs. Microorganisms break down the bodies of dead organisms, producing products such as nitrogen compounds that can be used by plants. Can you think of some other ways in which the members of a pond community interact? In the next two sections, ❷ you will learn about some of the specific interactions that take place within communities.

Populations

You, like all other living things on Earth, belong to an ecological community. Your community probably contains many different kinds of living things: people, dogs, cats, birds, insects, grass, and trees, to name a few. What other kinds of organisms are found in your community? ❸

Each kind of living thing makes up a **population** in the community. A population is a group of organisms of the same type, or species, living together in the same area. (A species is a group of similar organisms that can produce offspring. You and all other humans belong to the same species. But cats belong to another species.) For example, all the rainbow trout living in a lake are a population. All the redwood trees in a forest are a population.

1–1 (continued)

Compare the terms *community* and *population*. Point out that a population is made up of only one type of organism. All organisms of a particular type that live in the same general area make up a population.

• **What types of populations live in your area?** (People, squirrels, grasses, and so on.)

• **Why do you think these particular populations live where they do?** (They are able to find the resources needed for life such as food, water, and shelter.)

• **Which populations would be most likely to move to another area and survive?** (People and birds.)

• **What is another name for the kinds of living things that make up populations?** (Species.)

Explain to students that habitats sometimes overlap. If the organisms do not eat the same food, however, there is usu-

ally no problem. For example, a squirrel inhabits the inside of a hollow tree trunk and gets its food among the leaves on the ground. These leaves may be the habitat of a land snail. But since the snail is not looking for the same food as the squirrel, the overlapping of habitats causes little interaction between the two animals.

The mites that live in moth ears are almost always found in only one ear of the moth. This is because the mites interfere

But a group consisting of all the wildflowers in a meadow is not considered to be a population. Can you explain why? **4**

Habitats

Where would you go to find a lion? How about a pigeon? Where in a forest would you look for a squirrel? A mushroom? An earthworm? Would you discover all these organisms in the same place? Probably not. Lions live on the grassy plains of Africa. Pigeons live in cities, among other places. In a forest, squirrels live in the trees, mushrooms grow on the forest floor, and earthworms burrow in the soil. Each of these organisms lives in a different place.

The place in which an organism lives is called its **habitat.** A habitat provides food, shelter, and the other resources an organism needs to survive. Living things such as lions, pigeons, and mushrooms live in different habitats because they have different requirements for survival. Organisms such as lions, zebras, and giraffes also have different requirements for survival. Yet these organisms live in the same habitat. Why? Because their requirements—such as for temperature, water, and open space—overlap in many ways. The size of an organism's habitat depends on the organism's habits and needs. The habitat of a humpback whale is the open ocean. The habitat of a certain tiny mite, on the other hand, is the ear of a moth.

ACTIVITY
DISCOVERING

Home Sweet Home

1. Choose one of the following animals and find out what kind of shelter it builds: beaver, trapdoor spider, mud dauber wasp, prairie dog, cliff swallow, termite, weaver bird, mole rat, toucan, carrier shell (*Xenophora*), coral gall crab.

2. On a sheet of paper, draw a picture of the animal's shelter and make a list of the materials needed to build it.

3. Build a model of your animal's shelter using the same materials the animal would use whenever possible.

■ Predict what would happen if the materials that an animal uses to build its shelter were not available.

1–1 Section Review

1. Why do ecologists study both the nonliving and living things in an environment?
2. What is an ecosystem? Give an example of an ecosystem.
3. What is the difference between a community and a population?

Connection—*Architecture*
4. Explain why an architect designing a new home for the cheetahs in a zoo must know something about the natural habitat of cheetahs.

ACTIVITY
DISCOVERING
HOME SWEET HOME

Discovery Learning

Skills: Making models, relating, diagramming, applying, comparing, predicting

Students will gain a better knowledge of the habitats of various organisms through this activity. Encourage them to use everyday materials from home to construct their habitats. Place the best habitats on display when the activity has been completed.

---

with the moth's ability to detect predatory bats. If the mites lived in both ears, the moth's hearing would be so impaired that it would soon be eaten—along with its resident mites.

▶ *Activity Book*
Students will be challenged by the Chapter 1 activity, Carrying Capacity.

1-2 Food and Energy in the Environment

Guide for Reading

Focus on these questions as you read.

▶ How do producers, consumers, and decomposers interact?
▶ What is the difference between a food chain and a food web?

1-2 Food and Energy in the Environment

If you enjoy watching or playing team sports, you know that the members of a team usually play different positions. Basketball players may be centers, forwards, or guards. Baseball players may be pitchers, catchers, shortstops, center fielders, and so on. Each position has a particular role associated with it. For example, a pitcher throws the ball to the batters. A guard tries to prevent the members of the other team from scoring a basket. Similarly, organisms have special roles that they play in an ecosystem.

Energy Roles

Organisms may be **producers, consumers,** or **decomposers.** These three terms indicate how an organism obtains energy and how it interacts with the other living things in its community.

PRODUCERS Some organisms, such as green plants and certain microorganisms, have a very special ability that sets them apart from all other living things: They can make their own food. Such organisms are known as producers. Producers are able to use a source of energy (such as sunlight) to turn simple raw materials (such as water and carbon dioxide gas) into food (such as the sugar glucose). Organisms that cannot make their own food may eat the producers directly. Or they may eat other organisms that cannot make their own food. However, all organisms that cannot make their own food ultimately depend on producers. **Producers are the source of all the food in an ecosystem.**

Figure 1–8 *Towering redwood trees, indigo Texas bluebonnets, and bright pink phlox are examples of producers. Why are producers essential for life on Earth?* ●

18 ■ G

CONSUMERS Organisms that cannot make their own food depend on producers for food and energy. **An organism that feeds directly or indirectly on producers is called a consumer.**

There are many kinds of consumers. Some organisms, such as grasshoppers and rabbits, are plant eaters. Plant eaters are known as herbivores. The term herbivore comes from the Latin words *herba,* which means grass or herb, and *vorare,* which means to eat. Spiders, snakes, and wolves, which eat other animals, are known as carnivores. The Latin word *carnis* means of the flesh. Why is the term carnivore appropriate for organisms that eat meat? ❷

Organisms that eat both plants and animals are known as omnivores. (The Latin word *omnis* means all.) Crows, bears, and humans are just a few examples of omnivores.

There are many other terms that are used to group consumers according to what they eat. One such term is scavenger. A scavenger is an animal that feeds on the bodies of dead animals. Jackals, hyenas, and vultures are examples of scavengers. So are certain crayfish and crabs, who "clean up" watery environments by eating dead organisms.

DECOMPOSERS After living things die, organisms called decomposers use the dead matter as food. **Decomposers break down dead organisms into simpler substances.** In the process, they return important

Figure 1–9 *The caterpillars, shark, and hyena and vulture are all consumers.*

ACTIVITY DOING

Diet Delights

1. Use a dictionary to find out what these specialized feeders eat: piscivore, insectivore, detritovore, myrmecophage, frugivore, coprophage, necrophage, nectarivore, granivore, apivore, carpophage.

2. Invent a term to describe the feeding habits of Count Dracula (and other vampires).

Activity Bank

Garbage in the Garden, p.138

ACTIVITY DOING

DIET DELIGHTS

Skills: Comparing, classifying, relating, applying

Materials: Reference books

The foods eaten by the organisms are piscivore, fish; insectivore, insects; detritovore, decaying organisms; myrmecophage, ants; frugivore, fruit; coprophage, dung; necrophage, dead animals; nectarivore, nectar; granivore, grain; apivore, bees; carpophage, fruit.

Count Dracula might be called a bloodovore, a hemophage, or a sanguivore. The technical term is *hematophage.*

Integration: Use this Activity to integrate language arts into your science lesson.

Use the study of the Latin root words *herba* and *vorare* to integrate the topic of language arts in your lesson.

GUIDED PRACTICE

Skills Development

Skill: Interpreting illustrations

Use the photographs of the Malay lacewing butterfly caterpillars, the sand tiger shark, and the spotted hyena and hooded vulture feeding on a Cape buffalo. Have the students identify the group of consumers for each animal. (Caterpillars are herbivores; rest are carnivores.)

▶ *Laboratory Manual*

To reinforce the concept of interdependence, have students complete the Chapter 1 Laboratory Investigation, Investigating Relationships in an Ecosystem, in the *Laboratory Manual.*

REINFORCEMENT/RETEACHING

Distinguish between scavengers and decomposers by pointing out that scavengers use the energy in dead organisms to carry on their life processes. They store the nutrients as complex molecules. Decomposers also use the energy for life processes, but they release most of the nutrients into the environment as simple chemicals.

INDEPENDENT PRACTICE

▶ *Activity Book*

To help students understand the role of decomposers in an ecosystem, assign the Chapter 1 activity, Observing Decay.

ODD OR EVEN?

One ecological theory is that food chains with an even number of levels depress the number of plants in an ecosystem. In a two-level chain containing just plants and herbivores, the plants are limited. Add a third level of carnivores and the plants will increase (because their predators have decreased). Add a fourth level, and the plants are once again limited in number. If the theory is proven true, adding herbivore-eating organisms to ecosystems may make them "greener."

ACTIVITY
DOING

YOUR PLACE IN LINE

Skills: Classifying, diagramming, relating, applying

Students should understand that they are to trace each food back to a producer. For example, milk, cow, grain. For which foods would students be classified as herbivores? (Grains, bread, fruits, vegetables.) For which foods would they be classified as carnivores? (Meats, fish, and animal products such as eggs.) You might have students collect data for the entire class to see if more foods are on the second or third level of the food chain. Which foods are more often considered "good for you"? (Those on the second level.)

Integration: Use this Activity to integrate nutrition into your science lesson.

Figure 1–10 *Nestled among the fallen leaves on the forest floor, these mushrooms are slowly breaking down a dead branch for food. Why are mushrooms considered to be decomposers?* 1

ACTIVITY

Your Place in Line

Every time you eat, you are assuming a particular place in a food chain. You can determine your place in a food chain through the following activity.

Make a list of all the foods you ate for breakfast, lunch, and dinner. For each food, figure out the probable links in the food chain that lead up to you. Be sure to answer the following questions:
1. Who are the producers?
2. Who are the consumers?

materials to the soil and water. You may be familiar with the term "decay," which is often used to describe this process. Molds, mushrooms, and many kinds of bacteria are examples of decomposers.

Decomposers are essential to the ecosystem because they rid the environment of the bodies of dead plants and animals. Even more importantly, decomposers return nutrients (compounds containing chemicals such as nitrogen, carbon, phosphorus, sulfur, and magnesium) to the environment. These nutrients are then used by plants to make food, and the cycle of nutrients through the environment continues. If the nutrients were not returned to the environment, organisms within that ecosystem could not survive for long.

Food Chains and Food Webs

In general, food and energy in an ecosystem flow from the producers to the consumers, and finally to the decomposers. The food and energy links among the producers and consumers in an ecosystem are represented by **food chains** and **food webs**.

A food chain represents a series of events in which food and energy are transferred from one organism in an ecosystem to another. The first link in a food chain is always a producer. The second link is a herbivore. The third link and all the links after that are almost always carnivores.

Let's take a look at an example of a food chain. In an Antarctic food chain, the producers are one-celled organisms known as diatoms. The diatoms capture energy from the sun and use it to make food. When a diatom is eaten by a shrimplike animal called a krill, the food energy and matter in the diatom are transferred to the krill. In the following links of the food chain, the krill is eaten by a squid, which is eaten by a penguin, which is eaten by a leopard seal, which is eaten by a killer whale. Both food energy and matter are transferred at each successive link of the food chain. Figure 1–11 illustrates another food chain.

The "end" of a food chain is connected to the "beginning" by decomposers. In the Antarctic food chain, decomposers break down the body of the killer whale when it dies. This makes matter in the

---

1–2 (continued)

CONTENT DEVELOPMENT

Have students trace (on paper) the food energy from their last meal back to the sun.
• **Is this an example of a food chain or a food web?** (Unless students ate only one item, they should draw a food web.) Point out that in nature a food web is a far more accurate way of depicting the relationships among various organisms than a food chain is.

• **Why is a food web a better way of describing the path of food in an ecosystem?** (Because it is rare that an organism eats only one type of food.)
• **Why are so many plants needed to support herbivores?** (Most herbivores are not very efficient at converting the energy stored in plants into animal tissue, so they need large quantities of plants.)

Media and Technology

Use the transparencies in your *Transparency Binder* called Food Web and En-

ergy Pyramid to help develop the concepts in this section.

INDEPENDENT PRACTICE

▶ *Activity Book*

To help students better understand food chains and webs, assign the Chapter 1 activities, Find the Food Chain and A Food Web.

form of nutrients available to the producers. What do the producers do with these nutrients? **2**

A food chain gives you a glimpse of the food and energy relationships in an ecosystem. But it does not give you the whole picture. There are many organisms in an ecosystem, and few of them eat only one kind of food. Thus there must be more than one food chain in an ecosystem. Figure 1–12 on page 22 shows how a number of organisms in the Antarctic ecosystem are linked by food and energy relationships. This kind of diagram is known as a food web. Can you see why the name food web is an appropriate one? A food web consists of many overlapping food chains. One of the food chains in this food web was just described. Another food chain might be: a diatom is eaten by a tiny water animal that is eaten by a fish that is eaten by a penguin. Take a moment now to identify three of the many other food chains in this food web.

Feeding Levels and Energy

A feeding level is the location of an organism along a food chain. Producers form the first feeding level. Herbivores form the second feeding level. And carnivores form the third feeding level.

At each feeding level, organisms use the energy they obtain to digest their food, reproduce, move,

Figure 1–11 *The links of this desert food chain include a flowering Saguaro cactus (left), an iguana (top right), and a roadrunner (bottom right). What role does each organism play in this food chain?* **3**

G ■ 21

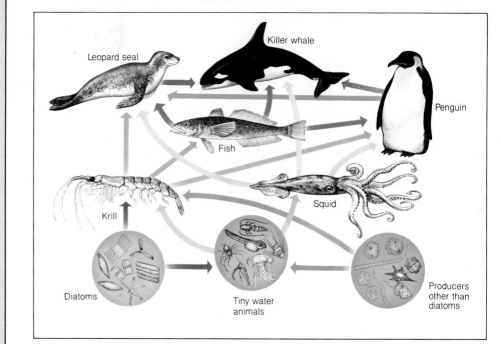

Figure 1–12 *Food webs can be quite complicated, even when they show only a few of the organisms in an ecosystem. What are the producers in this Antarctic food web? What are the herbivores and carnivores?* ❶

grow, and carry out other life activities. What does this mean for living things at higher feeding levels? It means that there is less energy available to them. As you can see in Figure 1–13, the amount of energy at the second feeding level is much smaller than that at the first feeding level. The amount of energy at the third feeding level is smaller still. At each successive level, there is less energy than there was before. Because a diagram that shows the amount of energy at the different feeding levels looks like a pyramid—wide at the base and narrowing toward the top—it is called a pyramid of energy.

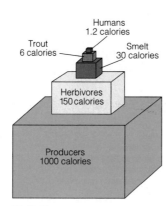

Figure 1–13 *With each successive feeding level, the amount of energy decreases greatly. How does the amount of energy in trout compare to that in smelt? Why can more people be fed if smelt is eaten instead of trout? Why do some experts think that a first step in solving the problem of world hunger might be to encourage people to eat lower on the food chain?* ❷

22 ■ G

1. Explain how producers, consumers, and decomposers interact. For each energy role, give two examples of organisms that perform that role in their ecosystem.
2. What is a food chain? A food web?
3. What is the relationship between feeding levels and amount of available energy?
4. How does energy flow through an ecosystem?

Critical Thinking—*Evaluating Diagrams*
5. Why are decomposers left out of almost all diagrams of food chains and food webs? Do you think this is a good practice? Why or why not?

1–3 Interaction and Evolution

Each organism in a community has its own unique role to play. This role, or **niche** (NIHCH), consists of more than the organism's place in a food chain. It includes everything the organism does and everything the organism needs in its environment. In other words, an organism's niche includes the place in which it lives, the food it eats, the organisms that feed on it, the organisms that interact with it in other ways, the amount of light and humidity it needs, and the physical conditions in which it can survive.

As you learned in the previous section, two or more species (kinds of organisms) can share the same habitat, or place in which to live. For example, the coral reef habitat is home to corals that build stony skeletons, soft flowerlike sea anemones, flat ribbons and thin threads of seaweed, spiny sea urchins, scuttling crabs, fishes in a rainbow of colors, and many other organisms. Two species can also share similar habits and food requirements. For example, flying fox bats and toucans are both flying animals that live in trees and eat fruit. Sharks and

Guide for Reading

Focus on this question as you read.
▶ *What are competition, predation, and symbiosis?*

ACTIVITY DOING

Eat or Be Eaten

Draw a food web that contains the following: bread crumbs, food scraps, pigeon, mouse, cockroach, cat, rat, bacteria, starling, spider, fly. Where would you be likely to find this food web? What feeding level is missing from this food web? Why is this feeding level missing?

G ■ 23

MULTICULTURAL OPPORTUNITY 1–3

In the classroom students typically interact competitively, cooperatively, individually, or in groups. Ask students to give examples of school activities where competition or cooperation is required, and tell whether it is more effective for them to work competitively or cooperatively. Note that competition, cooperation, and individualism are culture-bound concepts. In the United States, competitiveness is viewed as a positive trait, while other cultures—for example, the Japanese—place a much stronger emphasis on cooperation.

ESL STRATEGY 1–3

To reinforce some of the terms in this section, write the items below in two columns on the board. Have students match the words in Column A with their definitions in Column B. Then have them read their answers aloud.

Column A host, niche, competition, predators, prey, symbiosis, commensalism, mutualism, parasitism, parasite

Column B 1. symbiosis: one organism gains; other not harmed; 2. living things eaten by predators; 3. organisms living near, on, or inside another; at least one benefits; 4. flea; 5. symbiosis: one organism harmed; 6. all that organisms do and need in an environment; 7. symbiosis: both organisms benefit; 8. dog; 9. battle to survive; 10. living things that eat living things.

TEACHING STRATEGY 1–3

FOCUS/MOTIVATION

Display pictures from the textbook or other photographs of nature scenes. Ask students to identify an organism in the photograph and the habitat, or place in which it lives. Then have students identify or speculate about the following points: what the organism eats, what organisms could feed on it, what other organisms could interact with it, what physical conditions it needs to survive. After discussing several photographs, help students conclude that the role of the organism, or its niche, includes everything it does and everything it needs from its environment.

Then ask students to give the same information about themselves and their relationship with their environment.

CONTENT DEVELOPMENT

Explain that populations have different niches because they have different food needs, hunting methods, and ways of protecting themselves. Niche is often described as an organism's occupation, or the way it makes a living. Habitat is likened to an address, or place where an organism lives. Have students look at the organisms shown in Figure 1–12. They all share the same address—the Antarctic. Some eat the same things or are eaten by the same things, but no two species have exactly the same role or occupation in the ecosystem.

Figure 1–14 *The flying fox bat of Australia and the Toco toucan of Brazil both enjoy feasting on fruit. How are their niches similar? How are they different?* ❶

dolphins are fast-swimming ocean animals that both eat fish. Two or more species *cannot* share the same niche. If two species try to occupy the same niche for a long period of time, one of the species will become extinct, or die off. Why? The answer has to do with a special kind of relationship between organisms—a relationship you are now going to read about.

Competition

Ecosystems cannot satisfy the needs of all the living things in a particular habitat. There is only a limited amount of food, water, shelter, light, and other resources in an environment. Because there are not enough resources to go around, organisms must struggle with one another to get the things they need to survive. This type of interaction is known as **competition.**

One of the resources for which organisms compete is food. The shortage of other resources, such as water, light, and suitable places to live, also results in competition. Regardless of the specific causes, competition can have a powerful effect on the size and location of a population in an ecosystem.

Competition can occur within a species as well as between species. A male lion will fight with another male lion for control over a group of female lions. Pairs of penguins squabble with other pairs of penguins over the pebbles used in nest building. And if there is not enough space between two plants of the same species, they will compete with one another for

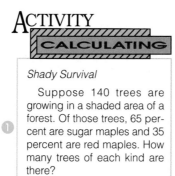

ACTIVITY
CALCULATING

Shady Survival

❶ Suppose 140 trees are growing in a shaded area of a forest. Of those trees, 65 percent are sugar maples and 35 percent are red maples. How many trees of each kind are there?

24 ■ G

---

24 ■ G

ACTIVITY
CALCULATING

SHADY SURVIVAL

Skills: Computational, calculator

Students should not have difficulty determining the percentages. Review with them how to change the percent to a decimal by moving the decimal point two places. Then ask students to multiply .65 × 140 and .35 × 140. There are 91 sugar maple trees and 49 red maples.

Integration: Use this Activity to integrate mathematics into your science lesson.

1–3 (continued)

Skills Development

Skill: Applying concepts

Have students make a list of animals native to their area and ask them to describe the habitats and niches of these animals. They may want to compile the information in chart form for easy reference.

REINFORCEMENT/RETEACHING

Make sure students understand the difference between a habitat and a niche. Often students incorrectly understand a niche as spatial rather than a role-related concept. Point out that a habitat is an area of the environment. To be successful, an organism's habitat must provide it with food and shelter. A niche is the particular role an organism plays in its habitat. That is, a niche includes only the part of the habitat that a particular organism needs or uses.

CONTENT DEVELOPMENT

A given environment has only a certain amount of space, food, water, and other life essentials. Because of this, the size of a population will be limited to the number of individuals that can obtain what they need. When there are many more individuals than there are resources, competition results.

water, nutrients, and light. (This is why gardeners have to thin out seedlings in a flower bed or vegetable patch.)

In order to better understand how competition works in nature, it might be helpful for you to think about some more familiar kinds of competition. People who read for a play, audition for a musical group, or try out for a sports team compete with one another for limited resources: roles, chairs, and positions, respectively. Nonliving things can also be thought of as being in competition with one another. Have you ever walked down the aisle of a supermarket and gazed in amazement at the number of different kinds of breakfast cereal displayed? Like living things, products such as breakfast cereals, cars, shampoos, blue jeans, and even science textbooks compete with one another for a limited resource. In this case, the resource is a customer's purchase choice. The products that are most successful at obtaining this resource (the ones that are bought most often) continue to be sold. The products that are least successful soon cease to be manufactured.

Predation

Slowly and silently, the cat sneaks up on an unsuspecting mouse. The cat crouches down. The tip of its tail twitches and its muscles tense. Then the cat pounces!

For thousands of years, people have valued the cat's ability to kill rats and mice. Living things, such as cats, that catch, kill, and eat other living things

Activity Bank

On Your Mark, Get Set, Grow!, p.141

"Avenues of Delight and Discovery"

The works of Rachel Carson (1907–1964) prove that scientific writings can be as beautiful and poetic as any work of literature. Although she was a marine biologist by training, two of her most famous books are not about the sea and its creatures. Read *The Silent Spring* and *The Sense of Wonder*, by Rachel Carson. Explore the beauty and mystery of the natural world by simply making a trip to the library!

G ■ 25

• **If an organism is involved in competition for life essentials, what are the possible outcomes for that organism?** (The organism may win the struggle and survive or it may lose the struggle and die; possibly the organism will be able to coexist with its competitor if the differences between them are great enough.)

• **Is there any other alternative for organisms that find themselves in competition with other organisms?** (If the competition is between different yet similar species, the organisms may change in ways that

will decrease the competition. In this way, both species may be able to survive.)

GUIDED PRACTICE

Skills Development

Skill: Predicting

Have students list factors that affect the survival of organisms, such as food, water, shelter, and space. Have students predict what factors will limit the number of people on the Earth. After you have listed several factors on the chalkboard, discuss

each one. Have students rank them from the most important to the least important.

INDEPENDENT PRACTICE

▶ *Activity Book*

Students who need practice with the concept of competition should complete the Chapter 1 activity, Competition.

ANIMAL INVASION

When European settlers arrived in Australia two hundred years ago, the only mammals on the continent were marsupials, bats, mice, rats, echidnas, and platypuses. The settlers wanted the familiar animals from their homes. They brought in horses, sheep, cattle, deer, foxes, goats, cats, pigs, camels, water buffaloes, and rabbits. Two dozen rabbits were imported into the country in 1859, and in less than fifty years there were millions of rabbits in Australia.

FACTS AND FIGURES

PREDATOR IN THE SEA

Predators come in many shapes and sizes. In the South Pacific Ocean the crown-of-thorns starfish preys on the creatures that build coral reefs. It pushes its stomach out over a coral colony, releases enzymes that dissolve the soft bodies of the creatures, and then absorbs the liquid. A recent invasion of these starfish has caused serious destruction of parts of the Great Barrier Reef off the northeast coast of Australia.

1–3 (continued)

CONTENT DEVELOPMENT

Competition is often described as a struggle, but most organisms evolve ways to reduce competition. Small differences in the place where organisms feed, what they feed on, and even the time they feed all help to reduce competition between organisms of different species.

• **What does the idea of niche tell us about competition?** (Because two species cannot occupy the same niche, they cannot directly compete with each other for all their needs. This is called the competitive exclusion principle.)

• **What about organisms of the same species?** (Most competition is between members of the same species because they have the same niche and the same adaptations to use the niche. This is called

Figure 1–16 *How can you tell that the lioness (right), the great blue heron (top left), and the hawk (bottom left) are predators? What kinds of prey do these predators* ❶ *hunt? By the way, the attacking redwing blackbird is not trying to prey on the hawk. The hawk simply flew too close to the blackbird's nest, upsetting the smaller bird.*

26 ■ G

are called **predators.** The organisms that are eaten by predators are called **prey.** Although people usually think of predators and their prey as being animals, ecologists consider just about all situations in which one organism kills and eats another as examples of predation.

Predation, like competition, plays an important part in shaping the structure of communities. In catching and eating prey, predators help to reduce the size of prey populations. By helping to control the size of prey populations, predators also help to maintain the diversity in an ecosystem. When predators are absent, prey species can become too numerous and crowd out other organisms.

This is exactly what happened with the rabbits that were introduced to Australia about 150 years ago by European settlers. The rabbits had few predators, so their population increased very quickly. These harmless-looking animals were soon stripping the grasslands bare of vegetation. Many of the native animals that also fed on this vegetation, such as kangaroos, starved. To save their herds, cattle ranchers put up special fences to keep the rabbits out of their pastures. This situation continued until the 1950s, when scientists introduced a rabbit-killing predator to Australia: a virus that caused a fatal rabbit disease. The disease killed off about 80 percent of the rabbits, making it possible to reclaim land for native Australian wildlife and livestock.

intraspecific competition.)

• **Give some examples of plant populations competing with one another.** (Answers will vary but should include competition for light, water, and nutrients.)

Point out that plants have also developed ways to avoid competition. Vines and air plants have developed adaptations to help them reduce competition for light.

ENRICHMENT

▶ *Activity Book*
Students will be challenged by the

Chapter 1 activity, What Goes Up Must Come Down.

CONTENT DEVELOPMENT

Point out to students that often both predator and prey benefit from their relationship. Predators obtain food from their prey. Prey also benefit because predators keep their population at a level that the environment can support in terms of food, shelter, water, and so on.

• **What might happen if all the prey of a certain predator were destroyed?** (The

PROBLEM Solving

To Bee or Not to Bee

The honeybees in the United States are in trouble! Pests from distant lands have been accidentally introduced into this country. These pests now threaten the $150-million-a-year beekeeping industry. Agricultural researchers, bee specialists, and other experts are searching frantically for a way to fight these pests before it's too late. Can you help them find a solution to the problem of the pests?

For each of the following situations, (1) identify the type of interaction involved, (2) describe the problem you perceive and propose a solution, and (3) predict the effects that the situation may have on the further evolution of the honeybee.

Evaluating situations

1. Tracheal mites live inside a bee's breathing tubes. There they suck fluids from the bee's body and interfere with its breathing. American honeybees are descendants of European honeybees, which rarely have tracheal mites. However, tracheal mites have been a major problem for American honeybees since 1984.

2. *Varroa* mites, which were first discovered in the United States in September 1987, attach to the outside of adult bees and young bees. The mites weaken the bees by feeding on their body fluids. In addition, they may transmit diseases from one bee to another.

3. Although "killer bees" belong to the same species as American honeybees, they are much more aggressive. Killer bees were accidentally released in Brazil in 1957. Since then, they have been expanding their range northward. In October 1990, the first swarm of killer bees entered the United States.

predator would either have to find a new food source or it too would die.)

• **What might happen if all the predators of a particular organism were killed off?** (The prey would first multiply. But after exhausting all available resources due to its increased numbers, the prey would soon begin to die off as well because the ecosystem could no longer support the entire population.)

PROBLEM SOLVING
TO BEE OR NOT TO BEE

This feature enables students to apply their knowledge of interactions among organisms to three situations.

1. Parasitism. The mites feed off the bees and weaken them. Accept all logical solutions and predictions. Over the course of many generations American honeybees have lost their resistance to the mites. Beekeepers are currently fumigating their hives with menthol to discourage the mites. Scientists have imported resistant bees from England, which they intend to breed with American bees. They hope that the resistant bees will pass their resistance to their offspring. In time, the bees may evolve so that they become resisant to the parasite.

2. Parasitism. The mites feed off the bees, weaken them, and make them more vulnerable to diseases. Accept all logical solutions and predictions. An insecticide is currently being used to control the *Varroa* mites. In time, the bees may evolve so that they become resistant to the parasite.

3. Competition. The "killer bees" may displace the American honeybees. Accept all logical solutions and predictions. Scientists hope that the aggressive qualities of the "killer bees" may be reduced as they interbreed with normal domestic bees. Some experts have proposed new ways of handling hives in order to work safely with these more aggressive bees. It is possible that the "killer bees" will interbreed with the American bees to produce a genetically diverse and useful strain of honeybee.

Mutualism between organisms often takes the form of a "cleaning" relationship. Certain fish clean parasites and dead tissue off other fish. Even predators such as sharks will not eat the cleaners. Often the cleaners are located in a fixed place, and their customers line up to visit the cleaning station!

In many examples of commensalism, one organism serves as a host—literally. That organism is usually better able to attract or gather food than its partner is. The partner hangs around waiting for the host to eat and then it gets some of the food, too—often the leftovers, but never enough to be a problem for the host. The cowbird follows the herd as it stirs up insects. The plover follows the farmer's plow for the same reason. Gulls follow ships and wait for scraps to be thrown overboard. The vulture follows the predators and waits for them to make a kill.

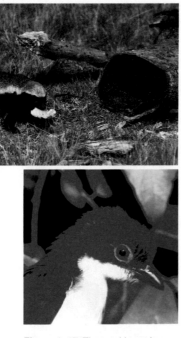

Figure 1–17 *The ratel loves honey, but cannot easily find beehives (top). The honeyguide can easily find beehives, but is too small, weak, and vulnerable to bee stings to get at the beeswax it likes to eat (bottom). Together, the ratel and honeyguide can obtain their favorite treats. What is this kind of partnership called?* ❷

Symbiosis

In a tropical ocean, a remora fish uses a structure on top of its head to attach itself to the belly of a shark and get a free ride. Chirping and fluttering, a honeyguide bird in Africa leads a furry black-and-white ratel to a wild beehive. With its sharp claws, the ratel rips open the hive. The ratel then laps up the honey as the honeyguide bird dines on beeswax. In the United States, a dog sleeping on a rug suddenly sits up and begins to scratch an itchy flea bite.

What do these events have in common? They are all examples of **symbiosis** (sihm-bigh-OH-sihs; plural: symbioses). **Symbiosis is a close relationship between two organisms in which one organism lives near, on, or even inside another organism and in which at least one organism benefits.** Symbioses are placed into three categories: **commensalism, mutualism,** and **parasitism.** In commensalism, one of the organisms benefits and the other is not harmed by the association. In mutualism, both organisms benefit. And in parasitism, one organism benefits and the other is harmed. Is the relationship between a dog and a flea an example of commensalism, mutualism, or parasitism? What kind of symbiosis do you have with a pet animal? ❶

As you read the following examples of commensalism, mutualism, and parasitism, keep in mind that science is a constantly changing body of knowledge. New observations may lead scientists to conclude that what was thought to be one kind of symbiosis is in fact another kind altogether. Try to think of additional ways in which the partners in a symbiosis may help—or harm—each other.

COMMENSALISM High in the branches of a tree, a large, fierce hawk called an osprey builds a big, flat nest for its eggs. Smaller birds, such as sparrows and wrens, set up their homes beneath the osprey's nest. Because the osprey eats mostly fish, these smaller birds are in no danger from the osprey. In fact, the little birds obtain protection from their enemies by living close to the fierce hawk.

Beautiful orchids and exotic bromeliads (relatives of pineapples) survive in dense, shadowy jungles by growing on tall trees. There among the tree branches, the plants get a great deal of sunlight. The roots

28 ■ G

1–3 (continued)

CONTENT DEVELOPMENT

Use the example of the osprey and the sparrow to illustrate the concept of commensalism. Point out that commensalism is a form of symbiosis in which one partner benefits and the other partner is neither benefited nor harmed.

• **In what ways are the sparrows helped by their relationship with the osprey?** (They are protected by the hawk, who scares off their natural enemies.)

• **In what ways is the osprey helped or hurt by its relationship with the sparrows?** (It is neither helped nor hurt. The sparrows do not give anything to the hawk that it needs, but neither do they take away anything that it needs.)

• **What do you think would happen to the sparrow population if there were a decrease in the osprey population?** (There would most likely be a decrease in the sparrow population because the sparrows would lose one of their protective mechanisms.)

• **What do you think would happen to the osprey population if there were a decrease in the sparrow population?** (The osprey population would most likely be unaffected.)

Discuss other examples of commensalism, such as orchids and trees, and humans and mites.

CONTENT DEVELOPMENT

Explain to students that mutualism is a type of symbiosis that occurs when both organisms benefit from the relationship.

of these plants are exposed, so they can take water and nutrients right out of the air or off the surface of the tree's bark. Can you explain why the relationship between a bromeliad and a tree is an example of commensalism? ❸

Like a giant tropical tree, you have smaller members of your community living on you. Dozens of tiny mites live at the base of the hairs that make up your eyebrows. Don't rush to the mirror to check—these mites can be seen only with a microscope. And don't worry about being a home to these mites. They are quite harmless, and everybody has them!

MUTUALISM Remember the ants and aphids you read about at the beginning of this chapter? This relationship is one of the many examples of mutualism that exist among Earth's living things.

The goby fish and snapping shrimp shown in Figure 1–19 on page 30 live in a sandy burrow built by the shrimp. Because the shrimp is nearly blind, it keeps one of its long feelers on the goby. When danger approaches, the goby warns its partner with flicks of its fins, and both partners retreat to their burrow. Neither the goby nor the shrimp can survive on its own. Gobies without homes and shrimp without guides are soon eaten up by predators.

Some of the most important (if not the most interesting) examples of mutualism involve microorganisms that live inside the body of much larger partners. The microorganisms obtain a safe home

Figure 1–18 *Sea anemones use stinging tentacles to catch and stun small fishes and other prey. This clownfish, however, is immune to the anemone's sting and thus is safe in the anemone's deadly embrace (left). The bromeliads that grow on forest trees are in turn involved in commensalism with smaller creatures, such as this red-eyed tree frog, that make their home in the vaselike center of the plant (right).*

G ■ 29

FACTS AND FIGURES

THE PLOVER

A tiny bird called the plover plays dentist to a crocodile in another example of mutualism. The plover hops inside the crocodile's mouth and feeds on the blood-sucking leeches found there. After its tasty meal, the bird hops out, leaving the crocodile free of pests.

FACTS AND FIGURES

ONE KILOGRAM EQUALS A TON!

To gain 1 kilogram of mass, a person must eat about 10 kilograms of fish. But these fish must eat 100 kilograms of animal plankton, which in turn must eat 1000 kilograms of plant organisms. So it takes 1000 kilograms (a ton) of producers to produce 1 kilogram of weight in a human.

Use the example of the ratel and the honeyguide bird to illustrate the concept of mutualism.

• **In what way is the ratel helped by its relationship with the honeyguide bird?** (The ratel is led to honey, its food source, by the honeyguide bird.)

• **In what way is the honeyguide bird helped by its relationship with the ratel?** (The ratel breaks into the bees' hive and exposes the beeswax that the honeyguide eats.)

• **What do you think might happen to the ratel population if there were a decrease in the honeyguide population?** (The ratel population might decrease if there were not a suitable food substitute.)

• **What do you think would happen to the honeyguide population if there were a decrease in the ratel population?** (The honeyguide population might decrease if there were not a suitable food substitute.)

Discuss other examples of mutualism with students, such as the ants and the aphids, and the goby fish and the snapping shrimp.

ENRICHMENT

Offer students the following situations and have them identify each as an example of commensalism or mutualism.

A worm lives in a shell with a hermit crab. When the crab feeds, the worm feeds, too.

Ants live in thorny plants. The ants get a nesting place and food. They drive off insect pests.

WASTE DISPOSAL

Many scientists hope that bacteria will help us with our garbage problem. They are working to develop plastics and other synthetic materials that are biodegradable; that is, that can be broken down into simple substances by bacteria, just as natural materials such as wood and wool are. But many people are not convinced that these processes will ever be safe or quick enough to reduce the garbage in our landfills. Encourage students to investigate the controversy about biodegradable products.

INTEGRATION

HEALTH

Many parasites are associated with diseases that affect humans. Assign each student to develop a report on the parasitic organism that causes each of these diseases: malaria, typhoid fever, cholera, African sleeping sickness, dysentery, tuberculosis, syphilis, typhus, Rocky Mountain spotted fever, yellow fever, trichinosis, elephantiasis, and schistosomiasis. Ask students to investigate how the disease is transmitted and how it can be prevented. Have students take turns giving their reports to the class. Then ask what conclusions they can draw about parasitic diseases based on the information.

1–3 (continued)

CONTENT DEVELOPMENT

When discussing parasitism, stress to students that a successful parasite lives off its host but rarely kills it. If the parasite were to kill its host, it would soon die as well unless it quickly found another host.

After discussing the examples of parasitism cited in the text, ask students the following questions.

• **What are some examples of parasitism in which humans act as hosts?** (Accept all logical responses such as lice, fleas, ticks, and tapeworms.)

• **Why do you think humans would make such excellent hosts for parasites?** (Human hosts are very unlikely to die because of predation or competition for food from other humans. They are unfortunately a very stable and reliable food source.)

GUIDED PRACTICE

Skills Development
Skill: Comparing concepts

• **What is the difference between parasitism and commensalism?** (The host is harmed in a parasitic relationship; it is not harmed in a commensalistic relationship.)

Figure 1–19 *In mutualism, both organisms benefit from the symbiosis. The small brown oxpeckers on the rhino's nose and belly feed on ticks and other parasites (right). (The white cattle egrets are involved in commensalism with the rhino—they eat insects flushed from hiding as the rhino walks through the grass.) The honeybee is extending a tubelike mouthpart to sip nectar (a sugary liquid) from a flower (top left). The yellow dust on the bee's head is pollen. Most flowers need to receive pollen from another flower in order for their seeds to develop. The goby and snapping shrimp depend on each other for survival (bottom left).*

inside their partner. In return, they help their partner in some way. Bacteria that live inside your digestive system help to produce certain vitamins that your body needs. Microorganisms in certain species of water animals (deep-sea tube worms, giant clams, corals, flatworms, and sea slugs, to name a few) produce food for their partners. Microorganisms in the intestines of cattle, horses, rabbits, termites, and other herbivores help these animals to digest the tough plant materials that they eat. Flashlight fish have structures beneath their eyes that contain symbiotic bacteria. These bacteria produce light, which the flashlight fish are able to turn on and off. The blinking lights of a school of flashlight fish are thought to confuse predators and perhaps enable the fish in the school to communicate.

PARASITISM Have you ever had a cold or been bitten by a mosquito or flea? If so, you have had firsthand experience with parasitism.

Parasites come in many shapes and sizes. Blood-drinking animals such as fleas, ticks, mosquitoes, leeches, and vampire bats are parasites. The fungi that cause athlete's foot and ringworm are also parasites. Some parasites live inside the body of another organism. Disease-causing bacteria and viruses are internal parasites. So are a number of worms, including the heartworm that affects pet dogs. Although they vary greatly in habit and appearance, all parasites have one trait in common: They are involved in a symbiotic relationship in which they harm their partner.

• **How does a predator differ from a parasite?** (Parasites live off their host for long periods of time; predators kill and quickly eat their prey; parasites are usually much smaller than their host; predators are usually much larger than their prey.)

• **How are they similar?** (Both get their energy from other organisms.)

ENRICHMENT

Parasitism is an effective method of controlling populations. Have students conduct library research and develop

Ecologists often regard parasitism and predation as being different forms of the same basic kind of interaction. In predation and almost all examples of parasitism one organism eats another organism. In predation, the predator usually kills its prey before it eats it. In parasitism, the **parasite** usually lives on or in a much larger organism and feeds on it while it is still alive. The parasite's unlucky "partner" is called its **host.** Parasites usually do not kill their host, although many weaken it greatly. Why do you think it is an advantage to a parasite not to kill its host? ❶

A few parasites do kill their host. For example, certain wasps lay their eggs on caterpillars. The eggs hatch into wormlike young wasps that burrow into the body of the caterpillar. The young wasps feed on the caterpillar's tissues, avoiding the caterpillar's major organs so that it stays alive. After about 30 or 40 days, the young wasps chew their way out of their dying host's body and spin cocoons. Inside the cocoons, the young wasps develop into adult wasps.

Some organisms are considered parasites even though they do not feed on their host. Cuckoos (and a few other types of birds) lay their eggs in other birds' nests. When the baby cuckoo hatches, it pushes the eggs and young of its foster parents out of the nest. The foster parents are tricked into feeding and caring for the intruder as if it were their own offspring. How does the cuckoo's behavior harm other birds? Why are cuckoos considered to be parasites? ❸

Figure 1–20 *The vampire bat bites host animals with its razor-sharp fangs, then drinks their blood (bottom right). The white ovals on this caterpillar are the eggs of a wasp (top right). When the young wasps hatch, they will slowly eat the caterpillar. The cuckoo continues to trick its unlucky foster parents into caring for it—even after it has grown much larger than they are (top left). Why are these animals considered to be parasites?* ❷

brief reports on instances where scientists have introduced parasites to control populations of certain organisms.

REINFORCEMENT/RETEACHING

Explain to students that the word *symbiosis* comes from the Greek words *sym*, meaning together, and *bios*, meaning life. To help them remember the types of symbiosis, point out that the word *mutual* has the meanings common, equal, and same. Mutualism involves two organisms in an equal relationship. The word *parasite* comes from a Greek word for a dinner guest who wouldn't leave! Tell students to visualize a parasite as a greedy and unwelcome visitor that won't go away.

List the three types of symbiosis—commensalism, mutualism, and parasitism—on the chalkboard.

• **In what relationship do both organisms benefit?** (Mutualism.)

• **In what relationship does one organism benefit and the second is harmed?** (Parasitism—the host is harmed or even killed.)

• **What kind of symbiotic relationship do flowering plants and bees have?** (Mutualism.)

Have students provide examples of each type of symbiotic relationship.

SYMBIOSIS

It is not always clear how a symbiosis should be classified. As scientists make new observations and reinterpret previously existing data, the understanding of the nature of a particular symbiosis may change. For example, plantlike growths known as lichens have long been thought to be one of the best examples of mutualism. A lichen is made up of an alga (a simple producer) and a fungus that are so closely associated that they look and act like a single organism. The alga makes food for itself and the fungus. The fungus, so the story goes, protects the alga from harsh conditions. This makes it possible for a lichen to live where the alga alone cannot. Recent experiments have shown, however, that some of the algae in lichens are able to survive by themselves under harsh conditions. And many of the algae grow much better by themselves than they do with a fungus partner. So it may well be that some lichens are examples of parasitism, not mutualism!

1–3 (continued)

CONTENT DEVELOPMENT

Direct students to Figures 1–21 and 1–23.

• **What do you observe in the photographs?** (Accept all logical responses.)

Ask students to read the captions and answer the questions posed. Then have students name different organisms. As a group, help students to identify the adaptations that help each organism to survive in its environment. Students may need to do additional research on the organisms they select. Volunteers should create presentations about the organisms, including handouts or displays.

Figure 1–21 *One adaptation to the environment involves the size of an animal's ears. Small ears, such as those of the arctic fox, help to conserve body heat (top). Large ears, such as those of the desert fox, help to get rid of excess heat (bottom). How else are these foxes adapted to their physical environment?* ❶

Adapting to the Environment

Have you ever heard the phrase "survival of the fittest"? Hiding behind this simple phrase is a complicated process. In response to the challenges of their environment, species evolve, or change over time. The evolutionary changes that make organisms better suited for their environment occur by means of a process known as natural selection. Natural selection works like this: Only the individuals that are best suited for their environment survive and produce offspring. These offspring inherit the characteristics that made their parents well suited for the environment. Over the course of a number of generations, these well-suited individuals continue to thrive and reproduce. At the same time, the characteristics that make individuals poorly suited for the environment disappear. This is because the individuals that have these characteristics are less likely to survive. Such individuals have few, if any, offspring to inherit their characteristics. The net result of natural selection are changes in the behavior and physical characteristics of species that make them better suited for their environment. This process is called adaptation.

Organisms cannot choose how they change. They also cannot invent new characteristics. Even with these limitations, living things have been changed in many strange and marvelous ways through natural selection to meet the challenges of their environment. Some of the most interesting adaptations have their origin in the way organisms interact with other living things in their community.

ADAPTING TO PREDATORS Organisms have evolved many adaptations to defend themselves against predators. Animals, such as deer and rabbits, are able to escape from predators by running very fast. Turtles, snails, and coconuts have hard shells that shield them from attackers. Skunks, stinkbugs, and mustard plants produce odors that repel predators. Fawns (baby deer) and many insects have colors and shapes that allow them to blend into their backgrounds. So do the flounder fish you read about earlier. Wasps, sea anemones, and nettle plants can sting. Roses, porcupine fish, hedgehogs, and sea urchins have long sharp thorns or spines. Toads,

32 ■ G

FOCUS/MOTIVATION

Use this demonstration of musical chairs to introduce the concept of survival of the fittest. Select seven students to play the game. The other students are to make their observations without comment. Arrange seven chairs in a circle. Play two rounds of musical chairs, allowing each student to find a seat. Remove one chair. Play another round, eliminating one student. Remove a second chair and repeat. Blindfold two of the remaining students. (Caution the players to be careful not to injure the two who are blindfolded.) Remind the class to observe carefully. Play this round with five students and five chairs. Remove one chair and play a final round. Then discuss what happened in the game. Ask students to explain why certain players ended the game with a chair and others did not. Relate the game to the concept of the survival of the fittest.

puffer fish, certain mushrooms, and many plants contain poisonous chemicals. And seventeen-year cicadas and the seeds of century bamboo plants show up so rarely that predators are not used to eating them. (Imagine waiting a hundred years—or even seventeen years—for your next meal!)

But predators are not so easily discouraged! They have evolved in ways that help them get around their prey's defenses. Cheetahs, for example, can achieve bursts of speed that allow them to catch swiftly running gazelles.

Some types of animals—prairie dogs, musk oxen, bees, and ants, to name a few—live in large groups. Individuals in these groups can take turns looking out for enemies. They can also band together to fight off predators. Can you think of other ways in which living in groups helps organisms to survive? Why can living in groups be considered an adaptation? ❸

ADAPTING TO COMPETITORS   Organisms have evolved many adaptations for dealing with competition. One strategy is for competing species to divide up the habitat. Take a look at the Central and South American hummingbirds in Figure 1–24 on page 34. What do you notice about them?

Although these birds are similar in form, it is obvious that they have very different beaks. Each different (specialized) beak limits a particular

Figure 1–22 *Some organisms defend themselves by looking like something they're not. This caterpillar looks like a bird-eating viper (right). What do the spiny bugs (left) and the praying mantis (center) resemble?* ❷

Figure 1–23 *Brilliant colors warn predators that the sea slug is too dangerous to eat. The orange projections on the sea slug's back are loaded with stinging structures from the sea anemones it eats (top). What adaptations has the cactus evolved that protect it from predators?* ❹

G ■ 33

HISTORICAL NOTE

CHARLES DARWIN

British naturalist Charles Darwin suggested that evolution occurred through a process he called *natural selection,* or *survival of the fittest.* He based his theories on evidence he collected while serving as a naturalist on a scientific expedition on the H.M.S. *Beagle* from 1831 to 1836. He published his theories in 1859 in a book now commonly known as *The Origin of Species.* It caused a revolution in the field of biology.

REINFORCEMENT/RETEACHING

• **If there were two kinds of goats living in high mountains and one kind could climb easily among the rocks to get the only available food and the other could not, which goats would be more likely to survive?** (The ones that could climb.)

• **If the climbing goats survived and had offspring, would the offspring be able to climb?** (Probably.)

• **What would happen to the goats that couldn't climb?** (They might starve; they

would be less likely to have offspring; any offspring they did have would be less likely to survive because they might starve; eventually, the goats would die out.)

CONTENT DEVELOPMENT

Ask students to take all the examples of organisms with protective adaptations mentioned in the text and list them by method. Categories could include speed, shells, smells, colors, sharp things, poison, groups, and so on. Have students go back through the chapter to look for oth-

er examples. They may want to do further research to add more categories and more organisms. All the information could be used in a bulletin board project titled Adaptations and could include pictures or drawings of all the organisms displayed in their appropriate categories.

GUIDED PRACTICE

▶ *Laboratory Manual*

At this point you may want to have students complete the Chapter 1 Laboratory Investigation in the *Laboratory Manual* called Observing Schooling Behavior in Fishes. In this investigation, students will observe a behavior that has evolved in response to predation.

Figure 1–24 *The long-tailed hermit (left), sicklebill (center), and green violet-ear (right), Central and South American hummingbirds, feed on the nectar of flowers. What is the most obvious way in which these birds have evolved to avoid competition?* ❷

hummingbird to drinking nectar from only certain flowers. Can you explain how this makes it possible for several species of these small, brightly colored birds to share the same habitat? ❶

A different sort of strategy is used by plants such as sunflowers, mesquite, and purple sage. Instead of sharing their habitat, these plants reduce competition by killing off their competitors. They release chemicals into their surroundings that discourage the growth of other plants.

The bacterium *Streptomyces* and the fungus *Penicillium* also produce chemicals that discourage the growth of competitors. You may be familiar with these chemicals in a more common form—that of antibiotics. Antibiotics help humans cure diseases by killing the microorganisms that cause them. The drug streptomycin is obtained from *Streptomyces*. Penicillin is obtained from *Penicillium*.

ADAPTING IN SYMBIOSIS The partners in many symbioses are extremely well-adapted to each other. For example, certain acacia trees in Latin America and Africa have huge hollow thorns or hollow swellings the size of Ping-Pong balls on their branches. These structures are inhabited by ants. The acacias also have other types of structures on or near their leaves that produce food for the ants. Thus the acacias feed the ants as well as provide them with a home. In return, the ants catch and eat small herbivores, such as grasshoppers, that land on their tree. If a large herbivore tries to nibble on the acacia's leaves (or if a curious person touches the acacia), the ants swarm onto the intruder, biting and stinging. The ants that live on the Latin American acacias also help their partner deal with competitors. They chew off any tree branches that come into contact with their acacia. This enables the tree to get plenty of light even though it lives in a dense tropical forest. Imagine the series of evolutionary adjustments that were necessary to make the ants and acacias so well suited to living together!

1–3 Section Review

1. Describe the three basic types of symbiosis. Give two examples of each.
2. What is competition? Why does it occur?

Critical Thinking—*Making Generalizations*

3. The myxomatosis virus is spread by mosquitoes. When the virus was first introduced to Australia, it killed many rabbits very quickly. Now, the virus is slower and less deadly. Explain how and why the rabbits and virus have changed. What impact might this have on the Australian ecosystem?

Figure 1–25 *The round structures on the whistling thorn acacia provide a home for symbiotic ants.*

1–4 Life in the Balance

Earlier in this chapter you learned that all of the living and nonliving things in an environment are interconnected, like the strands of a spider's web. Touching a single strand can cause the entire web to tremble. If too many threads are broken, the web collapses and must be built anew.

An ecosystem, however, is not an unchanging structure like a spider web. Changes are constantly occurring in an ecosystem. Populations increase and decrease. Trees fall and animals die. The weather changes with the seasons. Birds fly to warmer places for the winter. Each time a change occurs, an adjustment in the balance of an ecosystem is required.

Sometimes ecosystems are thrown completely out of balance by a natural disaster, such as a hurricane, landslide, forest fire, or volcanic eruption. Perhaps

Guide for Reading

Focus on this question as you read.

▶ *What are some ways in which humans can affect the balance of an ecosystem?*

Ask students to think about how the building of cities affects the environment. They will probably point out the destruction of natural animal habitats and may even mention the cutting down of trees. Have them also consider that paving large areas can prevent water from recycling to the water table and that the heat generated by cities can influence weather on a microscale.

Have students research ways in which the environment has been affected in different parts of the world—for example, the destruction of the Brazilian rain forest or the effects of air pollution in Mexico City.

ESL STRATEGY 1–4

Explain that the story of Great Gull Island is told chronologically (in time order). Ask students to find the expressions of time that help to organize the narrative: recently, by 1981, a hundred years ago, now, over the next three years, at first, then.

Have students write a description of the Laboratory Investigation at the end of the chapter, also organizing it chronologically and using similar time expressions: first, then, now, after three weeks, three weeks ago.

TEACHING STRATEGY 1–4

FOCUS/MOTIVATION

Use a simple demonstration of a structure built with index cards to illustrate the idea of the fragile balance of an ecosystem. Show how moving one card even a little or adding just one card too many can cause the whole structure to topple. Explain to students that unlike the card structure, an ecosystem is always working

to maintain a balance, but sometimes things can happen to upset that balance.

CONTENT DEVELOPMENT

The relationships in ecosystems evolved over thousands of years. The interconnectedness of these relationships was demonstrated when the food web was discussed. Symbiotic relationships are good examples of how closely "things" in natural ecosystems are tied together. Natural systems are very diverse and have many complex relationships.

INDEPENDENT PRACTICE

▶ *Activity Book*

Students who need practice on the concept of relationships among organisms should complete the Chapter 1 activity, Analyzing Relationships Among Organisms.

BACKGROUND INFORMATION

MOUNT ST. HELENS

In May of 1980, Mount St. Helens, a volcano in the state of Washington, exploded. Thousands of trees, shrubs, flowers, and animals were destroyed by the eruption. Volcanic ash covered the soil as far away as 14 kilometers from the volcano. What had once been a beautiful, green forest soon looked like the barren surface of the moon. Within a month, however, life began to return to the area. Roots of the red-flowered fireweed bush and other plants that had survived pushed growing stems up through the ash. These plants attracted insects such as aphids, which feed on the juices of the fireweed. In turn, birds came into the area to feed on the insects. Spiders crawled on the ash-covered surface. When these animals died, their bodies fertilized the ash, returning important nutrients to the soil. Hoofed animals such as elk wandered through the area, breaking up the ash cover and leaving holes through which more seeds could sprout.

Once plant and animal life started again, relationships among organisms were reestablished. What was once a bleak lifeless landscape is now an area filled with colorful flowers, green shrubs, and growing trees. Scientists are carefully studying this area for clues to the secret of how living things can turn a barren land into a lively ecosystem inhabited by interdependent organisms.

Figure 1–26 *In May 1980, the lush green forests of Mount St. Helens were destroyed by a volcanic eruption. The blast knocked over trees and covered the surrounding area in volcanic ash. But eventually life began to return to the area. The ecosystem of Mount St. Helens is slowly regaining its balance.*

you have read about or possibly even experienced the explosive eruption of Mount St. Helens in 1980, the forest fires in Yellowstone National Park in 1988, or Hurricane Hugo in 1989. What effects did these disasters have on the ecosystems in the area? In certain cases, however, events that seem like natural disasters are not really disasters at all. Instead, they are events that may actually help to maintain the balance in certain ecosystems. For example, naturally occurring forest and brush fires may clear away shrubs and dead wood, creating room for new plants to grow. Burning also breaks down dead plant materials and thus returns nutrients to the soil. Some organisms in fire-prone areas have evolved in ways that enable them to cope with periodic fires. A few even need fires. The seeds of the jack pine tree, for example, require the temperatures of a forest fire in order to be released from their protective pine cones.

Ecosystems are also put out of balance by human activities. **The damaging effects of activities such as chopping down forests or putting poisonous chemicals into rivers are quite obvious. Apparently harmless human actions may also cause widespread damage.** One of the more dramatic examples of the unexpected ways in which human activities can damage ecosystems involves Mono Lake, in eastern California.

1–4 (continued)

CONTENT DEVELOPMENT

Explain to students that other natural disasters that disturb ecosystems include wild fire, hurricanes, tornadoes, and floods. Discuss these examples with your students, pointing out that many organisms have evolved special ways of surviving natural disasters. For example, where fires are common, species may develop deep roots and can sprout new growth from the protected root system. Most tropical trees are flexible and bend during strong winds produced by storms.

CONTENT DEVELOPMENT

Stress to students that human activity tends to simplify ecosystems. Managed forests tend to have one or two primary species; large farms usually grow one or two crops for market; even cities tend to be less complicated than natural ecosystems. Mono Lake is a good example of how humans often fail to see the long-term effects of their actions.

- **Why were the islands in Mono Lake a good nesting place for birds?** (They were protected from predators, and the lake provided lots of food.)
- **Why did the water levels in the lake drop?** (People began to use the water from streams that fed the lake.)
- **What happened when the supply of water was reduced?** (The water got too salty and the shrimp, a major food source for the birds, died. In addition, land bridges formed and predators were able to reach

Mono Lake is a beautiful saltwater lake fed by streams of melting snow from the Sierra Nevada Mountains. Two small islands within Mono Lake attract thousands of birds, especially seagulls. More than 80 species of birds nest on these islands and feed on the lake's shrimp, flies, and algae. That is, they did until 1981. During the summer of that year, many baby seagulls were found dead. How strange this seemed to be for an ecosystem that had long provided food, water, and shelter for seagulls! As people investigated the situation, they discovered that the ecosystem had been disturbed by actions taken far away from the lake many years before.

About 40 years ago, the city of Los Angeles began to use water from the major streams that feed into Mono Lake. As less and less water emptied into Mono Lake, the lake began to dry up. Thousands of acres of dust formed where there was once water.

As the amount of water in the lake decreased, the concentration of salt dissolved in the water increased. The shrimp that seagulls fed on could not survive in water so salty. As the shrimp died, less food was available for the seagulls. Baby seagulls starved to death.

To make matters worse, as the water level in Mono Lake dropped, a land bridge that connected the shore to the nesting islands formed. Coyotes crossed this bridge, killed many seagulls, and invaded the gulls' nests.

Figure 1–27 *In January 1991, the Iraqi army occupying Kuwait dumped millions of liters of oil into the Persian Gulf, causing one of the world's worst environmental disasters. What effect did this oil spill have on wildlife?* ❶

Figure 1–28 *Mono Lake has the potential to be home to thousands of birds (left). But when too much of its water supply is taken away, the lake dries up and becomes virtually lifeless (right).*

G ■ 37

BACKGROUND INFORMATION
MONO LAKE

The final word on Mono Lake has yet to be written. The Committee to Preserve Mono Lake is working with scientists and environmentalists to gradually replenish the water supplies of the lake. However, the needs of society are also being taken into consideration in any environmental plans. Whether or not the lake will be saved is an open question, although most environmentalists believe it can be saved.

the islands.)

• **How might the Mono Lake ecosystem be saved?** (Find a new water supply for Los Angeles; start a campaign to conserve water.)

• **What have you learned from the Mono Lake story?** (Answers will vary but should include the idea of interconnectedness.)

● ● ● ● **Integration** ● ● ● ●

Use the discussion on the eruption of Mount St. Helens to integrate geology into your lesson.

Students can explore the complex "balancing act" of an ecosystem by using the interactive video called EcoVision. Have students relate what they discover about Heron Marsh to real-life ecosystems.

GUIDED PRACTICE

Skills Development
Skill: Predicting

Based on what students have learned about Mono Lake, challenge them to predict what will happen to the ecosystem if water is restored and if water is not restored. This activity could be set up as a debate with teams of students taking different positions on the possible future of the restored lake.

ENRICHMENT

Have students do library research on other disturbances to ecosystems. This research should include examples of damage caused by human activity and interference as well as by natural disasters.

ACTIVITY

Who Missed the Moose?

Isle Royale is a long, narrow island in Lake Superior, 25 kilometers from the shore of Canada. In the early 1900s, a few moose swam to the island. Within 20 years, the population had increased to more than 2000!

During the next 40 years, the moose population underwent several changes. Using books and other materials in the library, find out what changes occurred on Isle Royale and what caused the changes. Include answers to the following questions in your report.

1. What are limiting factors and in what ways do they affect a population?

2. How do birth and death rates affect a population?

3. What is a population cycle?

Many people want to save Mono Lake. But it will not be easy. In order to conserve water and save the lake, some profitable farmland must be allowed to turn back into desert. In addition, people must change their lifestyles and give up nice things like green lawns, swimming pools, decorative fountains, and weekly car washes. As you can imagine, the government of California is going to have a hard time getting people to cooperate with water-saving measures. To complicate the situation, the area around Los Angeles received less rainfall in the late 1980s and early 1990s than it usually does. This has made the water shortage even more severe.

Without a water conservation plan, Mono Lake will continue to dry up. And the delicate balance between living and nonliving things in this ecosystem may be altered beyond all hope for recovery.

The story of Mono Lake is only one example of the effects humans have on the balance in ecosystems. There are thousands and thousands of other stories. Some end sadly with something beautiful or strange lost forever. A few have happy endings. And many are unfolding even as you read these words. With careful planning, people can help these stories end happily. By understanding the interactions within the environment, people can both use the resources around them and preserve the beauty, diversity, and balance within ecosystems.

1–4 Section Review

1. How can human activities affect the balance of ecosystems?
2. How did humans change the balance in the Mono Lake ecosystem?

Connection—*You and Your World*

3. A picture-perfect lawn or golf course is usually a lush green expanse of just one kind of grass. Its appearance is kept up by a program of constant mowing, fertilizing, watering, and applying pesticides and weedkillers. Using what you have learned about interactions and balances in an ecosystem, explain why "perfect" lawns and golf courses are so difficult to maintain.

CONNECTIONS

Down for the Count

You might recall watching one of the adults in your household filling out a *census* form in 1990. Every 10 years, the government conducts a census of the people of the United States. Special forms are mailed out to every household in the country. People report the number of people in their household, the sex and age of each person, their income, the number of rooms in their dwelling, and many other facts. Then they mail back the forms.

Occasionally, there are problems. Some people give silly answers. Others fail to return their forms. And a few people may be overlooked by the census takers.

These problems seem minor compared to those faced by biologists performing a wildlife census. For one thing, wild animals do not have a mailing address! And even if they did, they could not fill out a census form! So the biologists must travel to the places where the animals live and put up with insect bites, awful weather, and other discomforts.

Some large, conspicuous organisms—such as caribou, elephants, and wildebeests—are simply counted from aerial photographs. The sizes of the populations of most other organisms are determined indirectly: Biologists count or estimate the size of part of a population, then use this figure to calculate the probable size of the entire population. For example, a

biologist studying wolves may let out a howl, then count the number of answering howls from real wolves. Suppose the biologist knows that about a quarter of the wolves in the area will respond to the fake howl. If the biologist hears eight responding howls, how many wolves are probably in the area?

Some wildlife census methods involve catching animals. As you can imagine, this can be more hazardous than ringing doorbells in a city or town for the Census Bureau! While counting animals, biologists have been bitten, scratched, pecked, sprayed by skunks, menaced by bears, and even chased up a tree by a moose that recovered too soon from a dose of tranquilizer delivered by a dart gun.

Faced with all these difficulties, why do biologists conduct a census of wildlife? Because knowing the size of populations and how populations have changed over time gives people some of the information they need for deciding how to manage wildlife and the environment.

CONNECTIONS
DOWN FOR THE COUNT

Students may have experiences to relate about the 1990 census. Ask them if they remember reading about it or seeing the form at their homes. Perhaps they helped to fill out the form. Discuss the kinds of questions that appeared on the form. Why is that information important to the government? How is the information used?

Encourage students to relate the ideas from their discussion of the human census to the need for a wildlife census. What kinds of problems might people have when they try to count animals? How does counting the animals help them?

If you are teaching thematically, you may want to use the Connections feature to reinforce the themes of evolution, patterns of change, and systems and interactions.

wildlife and natural land resources of the United States and other countries.

INDEPENDENT PRACTICE

Section Review 1–4

1. Many human activities, such as polluting the environment, introducing foreign species, and cutting down forests, can throw an ecosystem off balance. Other human activities, such as introducing a virus to limit the rabbit population in Australia, can sometimes help to restore the balance of disturbed ecosystems.

2. By diverting water that would normally run off into the lake and keep lake levels at a normal height.

3. "Perfect" lawns and golf courses are hard to maintain because they are out of balance and must be kept out of balance. To accomplish this, the interactions that normally occur in ecosystems are prevented or distorted. Pesticides get rid of the herbivores that eat the grass. Weedkillers destroy the weeds that would compete with the grass. Mowing also helps to prevent the growth of weeds by killing

tall plants before they have a chance to grow very much. By adding nutrients in the form of fertilizers and by watering, the grass can grow in spite of limited water and nutrients in its environment.

REINFORCEMENT/RETEACHING

Review students' responses to the Section Review questions. Reteach any material that is still unclear, based on their responses.

CLOSURE

▶ *Review and Reinforcement Guide*
Students may now complete Section 1–4 in their *Review and Reinforcement Guide.*

Laboratory Investigation

A LITTLE OFF BALANCE

BEFORE THE LAB

1. Divide the class into groups of three to six students per group.
2. Gather all equipment at least one day prior to the investigation. The size of the jars is not important as long as they are the same size. The large jars used in school cafeterias are perfect.
3. If *Elodea* is not available, other aquarium plants can be used. You might want to get students to measure the length of the plants or get a rough idea of the mass of the individual strands. Challenge students to develop a way to mark each individual plant so that it can be identified later.

PRE-LAB DISCUSSION

Have students develop data tables in which they can record their observations of jars A and B. Encourage them to quantify their observations and include observations of things that might affect the experimental results. Examples might be weather or a particularly warm spell during the experiment. You might wish to assign one student to record the temperature at the beginning and end of each school day. The water with the plant food may grow cloudy if there are algae present. This is an important observation because the algae are competing with the *Elodea* for nutrients.

If you do not cover the jars, water will evaporate. If you cover them tightly, gases can accumulate at the top and interfere with normal gas exchanges that occur in natural systems.

• **How can this problem be solved?** (Cover the jars and put two or three small holes in each lid.)

Laboratory Investigation

A Little Off Balance

Problem

How does adding lawn fertilizer affect the balance of an aquatic (water) ecosystem?

Materials *(per group)*

2 2-L wide-mouthed jars
pond water
8 *Elodea* (or other aquatic plant)
lawn fertilizer (or house plant food)
teaspoon

Procedure 🧪

1. Label the jars A and B.
2. Fill each jar about three-fourths full with pond water.
3. Place four *Elodea* in each jar.
4. Add one-half teaspoon of lawn fertilizer to jar B.
5. Place the jars next to each other in a lighted area.
6. Predict what will happen to the jars over the course of three weeks. Record your predictions.
7. Observe the jars daily for three weeks. Record your observations.

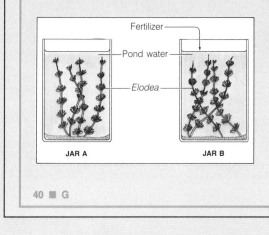

Fertilizer
Pond water
Elodea

JAR A   JAR B

Observations

1. Were there any differences between jars A and B? If so, what were the differences? When did you observe them?
2. How did your results compare to your predictions?

Analysis and Conclusions

1. What was the control in this experiment? The variable?
2. Why did you place the jars next to each other? Why did you place them in the light?
3. What effect did the fertilizer have on the *Elodea*?
4. Lawn fertilizer contains nitrogen, phosphorus, and potassium. These nutrients are often present in sewage as well. Predict the effects of dumping untreated sewage into ponds and lakes.
5. **On Your Own** Design an experiment to test the effects of different amounts of lawn fertilizer on the balance of an aquatic ecosystem. Predict the results of your experiment. If you receive the proper permission, you may perform your experiment and find out if your predictions are correct.

TEACHING STRATEGY

1. Have the teams work together to prepare their jars.
2. Make sure the teams record their observations daily. They may wish to take turns doing so or may choose one member to act as the recorder.

DISCOVERY STRATEGIES

Discuss how the investigation relates to the chapter ideas by asking open questions similar to the following.
• **How do the jars constitute an ecosystem?** (Each jar contains living and nonliving parts that interact with each other—Relating, Analyzing.)
• **What are the living and nonliving parts of this ecosystem?** (The plants and the organisms in the pond water are the living parts; the water, the nutrients, and the

Study Guide

Summarizing Key Concepts

1–1 Living Things and Their Environment

▲ All of the living and nonliving things in an environment are interconnected.

▲ An ecosystem consists of all the living and nonliving things in a given area that interact with one another.

1–2 Food and Energy in the Environment

▲ Producers are the source of all the food in an ecosystem.

▲ Consumers cannot make their own food. They feed directly or indirectly on producers.

▲ Decomposers break down dead organisms into simpler substances. In the process, they return important materials to the soil and water.

▲ A food chain represents a series of events in which food and energy are transferred from one organism in a ecosystem to another.

▲ A food web consists of many overlapping food chains.

▲ The amount of energy at each feeding level in an ecosystem can be diagrammed as a pyramid of energy.

1–3 Interaction and Evolution

▲ An organism's niche consists of everything the organism does and everything the organism needs in its environment.

▲ Two or more species cannot share the same niche.

▲ Interactions such as predation, competition, and symbiosis have had a powerful effect on the course of evolution.

1–4 Life in the Balance

▲ Ecosystems are sometimes thrown completely out of balance by natural disasters or by human activities.

Reviewing Key Terms

Define each term in a complete sentence.

1–1 Living Things and Their Environment

environment
ecology
ecosystem
community
population
habitat

1–2 Food and Energy in the Environment

producer
consumer
decomposer
food chain
food web

1–3 Interaction and Evolution

niche
competition
predator
prey
symbiosis
commensalism
mutualism
parasitism
parasite
host

---

3. The fertilizer probably caused an increase in the growth of *Elodea*.

4. Untreated sewage, when dumped into ponds and lakes, often causes increased growth of algae and other plants. This increased growth, in turn, upsets the natural balance of the lake or pond and increases the process of eutrophication. At this point you may want to discuss eutrophication, the nutrient enrichment of aquatic systems, with your class. You should point out that eutrophication is a natural process but is often accelerated by the activities of people.

5. Accept all logical, well-thought-out experiments. If students are allowed to perform their experiments, you may wish to ask them to report their findings to the class.

GOING FURTHER: ENRICHMENT

Part 1

You may want to repeat this experiment by doing the following.

1. Add measured amounts of plant food every week.

2. Use a different kind of aquatic plant.

3. Put the jars in a shady corner.

4. Compare various kinds of fertilizers.

5. Use a dish detergent with phosphate in place of the plant food.

Part 2

After students have completed the lab, have them investigate cultural eutrophication and the impact of human activities on freshwater lakes and ponds.

Part 3

What would happen if you used tap water instead of pond water? Ask students to write a hypothesis and then design an experiment to test the hypothesis. Encourage them to conduct the experiment and report on their results.

---

sun are the nonliving parts—Analyzing, Comparing.)

• **What prediction do you make about the plants in the jar with the fertilizer? Why?** (The plants in the jar with the fertilizer will probably grow more than those in the jar without the fertilizer. Fertilizer contains nutrients that help plants grow—Observing, Comparing, Relating.)

OBSERVATIONS

1. Students should observe more growth of *Elodea* in jar B than in jar A.

2. Answers will vary. Students probably predicted that the *Elodea* in the jar with the fertilizer would have better growth.

ANALYSIS AND CONCLUSIONS

1. Jar A was the control, and fertilizer was the variable.

2. The jars were placed next to each other so that both would be in the same environment in order to avoid any hidden variables. They were placed in the light so that the *Elodea* could perform photosynthesis.

Chapter Review

ALTERNATIVE ASSESSMENT

The *Prentice Hall Science* program includes a variety of testing components and methodologies. Aside from the Chapter Review questions, you may opt to use the Chapter Test or the Computer Test Bank Test in your *Test Book* for assessment of important facts and concepts. In addition, Performance-Based Tests are included in your *Test Book*. These Performance-Based Tests are designed to test science process skills, rather than actual content recall. Since they are not content dependent, Performance-Based Tests can be distributed after students complete a chapter or after they complete the entire textbook.

CONTENT REVIEW

Multiple Choice
1. c
2. b
3. a
4. a
5. d
6. b
7. b
8. a

True or False
1. F, Decomposers
2. F, symbiosis
3. T
4. F, prey
5. T
6. F, parasitism
7. F, Producers
8. F, less

Concept Mapping
Row 2: includes
Row 3: Nonliving things
Row 4: each species
Row 5: Community, part of

CONCEPT MASTERY

1. The term environment is used with a particular point of reference in mind—a tree's environment, the human population's environment, and so on. The term ecosystem refers to the system of living and nonliving things and their interactions as a whole.

2. Producers, such as green plants, turn simple raw materials into food. Consumers, such as animals, feed directly on the producers. Decomposers, such as certain fungi and bacteria, break down the remains of dead organisms, releasing raw materials back into the environment.

3. A population is a group of organisms of the same species that live in a given area. A community consists of all the interacting populations in a given area. An ecosystem consists of a community and the nonliving surroundings with which it interacts. The place in which a species lives is called its habitat. A species' feeding level is determined by where it fits in on a food chain. A species' niche includes its habitat and its feeding level.

4. A food chain describes a specific series of food and energy transfers from one feeding level to the next in an ecosystem. A food web is made up of the overlapping food chains in an ecosystem. A pyramid of energy describes the amount of energy that is available at each feeding level in an ecosystem. A pyramid of energy shows that energy is lost as you move along a food chain.

Chapter Review

Content Review

Multiple Choice

Choose the letter of the answer that best completes each statement.

1. The study of the interactions between living things and their environment is called
   a. commensalism.
   b. parasitism.
   c. ecology.
   d. botany.

2. Evolutionary changes usually occur by means of a process called
   a. mutualism.
   b. natural selection.
   c. predation.
   d. competition.

3. A desert is an example of a(an)
   a. ecosystem.
   b. population.
   c. food chain.
   d. niche.

4. A group of organisms of the same species living together in the same area is called a(an)
   a. population.
   b. ecosystem.
   c. community.
   d. niche.

5. Which term best describes the relationship between a honeybee and a flower?
   a. commensalism
   b. predation
   c. competition
   d. mutualism

6. An organism that eats plants is best described as a(an)
   a. omnivore.
   b. herbivore.
   c. scavenger.
   d. carnivore.

7. Everything an organism does and needs in its environment is known as its
   a. feeding level.
   b. niche.
   c. habitat.
   d. adaptation.

8. Which term best describes the relationship between a fox and a wolf?
   a. competition
   b. symbiosis
   c. predation
   d. mutualism

True or False

If the statement is true, write "true." If it is false, change the underlined word or words to make the statement true.

1. <u>Producers</u> break down dead organisms.
2. Any close relationship between two organisms in which one organism lives near, on, or even inside another organism and in which at least one organism benefits is known as <u>mutualism</u>.
3. The living part of an ecosystem is called a <u>community</u>.
4. The organisms on which a predator feeds are known as its <u>hosts</u>.
5. An animal that feeds on the bodies of dead animals is known as a <u>scavenger</u>.
6. The relationship between a dog and a flea is an example of <u>commensalism</u>.
7. <u>Consumers</u>, such as green plants, are the first link in a food chain.
8. Within a food chain, there is <u>more</u> energy available at each higher feeding level.

Concept Mapping

Complete the following concept map for Section 1–1. Refer to pages G6–G7 to construct a concept map for the entire chapter.

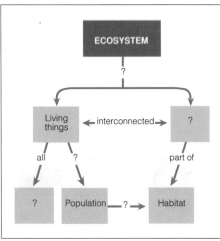

Concept Mastery

Discuss each of the following in a brief paragraph.

1. Explain how the terms environment and ecosystem differ in meaning.
2. Name and briefly describe the three basic energy roles in an ecosystem. For each role, give an example of an organism that plays that role.
3. Explain how the following terms are related to one another: community, ecosystem, feeding level, habitat, niche, population, species.
4. How are a food chain, a food web, and a pyramid of energy different from one another? Describe the relationship among the three.
5. Using specific examples, explain how predation, competition, and symbiosis can affect evolution.
6. Explain this statement. "In the environment, change is a two-way street."

Critical Thinking and Problem Solving

Use the skills you have developed in this chapter to answer each of the following.

1. **Applying concepts** African tickbirds can often be found perching on large animals such as Cape buffalo and rhinoceroses. The tickbirds eat bloodsucking ticks found on the skin of the large animals. What type of symbiosis is this? Explain.
2. **Making diagrams** Draw a food web that includes the following organisms: cat, caterpillar, corn, cow, crow, deer, hawk, human, lettuce, mouse, fox, grass, grasshopper, rabbit. Identify each organism as a producer or a consumer.

3. **Making predictions** How could the spraying of an insecticide interfere with the balance in an ecosystem?
4. **Relating concepts** Explain why the sun is considered to be the ultimate source of energy for almost all ecosystems.
5. **Identifying relationships** Take a look at the pyramid of energy in Figure 1–13 on page 22. What trend would you expect to see in the number of organisms at each level as you move from the bottom of the pyramid toward the top? Why?
6. **Assessing concepts** "If an ecosystem is properly selected, it contains four basic parts: the physical environment, the living things, energy, and the nutrients that circulate between its living and nonliving elements." Examine the accompanying photograph of a deer licking a block of salt. Explain whether you can identify each of these elements in the photograph. Then explain whether you think this description of an ecosystem is a useful one.
7. **Using the writing process** Write a short story or poem about a change in the balance of an ecosystem that you yourself have observed.

5. In response to predation, organisms have evolved a number of defenses. For example, horses can run away quickly and roses have thorns that discourage herbivores. Adaptations to competition include specialization and mechanisms to discourage the growth of competitors. For example, the warblers in a spruce tree look for food in only certain parts of the tree. Adaptations for symbiosis often involve many adjustments between the partners in the relationship. For example, the humans in African and Mediterranean countries have adaptations that make them more resistant to malaria. The protists that cause malaria have become resistant to certain drugs used to treat the disease. Student examples will vary.

6. Organisms are changed by their environment; the environment is changed by the organisms within it.

CRITICAL THINKING AND PROBLEM SOLVING

1. Mutualism, because both organisms benefit from the association. The tickbirds get a meal, and the large animals get rid of parasites.

2. Check student diagrams for accuracy. Producers: corn, grass, lettuce. Consumers: cat, caterpillar, cow, crow, deer, hawk, human, mouse, fox, grasshopper, rabbit.

3. Accept all logical answers. The insecticide might kill off herbivorous insects, causing producers to grow unchecked and possibly causing insect-eaters to starve. If the herbivorous insects are resistant to the pesticide, the insecticide might kill off the carnivorous insects that keep the population of herbivorous insects under control. The insecticide might, like DDT, build up in the food chain, causing carnivores at the top of the food chain to die off. If carelessly applied, the insecticide might pollute water or food and possibly poison organisms elsewhere in the food chain.

4. Most producers use the energy from the sunlight to power the process that turns raw materials into food.

5. The number of organisms at each level decreases. Not enough energy gets to the topmost levels to support many organisms.

6. Student explanations and opinions will vary but should attempt to identify the parts of the ecosystem and their relationships.

7. Student responses should be well written and creative and reflect an accurate understanding of the concept of balance in ecosystems.

KEEPING A PORTFOLIO

You might want to assign some of the Concept Mastery and Critical Thinking and Problem Solving questions as homework and have students include their responses to unassigned questions in their portfolio. Students should be encouraged to include both the question and the answer in their portfolio.

ISSUES IN SCIENCE

The following issue can be used as springboard for discussion or given as a writing assignment.

1. As human populations grow, the amount of land available for wildlife is dwindling. Should people be more concerned with their own needs or with the needs of the environment?

SECTION	HANDS-ON ACTIVITIES
2–1 Cycles in Time: Rhythms of Life page G46–G54 Multicultural Opportunity 2–1, p. G46 ESL Strategy 2–1, p. G46	**Student Edition** LABORATORY INVESTIGATION: Going in Cycles, p. G64 ACTIVITY BANK: Going Through a Phase, p. G142 **Laboratory Manual** Investigating Daily Cycles in Humans, p. G21 **Teacher Edition** Discussing the Biological Clock, p. G44d
2–2 Cycles of Matter pages G54–G59 Multicultural Opportunity 2–2, p. G54 ESL Strategy 2–2, p. G54	**Student Edition** ACTIVITY (Discovering): It Takes Your Breath Away, p. G56 ACTIVITY BANK: A Saucepan Simulation of a Cycle, p. G144 ACTIVITY BANK: Take It With a Grain of Salt, p. G146 **Laboratory Manual** Organisms and Carbon Dioxide, p. G25 **Activity Book** ACTIVITY: The Oxygen Cycle, p. G61 ACTIVITY: Water In—Water Out, p. G63 **Product Testing Activities** Testing Toilet Paper **Teacher Edition** Visualizing the Chemical Cycles, p. G44d
2–3 Cycles of Change: Ecological Succession pages G60–G63 Multicultural Opportunity 2–3, p. G60 ESL Strategy 2–3, p. G60	**Student Edition** ACTIVITY (Discovering): Backyard Succession, p. G62 **Activity Book** ACTIVITY BANK: Hay! Look at This! p. G177
Chapter Review pages G64–G67	

OUTSIDE TEACHER RESOURCES

Books

Andrews, W. A., ed. *Terrestrial Ecology,* Prentice Hall.

McNaughton, S., and L. L. Wolf. *General Ecology,* Holt.

Audiovisuals

The Aging of Lakes, film, Encyclopaedia Britannica

Sense of Timing, video, Coronet

The Water Cycle, film, Encyclopaedia Britannica

Water: A Precious Resource, video, National Geographic

OTHER ACTIVITIES	MEDIA AND TECHNOLOGY
Student Edition ACTIVITY (Reading): But What Will You Do When It Grows Up? p. G51 ACTIVITY (Writing): All the Right Moves, p. G52 **Activity Book** CHAPTER DISCOVERY: Discovering Life's Rhythms, p. G47 ACTIVITY: Swinging Hamsters, p. G59 **Review and Reinforcement Guide** Section 2–1, p. G13	**Prentice Hall Science Integrated Media** Travelin' Along **English/Spanish Audiotapes** Section 2–1
Student Edition ACTIVITY (Thinking): Miniature Worlds, p. G58 **Activity Book** ACTIVITY: Studying the Water Cycle, p. G51 ACTIVITY: The Water Cycle, p. G55 ACTIVITY: The Nitrogen Cycle, p. G57 ACTIVITY: The Unkindest Cut of All, p. G65 **Review and Reinforcement Guide** Section 2–2, p. G17	**Prentice Hall Science Integrated Media** Cycles in Nature **Transparency Binder** Oxygen/Carbon Dioxide Cycle Nitrogen Cycle **English/Spanish Audiotapes** Section 2–2
Review and Reinforcement Guide Section 2–3, p. G21	**English/Spanish Audiotapes** Section 2–3
Test Book Chapter Test, p. G31 Performance-Based Tests, p. G91	**Test Book** Computer Test Bank Test, p. G37

*All materials in the Chapter Planning Guide Grid are available as part of the Prentice Hall Science Learning System.

Chapter 2   CYCLES IN NATURE

CHAPTER OVERVIEW

Cycles affect individual organisms, ecosystems, and the non-living environment. Biological cycles and rhythms help organisms follow the cyclic changes in their environment. Such cycles may be daily, lunar, or annual. Some organisms are active only during the day or at night. Others behave in harmony with the lunar rhythms of the tides. Still others follow yearly patterns, migrating from one place to another or hibernating through the winter.

Matter flows in cycles from the nonliving part of the environment to living things and back again. The chemical cycles of water, oxygen, carbon, and nitrogen ensure that matter is cycled and recycled through an ecosystem. Water circulates between the Earth's surface and the atmosphere through the processes of evaporation, condensation, and precipitation. Air-breathing organisms take in oxygen and release carbon dioxide. Producers such as green plants take in carbon dioxide and release oxygen. Nitrogen gas is used by bacteria to make nitrates, which can then be taken in by plants. Plants use the nitrates to make proteins, which can be used by the organisms that consume plants. Eventually, decomposers break down the nitrogen compounds in dead organisms, returning the nitrates to the soil, where they can be used again or transformed into nitrogen gas, which is released into the air.

Ecosystems change over time as one ecological community succeeds another in a process called ecological succession. Eventually, a stable community of organisms, known as a climax community, may develop in a particular place. But the process of succession takes a long time, and because events can happen to set back the process, succession also moves in cycles.

2–1 CYCLES IN TIME: RHYTHMS OF LIFE
THEMATIC FOCUS

The purpose of this section is to introduce students to the concepts of biological cycles and rhythms, or patterns that occur over and over. Students will learn that living things have biological clocks, or internal timers, which help them stay in step with changes in their environment. These clocks are set by daily, lunar, or annual rhythms. These rhythms are linked to cycles of time—day and night, the tides, and the seasons.

The themes that can be focused on in this section are patterns of change, scale and structure, systems and interactions, and stability.

*Patterns of change: Stress the fact that cycles are repeated patterns of change. Whether they are daily, lunar, or annual, once completed, they repeat in the same way and over the same time period. Use the passage of the seasons as one of the best-known examples.

Scale and structure: As you discuss the different kinds of rhythms, make sure students understand that biological clocks keep track of cycles of time that can range from a few minutes to many years.

*Systems and interactions: Point out that interaction is responsible for the cyclic changes in the appearance and behavior of organisms. The organisms' biological clocks are regulated by the interaction of cycles in time and environment.

Stability: Organisms respond to environmental cues. But even without environmental cues, organisms will continue to be affected by cycles and rhythms because their biological clocks continue to operate.

PERFORMANCE OBJECTIVES 2–1

1. Describe how biological clocks affect organisms.
2. Compare diurnal and nocturnal organisms.
3. Discuss migrations as an example of annual rhythms.

SCIENCE TERMS 2–1

biological clock p. G47
diurnal p. G48
nocturnal p. G48
migration p. G52
hibernation p. G53
estivation p. G53

2–2 CYCLES OF MATTER
THEMATIC FOCUS

The purpose of this section is to introduce students to the concepts of the chemical cycles of water, oxygen, carbon, and nitrogen. The basic steps involved in each cycle are focused on in turn. Water circulates between the Earth's surface and the atmosphere. Some organisms take in oxygen and release carbon dioxide, while others take in carbon dioxide and release oxygen. Nitrogen moves from the air through bacteria to the soil through plants to animals and back again. The key idea in this section is that matter in an ecosystem, as demonstrated by water, carbon, oxygen, and nitrogen, must be cycled and recycled.

The themes that can be focused on in this section are energy, patterns of change, and unity and diversity.

*Energy: Be sure that students understand that energy in an ecosystem is constantly renewed, but matter, such as water, oxygen, carbon, and nitrogen, cannot be renewed; therefore, it must be recycled, or reused, in the ecosystem.

*Patterns of change: Emphasize that the chemicals change forms, sometimes many times, as they move in their cycles between the living and nonliving parts of the environment.

*Unity and diversity: Point out that the chemical cycles all have one thing in common: They involve the flow of matter from the nonliving part of the environment to living things and back again.

PERFORMANCE OBJECTIVES 2–2
1. Describe the steps in the water cycle.
2. Discuss the relationship between the oxygen cycle and the carbon cycle.
3. Explain how nitrogen moves in a cycle through an ecosystem.

SCIENCE TERMS 2–2
water cycle p. G55
oxygen cycle p. G55
carbon cycle p. G55
nitrogen cycle p. G55

2–3 CYCLES OF CHANGE: ECOLOGICAL SUCCESSION
THEMATIC FOCUS

The purpose of this section is to introduce students to the concept of ecological succession, yet another cycle that occurs in an ecosystem. Over time, one ecological community in a place is replaced by another until perhaps a stable community of organisms, or climax community, develops. Pollution, fire, floods, farming, and other factors that disturb the ecosystem can slow down or change the process of succession. The section concludes with the key idea that succession does not ensure that an ecosystem always returns to its original state; many factors influence the course of succession.

The themes that can be focused on in this section are evolution, patterns of change, and systems and interactions.

*Evolution: Encourage students to think of ecological succession as the evolution of an ecosystem. Use the pictures on page G61 to reinforce this idea.

*Patterns of change: Point out that the concept of ecological succession is based on change as one community of organisms replaces another community in a particular place.

*Systems and interactions: Emphasize that ecological succession does not mean that certain end results are guaranteed; many events can change the rate or affect the course of succession. This fact is important in understanding why an ecosystem may never be returned to its original state.

PERFORMANCE OBJECTIVES 2–3
1. Define ecological succession and describe its effect on an ecosystem.
2. Describe a climax community's place in ecological succession.

SCIENCE TERMS 2–3
ecological succession p. G61
climax community p. G61

Discovery *Learning*

TEACHER DEMONSTRATIONS MODELING
Discussing the Biological Clock

Introduce the chapter by making two columns on the chalkboard. Label the first column "Wide Awake at 8 AM" and the second "Wide Awake at 10 AM" Ask students when they are most alert and record their responses.
• **Why are some people alert and cheery in the morning whereas others don't seem to really get going until afternoon or evening?** (Answers will vary but should include that people are influenced by environmental stimuli, such as light intensity, lunar phases, and temperature.)

Point out that humans can condition themselves to different cycles.
• **Has anyone ever spent a vacation overseas or on the (East/West) Coast?** (Accept all answers.)

• **Was it difficult for you to adjust to a new time zone?** (Answers will vary. Have students describe how long it took them to adjust and how they felt during the adjustment period.)
• **What happened when you returned home?** (Answers will vary. If students spent more than a few days in a different time zone, they probably would have found it difficult to adjust when they returned home.)

Explain that the reason they have difficulty adjusting to new time zones has to do with their internal "biological clock." This clock is able to reset itself, but it takes a few days. During this time they may feel tired and sluggish. This is called "jet lag" or, sometimes, "jet exhaustion." You may wish to tell students that some scientists have experimented with helping to overcome jet lag through the use of bright lights at specific hours.

Visualizing the Chemical Cycles

Help students visualize the chemical cycles by having them act out each one. For example, assign one or two students to be nitrogen. A few other students can be nitrogen-fixing bacteria. Have other students be legumes. Assign one student to be a deer that eats the legumes and another student to be a mountain lion that eats the deer. After the mountain lion dies, nitrogen returns to the atmosphere, and the cycle begins again. Assign groups of students to develop similar plays for the water cycle and the oxygen/carbon dioxide cycle.

CHAPTER 2
Cycles in Nature

INTEGRATING SCIENCE

This life science chapter provides you with numerous opportunities to integrate other areas of science, as well as other disciplines, into your curriculum. Blue-numbered annotations on the student page and integration notes on the teacher wraparound pages alert you to areas of possible integration.

In this chapter you can integrate life science and astronomy (pp. 46, 51, 54), geology (p. 55), and mythology (pp. 55, 63).

SCIENCE, TECHNOLOGY, AND SOCIETY/COOPERATIVE LEARNING

The destruction of the rain forest is causing a disruption in the Earth's cycles of matter—the carbon, oxygen, and the nitrogen cycles. People in the Third World clear away the rain forest to create space for homes and crops. But the "slash-and-burn" method they use puts more carbon and nitrogen into the atmosphere and reduces the amount of oxygen produced by green plants.

In the slash-and-burn method, the rain forest is cut down and then burned. This method has a doubly harmful effect on the Earth's cycles of nature. First, by burning trees and other vegetation, huge amounts of carbon in the form of carbon dioxide are added to the atmosphere. Scientists calculate that the burning also transfers more nitrogen to the atmosphere than had been previously expected. Nitrogen compounds could accumulate in the air, reduce the amount of nitrogen available

INTRODUCING CHAPTER 2

DISCOVERY LEARNING

▶ *Activity Book*

You may want to begin your teaching of the chapter by using the Chapter 2 Discovery activity from the *Activity Book*. Using this Activity, students will discover some of their own personal life rhythms.

USING THE TEXTBOOK

Have students look at the photograph on page G44.
• **What type of animal do you see in the photograph?** (The photograph shows fish called grunion.)
• **What do you think these fish are doing on the beach?** (Answers will vary. Some students will probably realize that the fish are mating.)

• **Why do you think one fish is buried in the sand?** (Answers will vary. The fish that is buried is a female grunion that is laying eggs.)

Explain that the female grunion digs into the sand to deposit her eggs. After she deposits them, the male fertilizes them. Point out that the female deposits from 1000 to 3000 eggs at one time.

Cycles in Nature

Guide for Reading

After you read the following sections, you will be able to

2–1 Cycles in Time: Rhythms of Life
- Describe how biological clocks affect organisms.
- Give examples of the ways in which the rhythms of life are linked to cycles in time.

2–2 Cycles of Matter
- Discuss how matter flows through an ecosystem.

2–3 Cycles of Change: Ecological Succession
- Describe how ecosystems are changed by the process of succession.

On a cool spring night in southern California, the ocean waves surge up onto the beach. As each wave retreats, small silver fish known as grunion (GROON-yuhn) appear. The wet sand near the top of the high tidemark glitters with grunion.

The female grunion squirm into the sand tail first. They then deposit their pale orange eggs below the surface of the sand. The male grunion curve their bodies around their mates and fertilize the eggs. Then the next wave washes over the beach and sweeps the grunion back to sea.

Grunion deposit their eggs at places on the beach reached only once every two weeks by the highest tides. Hidden beneath the sand, the eggs are safe from the waves—and egg-eating predators in the ocean. By the time the tides are at their highest point again and the waves reach the eggs, the young grunion are ready to hatch. As the waves swirl the eggs from the sand, the tiny grunion pop out and are carried to the ocean. The process repeats itself year after year, generation after generation. It is an age-old cycle that ties the survival of a tiny fish to the movements of the sea, the Earth, and the moon. It is one of the many cycles in nature. Turn the page, and learn about more.

Journal *Activity*

You and Your World What is your favorite season? Why? What observations have you made about nature as the seasons change? Explore your thoughts and feelings in your journal.

◀ On spring and summer nights with a full moon or a new moon, grunion ride the ocean waves onto the beaches where they mate and lay their eggs.

---

for plants, and contribute to global warming, smog, and acid rain. Second, the reduced forest cover means there are fewer green plants using carbon in the process of photosynthesis and producing oxygen as a byproduct.

Another tragedy of the slash-and-burn destruction of the rain forest is that once cleared, the soil will grow crops for only a few years. It is very poor soil because minerals needed by crops are leached out by large amounts of rainfall. Soon the cleared area will no longer support the family, who then moves, and the cycle of destruction starts over.

Scientists worldwide are concerned about the effect on the Earth's cycles of matter produced by rain-forest destruction. People in Third World countries, however, argue that they cannot afford to preserve the rain forest at the expense of their own economic, social, and political development.

Cooperative learning: Using preassigned or randomly selected groups, have them complete one of the following assignments:
- Have groups illustrate the effect of rainforest destruction on the carbon and oxygen cycles and/or the nitrogen cycle.
- Have groups imagine that they are members of a commission studying the effects of rain-forest destruction on the carbon cycle. Each group is to propose at least two alternatives to the cutting and burning of the rain forest. In a chart, groups should predict the economic, social, political, and environmental effects of each alternative.

See Cooperative Learning in the *Teacher's Desk Reference.*

JOURNAL ACTIVITY

Encourage students to use the Journal Activity as the basis for a poem or short description about the seasons and nature's changes. Point out that they can compare their observations with the information in the chapter. Students should be instructed to keep their journal activity in their portfolio.

- **What is the advantage of producing so many eggs?** (Many eggs will not be fertilized; many eggs that are fertilized will not hatch; and many grunion that do hatch will not survive to reach adulthood.)

Have students read the chapter introduction on page G45.
- **How do the grunion get on and off the beach?** (They "ride" a wave.)
- **Once hatched, how do the young grunion get out to sea?** (They also are carried by waves.)

You may wish to remind students that the eggs are safe because they are deposited on the beach and covered by sand at a point reached by waves only at high tide.
- **What is the life cycle of the grunion dependent on?** (Students may answer that grunion are dependent on tides.)

Point out that because tides are caused mainly by the gravitational pull of the moon on the Earth's oceans, the life cycle of the grunion is actually an example of a lunar rhythm.

2-1 Cycles in Time: Rhythms of Life

MULTICULTURAL OPPORTUNITY 2-1

Students may not think of humans as migratory, but many people have to move on a regular basis to find natural and economic resources. This is true of nomadic cultures around the world as well as of laborers in agriculture. Point out that migrant workers must move in order to follow the seasonal demands of harvesting. Discuss the three major routes that families follow to find work, all starting from the south and moving northward. Students may be interested in researching some of the challenges faced by migrant workers.

ESL STRATEGY 2-1

For many LEP students, learning the months of the year presents difficulties, since new concepts as well as new words are involved. Review the months of the year and the months in each season before introducing the concept of annual rhythms.

Have students complete the sentences below by supplying the word that is defined. Note that each of the incomplete words ends in *-tion*.

-tion is a summer resting state.

-tion is a winter resting state.

-tion means to travel to a better environment.

Guide for Reading

Focus on these questions as you read.

▶ What controls the rhythms of life?

▶ What are some examples of daily, lunar, and annual rhythms?

Figure 2–1 *The elegant flowers of the night-blooming cereus open in the evening and close in the morning. In certain areas, the leaves of many kinds of trees change color during the autumn. Once a year, albatrosses woo a mate by strutting about and bobbing their heads. Why are these events considered to be examples of biological rhythms?* ❶

2-1 Cycles in Time: Rhythms of Life

What do you think of when you hear the word rhythm? A musician might think of the beat of a song or a dance. A soldier might think of the pace of marching in a parade. A biologist might think of the way a heart beats, a seagull flaps its wings, or a cricket chirps. Or a biologist might think of slower rhythms than these—for example, the way fiddler crabs change their color from light gray to dark gray and back again to light gray during the course of a day. Or the way whales travel from cold polar waters to warmer regions closer to the equator during the course of a year. A rhythm is any pattern that occurs over and over again.

Slower biological rhythms are often in harmony with certain natural cycles, such as the passage of day into night, the rise and fall of the tides, and the changing seasons. As summer changes to autumn, for example, the leaves of maple trees become red, yellow, and orange in color.

One of the most interesting things about many of the slower rhythms of life is that they continue even if an organism is removed from its natural environment. Once a year, ground squirrels will go into their winter sleep and starlings (small black birds) will breed as if it were spring—even when they live in a cage in the unchanging, seasonless world of a laboratory. Human volunteers living in a sunless cave

---

TEACHING STRATEGY 2-1

FOCUS/MOTIVATION

Have students feel their own pulse by gently placing two fingers (not a thumb—it has a pulse of its own) on the artery in the side of their neck or wrist. After they have felt the "thump-thump" from the surge of blood, have them move their heads up and down in rhythm to their heartbeat. Point out that this is an example of an internal rhythm—a rhythm that

operates inside our bodies and one over which we have no direct control. There are other rhythms in our environment that may affect what we do, when we do things, and even how we feel. Sometimes these environmental rhythms can be controlled, but for the most part they operate beyond our direct awareness and are beyond our control.

CONTENT DEVELOPMENT

• **What is a biological clock?** (It is a popular name given to a timing system that oc-

curs in plants and animals.)

Explain that biological clocks are not new, nor are they fully understood by scientists. The fact is that we really do not know much about these internal mechanisms. No one knows where a biological clock is located. No one knows exactly how they work. Some scientists think that biological clocks are set according to electromagnetic and gravitational forces of the Earth. Other scientists believe that forces both inside and outside the body keep biological clocks going. It is without any way to tell time still experience daily changes in blood pressure, body temperature, wakefulness, and other biological functions. Evidence from experiments such as these indicate that many of life's rhythms are not simply responses to changes in the environment. Something inside humans, squirrels, birds, and other living things keeps track of the passage of time. But what exactly is this something that monitors the passage of time?

Internal timers known as **biological clocks** may be responsible for keeping track of many different cycles of time. These cycles may range in length from a few minutes to many years. When the time is right, biological clocks "tell" organisms to change their appearance, behavior, or body functions in some way. For example, biological clocks tell grunion when to ride the waves onto a beach. **Biological clocks help living things stay in step with rhythmic cycles of change in their environment.**

To better understand why biological clocks are so important to living things, it might help you to think about the way alarm clocks help people stay in step with their daily activities. Have you ever used an alarm clock to help you get up in the morning? If you have, you know that it would be silly to set your alarm clock for the time that you want to leave for school. You need time to get out of bed, get dressed, eat breakfast, and so on. So if you need to be at school at 8:00, you might set your alarm clock for 6:45. This gives you time to get ready for your day. Biological clocks are important to living things for the same reason—although they may measure

Figure 2–2 *Biological clocks help living things stay in step with their environment. Biological clocks let snow geese know when it is time to fly south for the winter and tell morning glories to open their flowers during the day.*

G ■ 47

FACTS AND FIGURES

TERMS

The science that deals with the study of biological clocks is called chronobiology.

BACKGROUND INFORMATION

STOPPING THE CLOCK

Medical researchers recently reported that they had succeeded in stopping the biological clock in humans by exposing volunteers to bright light. Why is this exciting to physicians, psychologists, and other health professionals? Because stopping the clock has many useful medical applications. Biological clocks control such things as body temperature, sensitivity to drugs, levels of body chemicals, and tolerance to pain.

hoped that experiments on biological clocks performed in outer space, where organisms are far from the Earth's natural rhythms, will eventually provide more answers.

ENRICHMENT

Because the rhythms controlled by biological clocks tend to drift, scientists have developed some special terms for them: circadian, circalunar, and circannual. Each of these terms begins with the prefix *circa-*, which means approximately.

Diem means day. *Lunar* means of the moon and refers to months and tides. *Annual* means yearly.

CONTENT DEVELOPMENT

In humans, wakefulness and sleep are based on a circadian rhythm. This rhythm varies from one person to another and can be modified. Ask students to think about their own daily rhythms.

• **What other activities or processes may be controlled by a biological clock?** (Accept all reasonable answers, such as appetite, body temperature, heart rate, and so on.)

● ● ● ● **Integration** ● ● ● ●

Use the discussion on lunar rhythms and natural cycles to integrate astronomy into your lesson.

CAREERS

Forester

Foresters carefully study a possible recreation area to be sure that such items as cooking equipment, picnic tables, utility sources, and roads do not disturb the ecological balance of the forest. Other activities of foresters range from managing forest timberland to clearing away tree branches so that sunlight can reach the ground cover.

Those interested in pursuing a forestry career can get a start by studying chemistry, physics, math, earth science, and biological science in high school. Summer job experience in forest and conservation work is also helpful. Forestry applicants should enjoy working outdoors, be physically fit, and work well with people. For further information, write to the Society of American Foresters, Wild Acres, 5400 Grosvenor Lane, Bethesda, MD 20814.

time periods other than 24-hour days! How might having biological clocks be better for organisms than simply responding to changes in the environment as they happen? ❶

In nature, biological clocks are extraordinarily accurate. However, under unchanging conditions (in a laboratory, for example), biological clocks usually run a little too slow or a little too fast. For example, in a laboratory setting where light, temperature, and all other factors remain the same, a fiddler crab's cycle of color changes might take 23 hours rather than 24. Each day, the crab would change color an hour earlier than crabs in their natural environment. After a while, the crab's internal cycle would be completely out of step with its natural environment.

Why don't organisms get out of step in nature? The answer is simple: Biological clocks are set and reset by environmental cues such as dawn or dusk, day length, moisture, and temperature. But because biological clocks are influenced by the environment, it is not always easy to tell which changes in organisms are caused by a biological clock and which are caused by environmental cues. It is easy to see, however, that the rhythms of life are linked to natural cycles in time. In the next few pages, you will read about some of the ways the rhythms of life are in step with daily, lunar (of the moon), and annual (yearly) cycles.

Daily Rhythms

As night falls, the creatures of the day prepare to sleep. A flock of birds circles high above some trees, then suddenly drops into the branches. Colorful flowers close. A dog turns around several times before curling up on its bed with a sigh. Meanwhile, the creatures of the night are becoming active. A swarm of bats bursts from a cave. Mushrooms emerge and grow among the dead leaves on a forest floor. Certain microorganisms in the ocean begin to glow with an eerie bluish light.

Organisms that are active during the day are said to be **diurnal** (digh-ER-nuhl). Those that are active at night are said to be **nocturnal** (nahk-TER-nuhl). Are humans diurnal or nocturnal? ❷

Evolution has shaped the characteristics of organisms in such a way that diurnal organisms are well suited for the warm, dry, brightly lit day and nocturnal organisms are well suited for the cool, moist, dimly lit night. Take a look at the nocturnal night monkey and the diurnal emperor tamarin in Figure 2–3. What is the most obvious difference in the facial features of these two monkeys (other than the emperor tamarin's moustache)? That's right—the "eyes" have it! Like many nocturnal animals, night monkeys have much larger eyes than their diurnal relatives. Larger eyes gather a larger amount of the available light and allow the nocturnal animals to find their way in the darkness of the night.

Not all nocturnal animals have oversized eyes. Many rely on other senses to guide them in the dark. For example, owls and bats rely a great deal on their sense of hearing. And many nocturnal insects have extremely long feelers that allow them to explore the nighttime world through their senses of touch, taste, and smell.

Lunar Rhythms

Have you ever spent an entire day at the beach? If so, you might have noticed that each successive wave seemed to reach a little less far up the beach. After a while, you might have realized that the level of the ocean had dropped, revealing once-hidden rocks, seaweed, barnacles, and mussels.

Figure 2–3 *The nocturnal owl monkey (bottom) and the diurnal emperor tamarin (top right) both live in the forests of Latin America. How might different patterns of wakefulness in these monkeys help to reduce competition between them? Some organisms are neither nocturnal nor diurnal. The vole (top left) is most active at dawn and at dusk.*

Activity Bank

Going Through a Phase, p.142

G ■ 49

ANNOTATION KEY

Answers
❶ Biological clocks enable organisms to anticipate environmental conditions and prepare for them in advance. (Making inferences)
❷ Diurnal. (Drawing conclusions)

BACKGROUND INFORMATION
FIDDLER CRABS

Among the animals that show fascinating biological rhythms are fiddler crabs. The skin of these seashore crustaceans tends to darken at dawn and pale again at dusk. Their running activity coincides with the rise and fall of the tides. (This rise and fall changes by about 50 minutes every day.) Scientists experimented with fiddler crab rhythms by keeping some crabs in constant darkness inside laboratories. The crabs continued to change color and correlated their running behavior with the tides of their home beaches. When these same crabs were moved to a beach with different tidal times, they adjusted their activities to their new home. This seems to indicate that biological clocks can be automatically reset.

FOCUS/MOTIVATION

Collect photographs from magazines. Have students identify the animals as diurnal or nocturnal and explain their reasoning, which should include physical adaptations that are important for diurnal/nocturnal existence.

INDEPENDENT PRACTICE

▶ *Activity Book*
Students who need practice with the concept of diurnal/nocturnal animals should complete the chapter activity Swinging Hamsters.

REINFORCEMENT/RETEACHING

Make sure students are able to distinguish between diurnal and nocturnal animals. Construct a chart with two columns on the chalkboard. Label one column Diurnal and the other Nocturnal. Have students think of enough examples to fill the chart. You may want to have some students make a display of diurnal and nocturnal animals on a classroom bulletin board. Drawings or magazine photographs can be used for the display.

TIDES

All bodies of water are subject to tides. But tides rise and fall to different heights at different places. Lake Superior's tide rises and falls only 12.7cm, while the Bay of Fundy has a tide that rises and falls more than 15m. Why? On an inland body of water like Lake Superior, the tidal range is hardly noticeable. But the tide is much more noticeable at places where oceans and continents meet, like the Bay of Fundy. Also, the coastline itself plays a role; the water at the Bay of Fundy moves through a deep, narrow channel into the bay.

OIL SPILLS

Tides clean shorelines by carrying away wastes. They can also bring waste to the shore. That's how oil spilled from tankers and offshore rigs ends up on beaches. Ask students to think about what would happen to all the organisms they have been introduced to in this section if oil washed onto the organisms' beaches. Have students look up information on the effect of oil on marine organisms.

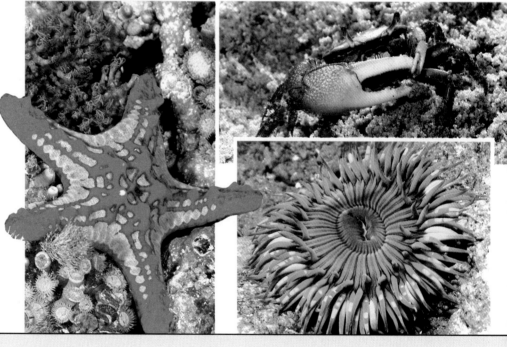

Figure 2–4 *Organisms that live at the edge of the ocean—such as the giant green sea anemone (bottom right), fiddler crab (top right), ringed top snail (top left), and red East African starfish (bottom left)—show patterns of activity that match the rise and fall of the tides.*

An examination of the rocks, wet sand, and tide pools at the water's edge might have revealed some interesting creatures becoming active at the low tide. Certain crabs pop out of their burrows and scurry around on the wet sand. Small starfish push their stomachs out of their mouths and absorb bits of food from the surface of the sand. Microscopic one-celled diatoms and small green worms rise to the surface of the sand, creating small, faint patches of brown and green.

Other organisms become inactive at low tide. Mussels and barnacles shut their shells tightly. Snails and other small animals hide beneath seaweed or within cracks in rocks. Sea anemones pull in their tentacles and contract into sand-covered blobs.

If you stayed at the beach long enough, you might have seen the waves come in once more, slowly washing away sand castles and gradually hiding the things that you had seen at low tide. With the return of the water at high tide, the crabs retreat to their burrows and block the entrances with sand. The diatoms and worms sink back under the sand to avoid being washed away by the waves. Snails begin to creep around. Mussels and barnacles open their

---

2–1 (continued)

FOCUS/MOTIVATION

Ask students what they know about tides. If you live near an ocean, tides will probably be a familiar phenomenon to students. Discuss what happens on a beach at high and low tides.

If you do not live near an ocean, encourage any students who have seen an ocean and watched the tides go in and out to describe the experience. Follow up with some discussion about what causes tides.

CONTENT DEVELOPMENT

Explain that tides are shallow water waves caused by the gravitational attraction of the moon, the Earth, and the sun. In particular, the moon's gravitational force causes ocean water to "bulge" on the sides of the Earth that face toward and away from the moon. The water is drawn away from the other sides. In the areas where the water bulges, there are high tides; in the other areas, there are low tides. Because the Earth rotates, most places have two high tides and two low tides every day. Tides also follow a twice-monthly rhythm. When the sun, the Earth, and the moon are aligned, the high tides are at their highest. When the sun, the Earth, and the moon form a right angle, the high tides decrease.

• **Which organisms are affected by the daily rhythms of the tides?** (Crabs, starfish, diatoms, anemones, mussels, barnacles, snails, worms.)

shells and filter food from the water. And sea anemones open up in flowerlike splendor.

The rise and fall of the tides are controlled by the moon (and to a lesser degree, the sun). As a result, tidal rhythms are considered to be lunar rhythms. (The word lunar means of the moon.) There are two kinds of tidal rhythms. You have just read about the high- and low-tide cycle, which occurs twice a day (every 12.4 hours, to be exact). The other type of tidal rhythm is roughly a two-week cycle (14.8 days) during which the high tides gradually become higher, peak, and then decrease.

Biological clocks in a number of organisms are in harmony with the two-week cycle of the tides. The grunion you read about at the beginning of the chapter are an example. They lay their eggs on the nights of the highest high tide. On a small island west of Australia, female red crabs release their eggs into the ocean during the lowest high tide. In tropical oceans, strange worms break in two at night during the lowest high tide. One half remains in its burrow at the bottom of the sea. The other half swims to the surface. There it joins millions of other half-worms. Many of these swimming half-worms are eaten by fishes, birds, and humans (who consider the worms a treat!). The remaining half-worms burst open at sunrise, releasing huge numbers of eggs and sperm.

As you might expect, 12-hour and 2-week tidal rhythms occur mostly in organisms that live near and in the ocean. However, some land organisms have rhythms that are in harmony with the lunar cycle. For example, the average length of a human pregnancy is exactly ten lunar months from the time the egg cell is released to the time the baby is born.

Annual Rhythms

Some of life's rhythms are closely associated with the seasons of the year. In the spring, for example, songbirds build their nests. Bears awaken from their winter sleep. Trees that were bare throughout the winter begin to grow a new cover of leaves. Daffodils, tulips, and primroses bloom. And many animals give birth to their young. Can you think of some other events that occur in the spring? How

Figure 2–5 *Chrysanthemums normally bloom in the autumn in response to lengthening nights. How do florists cause chrysanthemums to produce flowers for Mother's Day?* 1

G ■ 51

• **Why would some of these organisms become active at low tide and some at high tide?** (Those that get food from the water would be active when the high tides wash over them. Those that get their food from the sand or that have to protect themselves from being washed away would be active at low tide when the water has retreated.)

• **Which organisms are affected by the two-week cycle of the tides?** (Grunion, crabs, worms.)

• **What function in these organisms is tied to this cycle of the tides?** (Reproduction—in each case, the occurrence of the highest high tide or the lowest high tide triggers the release of eggs.)

• **Are people affected by lunar cycles?** (Yes, there is a large body of evidence that indicates behavioral patterns change with moon phases. For example, many police stations report an increase in crime during periods when there is a full moon.

● ● ● ● **Integration** ● ● ● ●

Use the discussion of lunar tides to integrate astronomy into your lesson.

GUIDED PRACTICE

Skills Development

Skills: Applying concepts, observing, recording data

At this point have students complete the in-text Chapter 2 Laboratory Investigation, Going in Cycles.

ACTIVITY

All the Right Moves

Write a report on the annual migrations of the animal of your choice. Some migratory animals include: springbok, monarch butterflies, ruby-throated hummingbirds, storks, certain eels, sea turtles, and certain bats. In your report, include a map that shows the route of the animal's migration.

Figure 2–6 *Caribou migrate between their summer home in the far north and their winter home in the forests hundreds of kilometers to the south. During their annual migration on Christmas Island, red crabs appear everywhere!*

about in summer, autumn, and winter? Stop for a moment and make a list of five events that occur in each season of the year. ❶

As you look over your list, you will probably discover that many of the events occur once a year, every year. Such events are examples of yearly, or annual, rhythms.

There are many examples of annual rhythms in nature. Many animals—such as grunion, deer, and red crabs—reproduce only during certain times of the year, when conditions are best for the young to survive. Can you explain why most animals bear their young in the spring, rather than in the winter? ❷

In response to seasonal variations in temperature, food supply, light, and other factors, some organisms migrate. This means they journey from one place to another. For example, many birds in the northern hemisphere migrate south for the winter. In the spring, the birds migrate back to northern regions to breed and raise their young. Birds are not the only organisms that migrate, however. Wildebeest, whales, bats, salmon, and red crabs are just a few of the other living things that migrate.

For the most part, **migrations** are annual rhythms in which organisms travel from the place where they breed to the place where they feed. In general, organisms migrate to more beneficial environments as seasonal changes make their old environment less favorable.

Some organisms have a different way of escaping unfavorable seasonal changes. They simply "sleep" through the bad periods of the year. These organisms are active only when conditions are favorable. For example, as winter approaches, the body functions of toads, bears, and certain other animals slow down. This enables these animals to wait out the cold winter months in sheltered hiding places. In their slowed-down state, the animals can survive without food or water until the coming of spring. This winter resting state is known as **hibernation.** (The Latin word *hibernus* means winter.)

In places where the summer months are extremely harsh, hot, and dry, organisms may enter a resting state known as **estivation.** (The Latin word *aestas* means summer.) For example, as the shallow lakes in which African lungfish live begin to dry up, the lungfish may bury themselves in the mud at the bottom of the lake. They can survive for many years in their shell of dried mud.

A few organisms, such as certain plants and insects, simply do not live through the harsh seasons in their environment. But before they die, these organisms produce weather-resistant eggs, spores, or seeds. The eggs, spores, or seeds are able to grow and develop when the seasons change and conditions become favorable once more. The life cycle of such organisms is usually an annual (yearly) cycle. For example, the plants known as annuals—such as marigolds, petunias, and sweet peas—start from seeds in spring, mature and bear seeds by autumn, and die in winter. The next spring, new plants sprout from the seeds and the cycle continues.

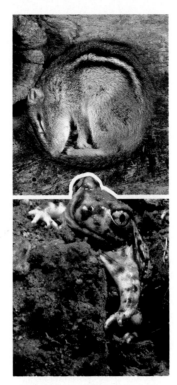

Figure 2–7 *A chipmunk escapes the cold, hungry days of winter by hibernating. A spadefoot toad avoids the harshest conditions of its desert home by estivating in an underground burrow.*

Figure 2–8 *Annual organisms, such as California poppies, simply do not live through the most unfavorable seasons. How do annual organisms ensure that their species continue from year to year?* ③

G ■ 53

HISTORICAL NOTE
FOLLOW THE BUFFALO

We think of the Plains Indians as having always followed the migrating herds of buffalo. But in fact, it was the horses that the Spaniards brought to North America in the 1600s that enabled the Plains Indians to give up their semi-agricultural life and follow the buffalo.

FACTS AND FIGURES
THE WOODCHUCK

During hibernation, the body temperature of a woodchuck may drop to as low as 4°C. Its heart beats once every 10 or 15 seconds. The woodchuck breathes at the same slow rate.

much lower body temperature. Animals that hibernate do so during the coldest part of the year. Hibernation appears to be an adaptation to surviving harsh environmental conditions, such as cold temperatures and scarce food supplies.

Estivation is a period of dormancy, like hibernation, during which metabolic rate and body temperature decrease. Estivation occurs in response to hot, arid conditions and helps organisms avoid overheating and water loss.

• **In what biomes would you expect to find hibernating animals?** (Tundra, coniferous forests, and deciduous forests.)

• **In what biome would you expect to find animals in estivation?** (Desert.)

2-2 Cycles of Matter

Guide for Reading

Focus on this question as you read.

▶ *How do water, oxygen, carbon, and nitrogen flow through the environment?*

2-2 Cycles of Matter

There are many types of cycles in nature. The changing seasons form a cycle, as do the rising and falling tides and the passage of day into night. Organisms have life cycles in which they are born, grow, reproduce to create the next generation, and eventually die. Stars also undergo a series of changes from the time they are "born" as hot spinning clouds of gases to the time they "die" explosively. Rocks are worn down into sand, which may then be transformed by heat and pressure back into rock. Circular series of chemical reactions, or chemical cycles, turn carbon dioxide gas into food and break down food to release energy and carbon dioxide.

In Chapter 1, you learned about the way energy flows through an ecosystem. As you may recall, energy is used up at each feeding level. But ecosystems constantly receive a new supply of energy—usually in the form of sunlight.

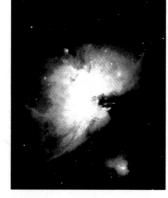

Figure 2–9 *Cycles in nature do not always involve living things. New stars may be formed from the matter that remains after a star explodes.*

54 ■ G

Figure 2–10 In the rock cycle, sand may be transformed into rock, which may then be worn down to sand. The slow wearing-down of sandstone may produce arches and other amazing rock formations.

The supply of matter in an ecosystem, however, is not renewed. But matter, unlike energy, can be recycled, or reused. **Matter, in the form of chemicals, flows in cycles from the nonliving part of the environment to living things and back again.**

There are many cycles of matter, and most of them are quite complex. Fortunately, you do not need to know every detail of every cycle. In this section, you will learn about the basic steps (and only the basic steps!) of four of the most important cycles of matter: the **water cycle,** the **oxygen cycle,** the **carbon cycle,** and the **nitrogen cycle.**

The Water Cycle

For many of the world's cultures, water has long symbolized life. Countries with water usually prospered—and those that lacked water often faced disaster. Knowing where water was and where it would be was a key to success. Many thousands of years ago, people became aware that there is a natural cycle to the flow of water on this planet—a cycle people still rely on today.

"Earth" is not a particularly appropriate name for our planet. "Water" would actually be more fitting, for three fourths of the planet Earth is covered by lakes, streams, rivers, and oceans. Water circulates continuously between the Earth's surface and the atmosphere (the envelope of air surrounding the Earth). Water on the Earth's surface is heated by the sun and evaporates. In other words, it changes from a liquid into a gas, or vapor. The water vapor then

Figure 2–10 *In the rock cycle, sand may be transformed into rock, which may then be worn down to sand. The slow wearing-down of sandstone may produce arches and other amazing rock formations.*

③ Activity Bank

A Saucepan Simulation of a Cycle, p.144

Figure 2–11 *From a distance, the Earth is blue with large bodies of water and white with clouds. In Chinese mythology, dragons were in charge of the Earth's rivers, bodies of water, and rain. Why is this dragon surrounded by tiny clouds?* ①

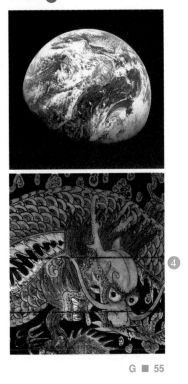

Use the photograph showing the arch to integrate geology into your lesson.

CONTENT DEVELOPMENT

Point out to students that although water covers more than 71 percent of the Earth's surface, less than one tenth is pure enough for land organisms to use.

Draw a simple diagram of the main steps in the water cycle on the chalkboard. (See Figure 2–12.) Ask the following questions:

• **How are clouds formed?** (When the water vapor reaches a certain temperature called the dew point, it condenses, forming clouds.)

• **Is more water evaporated from rivers and lakes than from the oceans?** (Oceans contain 97 percent of the Earth's water supply; lakes and rivers contain less than 1 percent, so the oceans contribute far more to the water cycle.)

• **Why don't we run out of water?** (Because water cycles through the environment and its destruction [in photosynthesis] is balanced by its manufacture [in respiration].)

• **If the water cycle replaces water, why do we worry so much about water pollution?** (Some pollutants are not removed during the water cycle and may eventually affect human water supplies.)

● ● ● ● **Integration** ● ● ● ●

Use the picture of the Chinese dragon to integrate mythology and multicultural studies into your lesson.

TEACHING STRATEGY 2–2

FOCUS/MOTIVATION

On the chalkboard, draw a circular arrow. Explain to students that this figure represents a cycle. The word *cycle* comes from the Greek word meaning circle. Ask students to think of some cycles they are familiar with in their lives (seasons, day and night, life cycles of plants or animals, daily or weekly schedules, recycling).

CONTENT DEVELOPMENT

Ask students to choose one of the cycles they discussed in class and draw its steps in a circular pattern like the arrow on the board. Have them compare their pictures. Ask them what all the cycles have in common. (They are repeating patterns.)

● ● ● ● **Integration** ● ● ● ●

Use the discussion on cycles in nature and the photograph of the exploding star to integrate astronomy into your lesson.

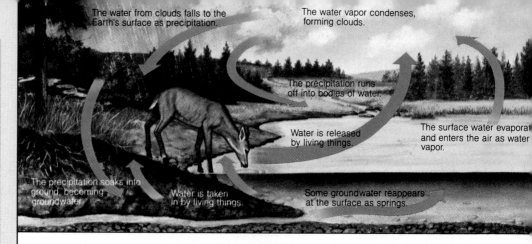

The water from clouds falls to the Earth's surface as precipitation.

The water vapor condenses, forming clouds.

The precipitation runs off into bodies of water.

The surface water evaporates and enters the air as water vapor.

Water is released by living things.

The precipitation soaks into ground, becoming groundwater.

Water is taken in by living things.

Some groundwater reappears at the surface as springs.

Figure 2–12 *Water cycles through both the living and the nonliving part of the environment. What happens to water that falls as precipitation?* ❶

Activity Bank

Take It With a Grain of Salt, p. 146

ACTIVITY DISCOVERING

It Takes Your Breath Away

Hold a mirror a few centimeters from your mouth. Say "Horace the horse hulas in Hilo, Hawaii." What happens to the mirror? Why does this happen?

■ How does this relate to the water cycle?

rises up into the air. In the upper atmosphere, water vapor cools and condenses into liquid droplets. It is these droplets that form clouds. Eventually, the droplets fall back to the surface of the Earth as precipitation—rain, snow, sleet, or hail.

Most precipitation falls directly back into the oceans, lakes, rivers, and streams. Some of the rest falls on the surface of the land and then runs off into these bodies of water. In either case, water that evaporates into the air returns to the surface of the Earth, and the cycle repeats itself.

Not all water, of course, goes directly back into the Earth's bodies of water. Some is taken in by living things and later returned to the nonliving part of the environment. For example, plants take in liquid water through their roots and release some water vapor through their leaves. Animals drink water, but they also give water back to the environment when they breathe and in their wastes.

The Oxygen and Carbon Cycles

Like most living things, you need oxygen to survive. The atmosphere, which is 20 percent oxygen, supplies you and other air-breathing organisms with this vital gas. Oxygen from the atmosphere that has dissolved in water is breathed by fish and other

---

Discovery Learning

Skills: Making observations, relating concepts

Materials: Hand mirror

Using this simple activity, students will be able to see that when we breathe, we release water vapor into the air. When they breathe onto the mirror, it fogs up. The water in our breath cools as it reaches the outside air and condenses on the mirror.

The water vapor we release into the air when we exhale is part of the cycle in which water moves from living things to the nonliving part of the environment.

2–2 (continued)

INDEPENDENT PRACTICE

▶ *Activity Book*

Students who need practice on the concept of the water cycle should complete these two chapter activities: Studying the Water Cycle and The Water Cycle.

ENRICHMENT

▶ *Activity Book*

Students will be challenged by the chapter activity Water In—Water Out in the *Activity Book.*

CONTENT DEVELOPMENT

The two major processes involved in the oxygen and carbon cycles are photosynthesis and respiration. Compare the two processes by pointing out that during photosynthesis, plants take in carbon dioxide and water and produce carbon compounds and oxygen. During respiration, both plants and animals give off carbon dioxide and water vapor. Have students observe Figure 2–14 on page G57 and trace the paths of the carbon dioxide and the oxygen. Point out that this is a simple example of the oxygen and carbon cycles.

aquatic organisms. Clearly, living things would have used up the available oxygen supply in the atmosphere millions of years ago if something did not return the oxygen to the air. But what could that something be?

Consider this: When you inhale, you take in oxygen. When you exhale, you release the waste gas carbon dioxide. If something used carbon dioxide and released oxygen, it would balance your use of oxygen. That something, as you may already know, are producers such as green plants and certain microorganisms. These producers use carbon dioxide gas, water, and the energy of sunlight to make carbon-containing compounds that are often referred to as "food." During the food-making process, the producers also produce oxygen, which is released into the environment. Through this process, known as the oxygen cycle, there is always a plentiful supply of oxygen available for air-breathing organisms.

But what happens to the carbon in food? How is it transformed back into carbon dioxide? In order to extract energy from food, organisms must digest the food, or break it down into simpler substances. This process ultimately produces water and carbon dioxide, which are released back into the environment. Figure 2–14 illustrates the oxygen and carbon cycles. Can you explain why these two cycles are usually discussed together? ❸

The Nitrogen Cycle

About 78 percent of the atmosphere is made up of "free" nitrogen, or nitrogen that is not combined with other elements. All living things need nitrogen to build proteins and certain other body chemicals. However, most organisms—including plants, animals, and fungi—cannot get the nitrogen they need from the free nitrogen in the air. They can use only nitrogen that is combined with other elements in compounds. But how are these nitrogen-containing compounds made?

Certain kinds of bacteria are able to use the free nitrogen in the air to make nitrogen compounds through a process known as nitrogen fixation. Most of the nitrogen fixation on Earth occurs as a result of the activity of bacteria. Some of these bacteria live

Figure 2–13 *The water in this tiger's breath is visible as white droplets condensing in the cold winter air. What other substances does the tiger exhale?* ❷

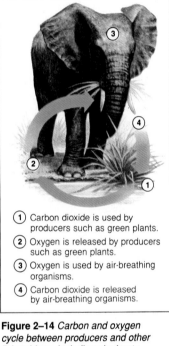

① Carbon dioxide is used by producers such as green plants.

② Oxygen is released by producers such as green plants.

③ Oxygen is used by air-breathing organisms.

④ Carbon dioxide is released by air-breathing organisms.

Figure 2–14 *Carbon and oxygen cycle between producers and other living things, including elephants. How does the carbon in carbon dioxide become the carbon in food?* ❹

G ■ 57

🖵 **Media and Technology**

Use the transparency in your *Transparency Binder* called Oxygen/Carbon Dioxide Cycle to help develop the concepts of the oxygen and carbon cycles.

ENRICHMENT

For each 900 kilograms of coal that is completely burned, about 25,000 kilograms of carbon dioxide are added to the atmosphere. This massive addition of carbon dioxide has been called the greenhouse effect. Encourage students to develop reports on the greenhouse effect and its importance to the oxygen and carbon cycles.

GUIDED PRACTICE

▶ *Laboratory Manual*

Skills Development

Skills: Observing, recording data

At this point you may want to have students complete the Chapter 2 Laboratory Investigation called Organisms and Carbon Dioxide in the *Laboratory Manual.* In this investigation, students will discover the importance of carbon dioxide in the environment.

INDEPENDENT PRACTICE

▶ *Activity Book*

Students who need practice on the concept of the oxygen cycle should complete the chapter activity The Oxygen Cycle.

ACTIVITY
THINKING
MINIATURE WORLDS

Skill: Applying concepts

Using what they know about the chemical cycles, students should be able to explain how the cycles would function in the miniature ecosystem. Any explanation should be based on the need for balance between organisms that use oxygen and produce carbon dioxide and those that use carbon dioxide and produce oxygen, as well as for organisms that use, convert, and cycle nitrogen in its various forms.

ACTIVITY
THINKING

Miniature Worlds

Certain companies make sealed glass globes that contain air, water, some small water plants, a few tiny shrimp, and certain microorganisms. If kept in a sunny place, the living things in the glass globe can survive indefinitely. How do the nitrogen, oxygen, and carbon cycles work in these miniature ecosystems?

in the soil. Others live in the water. Others grow inside special structures on the roots of certain plants, including beans, clover, alfalfa, peas, and peanuts.

One family of nitrogen compounds produced by nitrogen-fixing bacteria consists of substances called nitrates. Nitrates can be taken from the soil by plants. Inside the plants, the nitrogen in the nitrates is used to make compounds such as proteins. The compounds made by the plants can be used by animals, fungi, and other organisms that cannot use nitrates directly. Take a moment now to look at Figure 2–15. Trace the steps of the nitrogen cycle from the free nitrogen in the air to the nitrogen in the bodies of animals.

You have just read about the part of the nitrogen cycle in which nitrogen is transferred from the nonliving portion of the environment into living things. Now let's look at the part of the nitrogen cycle that returns nitrogen to nonliving things.

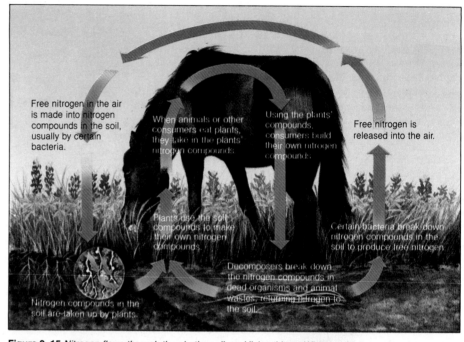

Figure 2–15 *Nitrogen flows through the air, the soil, and living things. What would happen to the nitrogen cycle if all bacteria suddenly vanished from the Earth?* ❶

58 ■ G

2–2 (continued)

CONTENT DEVELOPMENT

Emphasize that all living things are linked to the abiotic (nonliving) part of the ecosystem by their need for chemicals. There are about 30 chemicals essential for life. When an organism dies, these chemicals are returned to the Earth or get into the air, where they are available for other organisms. This movement forms a cycle.

Ask students to observe Figure 2–15 on page G58 and trace the steps in the nitrogen cycle. Point out that most of the Earth's nitrogen is in the form of a gas. This gas is combined with hydrogen during the process of nitrogen fixation and after several more chemical steps is changed to nitrates.

• **What are some other sources of nitrates?** (Certain decay bacteria also change organic material into nitrates.)

Remind students that nitrates can be used by plants.

• **What do plants do with the nitrates?** (They use the nitrogen in the nitrates to make proteins and other nitrogen-containing compounds.)

Point out that not all the nitrates go into plant and animal tissue.

• **What happens to nitrogen compounds that do not get absorbed by plants?** (Certain kinds of bacteria "free" the nitrogen from the compounds and release nitrogen gas back into the atmosphere.)

INDEPENDENT PRACTICE

▶ *Activity Book*

Students who need practice on the concept of the nitrogen cycle should complete the chapter activity The Nitrogen Cycle.

▶ *Product Testing Activity*

Have students perform the product test on toilet paper from the Product Testing worksheets. Ask students to consider how long it takes for the paper to degrade and for its components to be recycled in the environment.

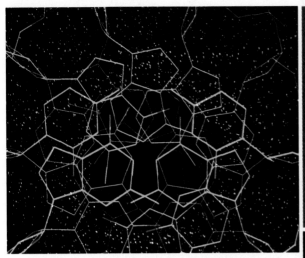

Decomposers, such as certain bacteria, break down the complex nitrogen compounds in dead organisms and animal wastes. This returns simple nitrogen compounds to the soil. These simple compounds may be used by bacteria to make nitrates.

Nitrogen can go back and forth between the soil and plants and animals many times. Eventually, however, certain kinds of bacteria break down nitrogen compounds to produce free nitrogen. The free nitrogen is released into the air, completing the cycle.

Figure 2–16 *Lightning may cause chemical reactions that change free nitrogen into nitrogen compounds. Most nitrogen fixation on Earth, however, is performed by bacteria (top right). The fixed nitrogen can then be used to produce proteins and other important compounds, including DNA (top left).*

2–2 Section Review

1. Show the basic steps of the nitrogen, water, oxygen, and carbon cycles by drawing a simple diagram for each cycle. (Do not copy the diagrams in your textbook!)
2. Why is it important for matter to be recycled in ecosystems?

Connection—*Ecology*
3. Every fourth year, a farmer plants alfalfa or clover on a field instead of wheat. Explain this practice.

2–3 Cycles of Change: Ecological Succession

MULTICULTURAL OPPORTUNITY 2–3

Ask students to examine a mini-ecosystem—perhaps in their backyard, in a park, or on the school grounds. They should make daily observations of their ecosystem over an extended period of time (at least one month) and note any changes. How many of these changes are the result of human activity?

ESL STRATEGY 2–3

As a group project, assign two specific incidents where environmental damage has occurred recently and have students give brief oral reports on the types of ecological succession that followed. Ask an English-speaking student to take the role of tutor in helping a LEP student to prepare the report.

Note: Follow study suggestions regarding pre-Chapter Review found at the end of Chapter 1.

Guide for Reading

Focus on this question as you read.

▶ What is ecological succession?

Figure 2–17 *The process of succession is considered to begin with bare rock, such as that resulting from a lava flow, or with a newly formed pond. Succession then gradually changes the area. How did succession affect this pond up to now? How will it probably change the pond in the future?* ❶

2–3 Cycles of Change: Ecological Succession

Imagine that you have built a time machine in a secret clearing in a forest. The big day has arrived—you are finally ready to test your invention! Your hands shake with excitement as you set the controls. You are about to travel hundreds of years back in time. You start the machine, and . . .

Splash! You find yourself in the middle of a pond. What's going on here? You started in a forest and now you're in a pond. Can a forest have once been a pond? You decide to use your time machine to discover an answer to this question. (Fortunately, your time machine is waterproof!) On your way back to the future, you will make a few stops so you can look around and see if your surroundings change over time.

At first, the pond is quite deep. No plants grow at the very bottom of its center. Not enough light can penetrate through the deep water for plants to survive. The pond is inhabited by fishes, the young of insects such as dragonflies, and a huge number of small aquatic animals and microorganisms.

As time passes, particles of dirt, fallen leaves, and the remains of dead water organisms begin to accumulate at the edges and bottom of the pond. As the pond becomes more shallow, new organisms can get a foothold. Underwater plants line the bottom of the pond. Eventually, water plants that poke out of the water—such as water lilies, reeds, and cattails—start growing around the edges of the pond.

TEACHING STRATEGY 2–3

FOCUS/MOTIVATION

Draw an arrow pointing to the right on the chalkboard. Tell students that ecological succession describes gradual and often predictable community change. It is not exactly linear change, not exactly circular or cyclic change. Draw an arrow pointing to the left to show that succession can be set back. This second arrow should not be as long as the first one and should

be above the first one. Draw a third arrow above the second one, pointing to the right; it should extend farther than the first arrow. Connect the ends of the arrows. The pattern will resemble a zigzag but will be moving to the right. Point out that over long periods of time, succession moves in one direction, even though it is set back occasionally.

CONTENT DEVELOPMENT

Many students will be familiar with old-field succession, which occurs when areas are no longer used for crops. Annuals, then perennials, invade the field, followed by a variety of shrubs and trees. Eventually, a forest with a well-developed canopy and understory forms. This process of old-field succession to forest can take place in a person's lifetime. The gradual change from a lake to a forest takes hundreds of

As the pond continues to fill in, the fish begin to die off. They are replaced by air-breathing animals such as frogs and turtles. The water lilies, reeds, and other plants grow all across the pond. Materials from the dead plants further fill in the pond.

Eventually only a few patches of open water are left. The pond has become a marsh. Like the pond, the marsh keeps filling in. In time, it becomes dry land. Rabbits and deer roam where fish and frogs once lived. Bushes and then trees take root. What began as a pond has become a forest.

Over time, one ecological community succeeds, or follows, another. **The process in which the community in a particular place is gradually replaced by another community is called ecological succession.** And, as your time-machine adventure has shown you, the process of **ecological succession** can completely change what a place looks like.

If the community in a particular place is left alone, it may in time consist of a group of species that are not replaced by new arrivals. This stable collection of plants, animals, and other organisms is known as a **climax community.** The climax community varies from place to place. In the northeastern United States, for example, a climax community may be characterized by oak and hickory trees. In certain areas of northern California, the climax community may be dominated by huge redwood trees.

The process of succession does not have to start with a pond or other body of water. It can begin with the bare rock formed by a lava flow or landslide. It can also occur on soil that has been cleared of vegetation by a disaster or in areas where some sort of ecological disturbance such as logging or farming has been stopped.

Succession usually takes a long time. To go from a tiny pond to a forest can take more than a hundred years. Outside forces, however, can affect the rate of succession. For example, certain pollutants, such as sewage and phosphate-containing detergents, can cause the plants in a body of water to grow extremely quickly. How would this affect succession? ❷

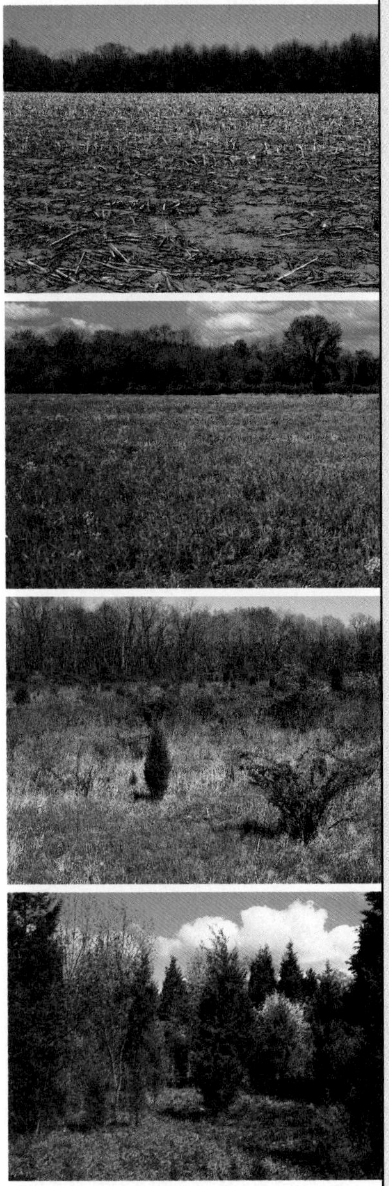

Figure 2–18 *Succession resumes when an area, such as a corn field, is left alone. The first year, a few weeds and grasses take root. After two years, the field is covered with grass. After ten years, there are shrubs and young trees. After twenty years, the field has become a young forest.*

ANNOTATION KEY

Answers

❶ The pond has slowly filled up with debris, water plants, and air-breathing animals and has become a marsh. In time it may fill in even more and become dry land where a forest can grow. (Drawing conclusions, Making predictions)

❷ It speeds up succession by causing plants to grow faster. (Making inferences)

BACKGROUND INFORMATION

ECOLOGICAL SUCCESSION

There are actually two types of ecological succession—primary succession and secondary succession. Primary succession is the establishment and development of communities in newly formed areas. Cooled lava, rocky surfaces, and sandy areas are examples of regions in which primary succession occurs. Primary succession also occurs in newly formed lakes and ponds. Secondary succession is succession that occurs in disturbed areas, such as abandoned farmland and vacant lots.

years unless it is accelerated by human activities.

- **Why do we still have lakes and ponds? Why haven't they all changed into forests?** (Many lakes are still very young in geological time. In addition, erosion and other geological processes are constantly forming new lakes.)
- **Why can succession be considered a type of evolution?** (The lake changes over time.)

FOCUS/MOTIVATION

Take a ten-minute field trip around the schoolyard to look for evidence of succession. Find grassy areas where mowers cannot reach and point out any young trees or tall weeds that may be invading the area. If there is a hedge, look for evidence of trees trying to grow nearby. Also, look for trees trying to grow along rows of fence. Have students take notes about their observations.

CONTENT DEVELOPMENT

Point out that the spores and seeds that germinate in newly colonized areas are not a result of spontaneous generation. They have arrived via wind, water, and animals. Discuss how a newly formed island might get spores and seeds. Encourage students to collect different seeds and test their ability to be blown by the wind or carried by water or animals.

Discovery Learning

Skills: Making observations, relating concepts

Students are able to reinforce their understanding of ecological succession through this project. Caution students to find an area that is likely to remain undisturbed for the period of time and to be sure to get permission to conduct the experiment there. Students should first explore their area and record their observations before the grass grows.

Students should check on their area each week during the period of time to be sure that the area has not been disturbed. They may also want to make notes each week to use along with their initial and final observations.

Encourage students to use some form of chart to present the information they collect on the organisms in the two areas. They should conclude that many more and different kinds of organisms are found in their area than in the mowed area because they can live there undisturbed.

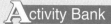

Activity Bank

Hay! Look at This! Activity Book, p. G177. This activity can be used for ESL and/or Cooperative Learning.

Figure 2–19 *In 1988, terrible fires destroyed much of the forest in Yellowstone National Park. How did this affect succession?* ❶

ACTIVITY

DISCOVERING

Backyard Succession

1. Locate a backyard, field, or park lawn that is usually mowed.

2. After obtaining the proper permission, measure an area that is 1 meter on each side.

3. Do not mow or disturb that area for six weeks or longer.

4. After six weeks, carefully explore your area to see what organisms are living in it.

■ Compare the organisms you find in your area with the ones that are growing in the mowed area. What conclusion can you reach?

Some events can slow down succession or set it back a few steps. Plowing a field prevents bushes and trees from gaining a foothold. Fire can burn a developing forest and set it back. Floods can fill a dying pond with water again. Because of these kinds of changes in the environment, succession usually moves in cycles rather than in a straight line.

When making decisions about how natural resources should be used, it is important to keep this in mind: Succession can take many different paths and can lead to different climax communities. The end result of succession is due in a large part to chance. A particular pond, for example, may end up as a forest of willow and alder trees or a treeless peat bog. Because of this, people cannot assume that an ecosystem will recover and return to the way it was after it has been disturbed. It is possible that succession will restore an ecosystem after trees are cut down, land is dug up for mining, oil is spilled, or any other kind of environmental damage occurs. But it is also possible that succession will take a different path and the ecosystem will never be the same again. Because of this, people must be very careful in deciding which resources should be used. Succession will occur—but no one can accurately predict the course it will take.

2–3 Section Review

1. What is ecological succession? How do ecosystems change as a result of succession?
2. What is a climax community?

Critical Thinking—*Appraising Conclusions*
3. Logging companies often plant pine seedlings in places where they have cut down all the trees. They argue that there is nothing wrong with harvesting trees from any forest, as long as measures such as replanting are taken. Many ecologists argue that forests that have not yet been affected by logging should be left alone. Using what you have learned about succession, explain why the ecologists take this position. Do you think this is reasonable?

2–3 (continued)

ENRICHMENT

Explain how the establishment of some type of plant in an area can either pave the way for the next species or make the area unsuitable for a former species. For example, small plants can create a layer of soil in which larger trees can then grow, but the shade of the trees can then make growth impossible for the smaller plants. Can students think of other situations in which one species is forced out of an area by another?

REINFORCEMENT/RETEACHING

Some students may still be confused by the concept of ecological succession. To help reinforce the concept, have them draw a series of pictures or a diorama showing different stages of ecological succession. The pictures on page G61 can serve as a starting point, but encourage students to create their own series of pictures. Display the pictures on a bulletin board labeled Ecological Succession.

INDEPENDENT PRACTICE

Section Review 2–3

1. Ecological succession is the process in which the community in a particular place is gradually replaced by another community. Succession changes the types of animals, plants, and other organisms that are found in the ecosystem.
2. A climax community consists of a set of organisms that are not replaced by

CONNECTIONS

Cycles and Stories ❶

Why are there seasons? What causes day to turn into night? Why does the moon seem to grow and then shrink during the course of a month?

Today we know that these never-ending cycles of change are caused by the movement of the Earth and the moon. But long ago, people did not know about the way the Earth and moon spin through space. As they looked in wonder at the world around them, people created stories, or *myths* (MIHTHS), to explain what they saw. Here is one such myth from Nigeria, a country in Africa.

Why the Moon Grows and Shrinks

The bush baby (a small monkeylike animal) was very poor. His friend the mouse-deer felt sorry for him, and wanted to help. So the mouse-deer, who had two pairs of eyes, gave one pair to the bush baby.

The mouse-deer's eyes were large, round precious stones that shone with a light of their own. But no one could afford

to buy such fine gems. So the bush baby broke the eyes into tiny pieces.

Unfortunately, when the bush baby went to sell the tiny sparkling gems, the wind blew them all over the town. It took the children of the town a month to gather up the tiny gems and put them in a box. But as soon as they had finished, the wind began to blow them out of the box once more.

Every month, the wind scatters the bush-baby's tiny gems across the town of the sky, where they glitter as stars. And each month, the children gather up the stars and put them into the box of the moon. But as soon as the moon is full, the wind begins to blow away the gathered gems.

■ What are some myths about nature that belong to your own cultural heritage? Discover the myths of your ancestors by talking to the older members of your family or by going to the library.

G ■ 63

CONNECTIONS
CYCLES AND STORIES

Some students may be fascinated by the idea of myths as explanations for natural phenomena. Many students may not have connected the concept of myths or stories with scientific theories. Explain that in most cultures myths were people's attempts to explain phenomena that we now often turn to science to answer.

When students have investigated myths either through their families or through the library, encourage students to share their findings with the class. Group the presentations by subject (sun, moon, stars, seasons, and so on), if possible, so that students can see the variety and ingenuity of myths.

If you are teaching thematically, you may want to use the Connections feature to reinforce the themes of patterns of change or systems and interactions.

Integration: Use the Connections feature to integrate mythology and multicultural studies into your lesson.

new arrivals. It is the stable end product of succession.

3. Ecologists take this position because it is never certain that succession will eventually cause an ecosystem to return to the way it was before being disturbed. In addition, a natural forest consists of many different kinds of trees and plants at various stages of development, whereas a replanted area has trees that are the same age and are of the same species. Students' assessment of this position will vary.

REINFORCEMENT/RETEACHING

Review students' responses to the Section Review questions. If they appear to have difficulty with any of the questions, review the appropriate material in the section.

CLOSURE

▶ *Review and Reinforcement Guide*

At this point have students complete Section 2–3 in their *Review and Reinforcement Guide.*

Laboratory Investigation

GOING IN CYCLES

BEFORE THE LAB

1. This activity requires one class period to set up and a few minutes of observation time each day thereafter for about three weeks. The lab can be done at any point within the chapter. Although this activity is designed for houseflies, several other common insects, such as mealworms, are suitable for observing life cycles.

2. Before beginning the lab, you should gather all the necessary equipment. Plan for enough space to keep students' jars for three weeks. The space should be easily observable. You should also be certain that you have enough female flies for each group to have at least one.

PRE-LAB DISCUSSION

Review the laboratory procedure with students.

• **What is the purpose of the laboratory investigation?** (To trace the steps in the life cycle of a housefly.)

• **How is the gauze cloth used?** (To prevent the flies from escaping while allowing them fresh air.)

• **What is the purpose of the wet cotton, the bran flakes, and the milk?** (The wet cotton provides moisture, and the bran flakes and milk provide food.)

• **What are the differences between male and female houseflies?** (Females have pointed tails and small eyes. Males have rounded tails and large eyes.)

It is a good idea to have one male and one female fly in a clear plastic vial so that students can become familiar with their different structures.

The eggs should be kept in a warm place with adequate moisture. Putting the jars in indirect sunlight for a few days will reduce the growth of mold.

Laboratory Investigation

Going in Cycles

Problem

What are the steps in the life cycle of a housefly?

Materials *(per group)*

> magnifying glass
> rubber band
> cotton ball
> glass jar
> piece of gauze cloth large enough to cover the top of the glass jar
> 20 mL bran flakes
> 10 mL diluted canned milk
> paper towel
> houseflies
> metal bottle cap

Procedure 🧪 🐁

1. To make a fly cage, place a paper towel in the bottom of a glass jar. Put 20 mL of bran flakes and 10 mL of diluted canned milk on the towel.

2. Wet a cotton ball with water and put it in the metal bottle cap. Put the bottle cap, with the cotton ball facing up, into the glass jar.

3. Put the flies your teacher gives you into the cage. Stretch the gauze cloth over the mouth of the jar and hold it in place with the rubber band.

4. Using the magnifying glass, check to be sure there is at least one female fly. Female flies have pointed tails and small eyes. Males have rounded tails and large eyes.

5. When eggs appear, release your adult flies outdoors. Fly eggs are small, white, and shaped like sausages.

Observations

1. Each day, check the jar and write a description of what you see.

2. For how many days do you see eggs?

3. Larvae (wormlike young flies) come from the eggs. Draw a larva. For how many days do you see larvae?

4. A larva becomes a pupa. Draw a pupa. For how many days do you see pupae?

5. What does a pupa become?

Analysis and Conclusions

1. Using your drawings and other data from your investigation, prepare a diagram showing the life cycle of a housefly.

2. **On Your Own** Design an investigation to examine the life cycle of another kind of organism—a bean plant, fruit fly, guppy (a fish), or frog, for example. If you receive the proper permission, you may perform the investigation you have designed.

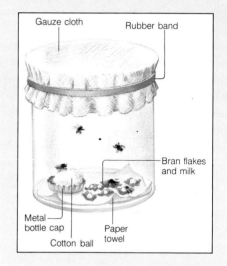

TEACHING STRATEGY

1. Have students set up their fly cages before you distribute the flies.

2. Have students identify their flies after they are in the cages to be sure that they have at least one female.

3. Make sure students remember to record their observations each day.

DISCOVERY STRATEGIES

Discuss how the investigation relates to the chapter ideas by asking open questions similar to the following.

• **Think about the different cycles you have studied in this chapter. What is a cycle?** (A cycle is a repeating, or circular, process—a set of events that occur in the same sequence over and over—analyzing, inferring.)

Study Guide

Summarizing Key Concepts

2–1 Cycles in Time: Rhythms of Life

▲ Biological clocks help living things stay in step with rhythmic cycles of change in their environment.

▲ Biological clocks are set and reset by environmental cues such as dawn or dusk, day length, moisture, and temperature.

▲ The rhythms of life are linked to daily, lunar, and annual cycles in time.

▲ Organisms that are active during the day are said to be diurnal. Those that are active at night are said to be nocturnal.

▲ Tidal rhythms are one type of lunar rhythm. There are two kinds of tidal rhythms: a roughly two-week cycle and a roughly 12-hour cycle.

▲ Events that occur once a year, every year are examples of annual rhythms.

▲ Migration is the movement of organisms from one place to another. Many animals have annual migrations.

▲ In winter, some organisms enter a resting state known as hibernation.

▲ In summer, some organisms enter a resting state known as estivation.

2–2 Cycles of Matter

▲ Unlike energy, matter can be recycled. Matter flows in cycles from the nonliving part of the environment to living things and back again.

▲ There are many cycles of matter in ecosystems. Four of the most important are the water, oxygen, carbon, and nitrogen cycles.

2–3 Cycles of Change: Ecological Succession

▲ The process in which the set of living things in a particular place is gradually replaced by another set of living things is called ecological succession.

▲ In time, a particular place may possess a stable collection of plants, animals, and other organisms known as a climax community. The climax community varies from place to place.

▲ Succession usually takes a long time. Outside forces, however, can affect the rate of succession and may even reset the cycles of succession.

Reviewing Key Terms

Define each term in a complete sentence.

2–1 Cycles in Time: Rhythms of Life
biological clock
diurnal
nocturnal
migration
hibernation
estivation

2–2 Cycles of Matter
water cycle
oxygen cycle
carbon cycle
nitrogen cycle

2–3 Cycles of Change: Ecological Succession
ecological succession
climax community

ANALYSIS AND CONCLUSIONS

1. Check student diagrams for accuracy.
2. Accept all logical, well-thought-out plans. Remind students to do some research on the needs and life cycle of the organism they have selected before they begin devising their plan. If students are allowed to perform their investigations, you may wish them to keep a daily log in which they note observations, feedings, waterings, and so on.

GOING FURTHER: ENRICHMENT

Part 1

Have students vary conditions of the laboratory activity (such as temperature) to observe the effect of such changes in the life cycle of the flies and, specifically, on the duration of each stage of their cycle.

Part 2

Have students investigate the life cycles of a mammal, reptile, bird, and fish of their choice and compare the type, sequence, and duration of the stages of these life cycles to those of the housefly's life cycle.

• **How is the life cycle of a housefly like the water cycle?** (Certain events take place in a certain order in the life of every housefly—egg, larva, pupa, adult; certain events occur in a certain sequence—evaporation, condensation, precipitation—in the cycle of water through an ecosystem—analyzing, applying, comparing.)

OBSERVATIONS

1–2. The white elongated eggs appear after about one day.
3. The larvae (maggots) appear after about eight more days.
4. The pupae appear after about seven more days.
5. A pupa becomes an adult fly.

Chapter Review

ALTERNATIVE ASSESSMENT

The *Prentice Hall Science* program includes a variety of testing components and methodologies. Aside from the Chapter Review questions, you may opt to use the Chapter Test or the Computer Test Bank Test in your *Test Book* for assessment of important facts and concepts. In addition, Performance-Based Tests are included in your *Test Book*. These Performance-Based Tests are designed to test science-process skills, rather than factual-content recall. Since they are not content dependent, Performance-Based Tests can be distributed after students complete a chapter or after they complete the entire textbook.

CONTENT REVIEW

Multiple Choice

1. b
2. c
3. d
4. d
5. a
6. a
7. b
8. b

True or False

1. T
2. F, can
3. F, migration
4. F, lunar
5. F, evaporation
6. T
7. T

Concept Mapping

Row 1: Lunar, Annual
Row 3: Migration, Estivation

CONCEPT MASTERY

1. Possible answers: Caribou migrate from their summer home in the far north, where they breed, to their winter home in the southern forests, where they can find food. Bears hibernate or "sleep" through the winter until spring brings more favorable conditions. Toads estivate in burrows during the hot, dry summers until winter brings more favorable conditions. Marigolds produce seeds before they die in winter, and in spring the seeds grow into next year's marigolds.

2. The grunion move up onto the beach

Content Review

Multiple Choice

Choose the letter of the answer that best completes each statement.

1. Organisms that are active during the day are said to be
   a. nocturnal.   c. lunar.
   b. diurnal.   d. annual.
2. In the winter, frogs and ground squirrels enter a resting state known as
   a. succession.   c. hibernation.
   b. estivation.   d. migration.
3. Fiddler crabs are most active at low tide. What kind of rhythm are the fiddler crabs showing?
   a. annual   c. daily
   b. diurnal   d. lunar
4. The act of traveling to a new environment when seasonal changes make the old environment less favorable is known as
   a. succession.   c. hibernation.
   b. estivation.   d. migration.
5. Clouds are formed from water vapor by
   a. condensation.   c. precipitation.
   b. evaporation.   d. denitrification.
6. Organisms that are active at night are said to be
   a. nocturnal.   c. lunar.
   b. diurnal.   d. annual.
7. Succession may result in a stable set of organisms known as a(an)
   a. ecosystem.
   b. climax community.
   c. transitional community.
   d. migration.
8. Most nitrogen fixation on Earth occurs through the activity of
   a. plants.   c. animals.
   b. bacteria.   d. fungi.

True or False

If the statement is true, write "true." If it is false, change the underlined word or words to make the statement true.

1. Biological clocks are inner timers that help organisms stay in step with natural cycles in time.
2. Unlike energy, matter cannot be recycled.
3. The movement of organisms from the place where they feed to the place where they breed is known as estivation.
4. The approximate 12-hour cycle of the tides is an example of a daily rhythm.
5. Liquid water changes into water vapor through precipitation.
6. Succession can be speeded up, slowed down, or reset by outside forces.
7. Air-breathing organisms exhale carbon dioxide, which can then be used by producers such as green plants.

Concept Mapping

Complete the following concept map for Section 2–1. Refer to pages G6–G7 to construct a concept map for the entire chapter.

---

to deposit their eggs only at night (daily cycle). They appear only with the highest tides (lunar cycle). They appear at two-week intervals during the spring and early summer (annual cycle).

3. Students' answers will vary but should be based on observations of whether organisms in their community are continuing to change or have been established there for a long time.

4. If matter did not cycle through the ecosystem, it would soon be used up, and living things would die off.

5. People take in oxygen and release carbon dioxide. Green plants take in carbon dioxide and produce oxygen. Green plants need carbon dioxide to make food, and people need the food and the oxygen that green plants produce.

6. Bacteria use nitrogen from the air to make compounds. These compounds can then be used by plants to make other compounds. These compounds can then be used by animals. When the animals die, bacteria break down the compounds and return the nitrogen to the soil or to

describe the 4 steps of the oxygen & carbon cycles. Who participates in this cycle? (handwritten)

Concept Mastery

Discuss each of the following in a brief paragraph.

1. Using specific examples, describe four different strategies for dealing with seasonal changes in the environment.
2. How is reproduction in grunion tied to daily, lunar, and annual cycles of time?
3. Do you live in a climax community? What observations lead you to this conclusion?
4. Why are cycles of matter important to living things?
5. How do the oxygen and carbon cycles link you to green plants?
6. Describe the basic steps of the nitrogen cycle.
7. What is succession? Explain how succession can change a marsh into a forest.

Critical Thinking and Problem Solving

Use the skills you have developed in this chapter to answer each of the following.

1. **Relating cause and effect** There is much evidence to support the theory of the "greenhouse effect." According to this theory, excess amounts of carbon dioxide in the atmosphere can cause temperatures all over the world to rise. Explain how destruction of the world's forests may contribute to the greenhouse effect.
2. **Making predictions** A volcano is forming a new island in the ocean southeast of the island of Hawaii. This island will emerge from the sea in a thousand years or so. How might succession change this island over time? How might further volcanic eruptions on the island affect succession?
3. **Relating cause and effect** The accompanying photograph shows one use of fossil fuels—to power cars, buses, and trucks. As they burn, fossil fuels (coal, oil, natural gas, and gasoline, to name a few) release energy and carbon dioxide. For about two hundred years, people have been burning huge amounts of fossil fuels for energy. How does this affect the oxygen and carbon cycles?
4. **Making diagrams** Nitrogen in your food today may have once been part of a dinosaur. Draw a diagram that shows how the nitrogen might have gotten from the dinosaur to you.
5. **Assessing concepts** Is it better to think of succession as a one-way street or as a series of cycles? Explain your answer.
6. **Using the writing process** Imagine that you are a drop of water. Describe your journey through the water cycle. What changes do you undergo along the way? What living and nonliving things do you meet? What do you think about them? Is going through the water cycle fun or is it an unpleasant chore?

of plants; small plants will lead to bigger plants. Plants will bring animals to feed on them. And eventually, the volcanic island will be a lush tropical island like the other Hawaiian Islands. Subsequent volcanic eruptions leading to more lava flows will, however, kill off the plants and animals. The island might become bare rock again, but then tiny plants would appear . . .

3. Huge amounts of carbon dioxide have been added to the atmosphere, thus disrupting the balance of the gases. The oxygen and carbon cycles cannot cope with such an overabundance of one gas.
4. Students' diagrams will vary but should show that when the dinosaur died, its chemicals returned to the soil to be used by plants, which we then eat.
5. Succession is best thought of as a series of cycles because many events can occur to stop, slow down, or even alter its course.
6. Students' descriptions should be scientifically consistent with the chapter material. The description should include the cycle of evaporation, condensation, and precipitation.

KEEPING A PORTFOLIO

You might want to assign some of the Concept Mastery and Critical Thinking and Problem Solving questions as homework and have students include their responses to unassigned questions in their portfolio. Students should be encouraged to include both the question and the answer in their portfolio.

ISSUES IN SCIENCE

The following issues can be used as springboards for discussion or given as writing assignments.

1. The use of pesticides to control insect populations selectively produces insects that are immune to certain chemicals. On the other hand, pesticides have helped people to increase crop yields and get rid of diseases that are carried by insects. Should pesticides continue to be used?
2. The massive destruction of tropical rain forests and other large ecosystems has led many scientists to predict that the oxygen and carbon cycles are being disrupted. Assign students to seek evidence supporting or denying this prediction.

the air, and the cycle continues.

7. Succession is the process in which the community of organisms in one place is gradually replaced by another community. The marsh will slowly fill in with plants, dirt, leaves, and other materials. The water disappears, and the area becomes dry land. Now rabbits and deer, rather than frogs and fish, can live there. There is soil for trees and other plants to take root in. Eventually, the area becomes a forest.

CRITICAL THINKING AND PROBLEM SOLVING

1. When forests are cut down, they are often burned. The burning releases huge amounts of carbon dioxide into the atmosphere. Also, cutting down the forests means that there are fewer trees to take in carbon dioxide and produce oxygen.
2. Initially, the island will be bare rock, but gradually, tiny plants will appear, their seeds carried in by the wind or the water. A few scattered plants will become fields

SECTION	HANDS-ON ACTIVITIES
3–1 Biogeography pages G70–G74 Multicultural Opportunity 3–1, p. G74 ESL Strategy 3–1, p. G74	**Student Edition** LABORATORY INVESTIGATION: Building a Biome, p. G94 **Teacher Edition** Demonstrating Dispersal, p. G68d
3–2 Tundra Biomes pages G75–G76 Multicultural Opportunity 3–2, p. G74 ESL Strategy 3–2, p. G74	**Laboratory Manual** Adapting to the Cold, p. G29
3–3 Forest Biomes pages G77–G83 Multicultural Opportunity 3–3, p. G76 ESL Strategy, 3–3, p. G76	**Student Edition** ACTIVITY (Doing): Forest Food Webs, p. G78 ACTIVITY (Discovering): Comparing Forest Biomes, p. G80 ACTIVITY BANK: Cutting Down the Rain, p. G148
3–4 Grassland Biomes pages G83–G85 Multicultural Opportunity 3–4, p. G83 ESL Strategy 3–4, p. G83	**Student Edition** ACTIVITY BANK: Grandeur in the Grass, p. G149 **Teacher Edition** Identifying Grassland Animals, p. G68d
3–5 Desert Biomes pages G85–G87 Multicultural Opportunity 3–5, p. G85 ESL Strategy 3–5, p. G85	**Student Edition** ACTIVITY (Discovering): A Desert Terrarium, p. G86 **Activity Book** ACTIVITY: Cactus Adaptations, p. G101
3–6 Water Biomes pages G88–G93 Multicultural Opportunity 3–6, p. G88 ESL Strategy 3–6, p. G88	**Laboratory Manual** Investigating Habitats, p. G35
Chapter Review pages G94–G97	

OTHER ACTIVITIES	MEDIA AND TECHNOLOGY
Activity Book CHAPTER DISCOVERY: Climate, Plants, and Animals, p. G73 ACTIVITY: Microbiomes, p. G91 ACTIVITY: Identifying a Biome, p. G97 **Review and Reinforcement Guide** Section 3–1, p. G23	**Prentice Hall Science Integrated Media** Earth's Many Biomes **English/Spanish Audiotapes** Section 3–1
Review and Reinforcement Guide Section 3–2, p. G25	**Prentice Hall Science Integrated Media** Earth's Many Biomes **English/Spanish Audiotapes** Section 3–2
Student Edition ACTIVITY (Thinking): Saving the Rain Forests, p. G83 **Activity Book** ACTIVITY: Precipitation on the Earth's Land Biomes, p. G99 **Review and Reinforcement Guide** Section 3–3, p. G27	**Prentice Hall Science Integrated Media** Earth's Many Biomes **English/Spanish Audiotapes** Section 3–3
Activity Book ACTIVITY: Designing a Habitat, p. G105 **Review and Reinforcement Guide** Section 3–4, p. G29	**Prentice Hall Science Integrated Media** Earth's Many Biomes **English/Spanish Audiotapes** Section 3–4
Activity Book ACTIVITY: Scenic View from Around the World, p. G87 ACTIVITY: Land Biomes of the Earth, p. G89 ACTIVITY: Name That Biome! p. G103 **Review and Reinforcement Guide** Section 3–5, p. G31	**Prentice Hall Science Integrated Media** Earth's Many Biomes **English/Spanish Audiotapes** Section 3–5
Student Edition ACTIVITY (Reading): Life Near a Trout Stream, p. G91 **Activity Book** ACTIVITY: There's No Place Like Home, p. G85 ACTIVITY: Neighborhood Water Habitat, p. G93 ACTIVITY: A Water Environment, p. G95 **Review and Reinforcement Guide** Section 3–6, p. G33	**Prentice Hall Science Integrated Media** Earth's Many Biomes **English/Spanish Audiotapes** Section 3–6
Test Book Chapter Test, p. G51 Performance-Based Tests, p. G91	**Test Book** Computer Test Bank Test, p. G57

* All materials in the Chapter Planning Guide Grid are available as part of the Prentice Hall Science Learning System. G ■ 68b

CHAPTER OVERVIEW

Biogeography is the study of the distribution of the Earth's plants and animals. Dispersal of plants and animals in the environment is accomplished in many ways. Sometimes water, wind, animals, and people help dispersal. Natural and people-made barriers can prevent dispersal.

Plants and animals live in different biomes. The major land biomes are tundra, coniferous forest, temperate deciduous forest, tropical rain forest, grassland, and desert. Differences in temperature and amount of rainfall largely determine these biomes. Tundra is very cold and dry. Coniferous forests have more precipitation and high enough temperatures to support the growth of cone-bearing trees and a greater diversity of animal life than is found in the tundra. Deciduous forests are characterized by trees that seasonally shed their leaves and grow new ones. A rich di-versity of animal life is found in these forests. Tropical rain forest biomes have large amounts of rain and year-round warm temperatures. Such climatic conditions give tropical rain forests the most abundant and varied plants and animals of any land biome. Grasslands receive between 25 and 75 centimeters of annual rainfall and have grasses as the main plants. Deserts have a yearly rainfall of less than 25 centimeters.

Water biomes are either marine or freshwater. Marine biomes, consisting of the world's oceans, cover more than 70 percent of the planet. A variety of chemical and physical factors determine the numbers, kinds, and distribution of organisms in the oceans. Freshwater biomes include still and running water. As in oceans, an interaction of several factors determines the kind of organisms that are present.

3–1 BIOGEOGRAPHY

THEMATIC FOCUS

The purpose of this section is to introduce the concept of biomes, focusing on climate and organisms as determining factors in classifying biomes. The section opens with a discussion of biogeography as the study of where organisms live and examines dispersal of organisms and barriers to dispersal.

The themes that can be focused on in this section are patterns of change and stability.

*Patterns of change: Stress the fact that organisms disperse into new areas. Dispersal is accomplished often with help from wind, water, animals, and humans. Barriers can prevent dispersal.

Stability: As you discuss the determining factors of biomes, stress that climate and organisms are criteria for classifying biomes. Identification of biomes are based on the common factors within the biome.

PERFORMANCE OBJECTIVES 3–1

1. Identify methods of dispersal.
2. Describe types of dispersal barriers.
3. Define biome.

SCIENCE TERMS 3–1

biogeography p. G70
dispersal p. G71
biome p. G73

3–2 TUNDRA BIOMES

THEMATIC FOCUS

The purpose of this section is to introduce the characteristics of the tundra biomes. Because of the climate, plants and animals in this biome have adapted to extreme cold and short growing seasons. The term *permafrost* is defined and described as one factor that inhibits plant growth.

The themes that can be focused on in this section are patterns of change and systems and interactions.

*Patterns of change: Stress the seasonal changes that take place within the tundra biome. Point out that although the growing season is short, it attracts a wide variety of migrating birds.

*Systems and interactions: As you discuss the tundra biome, make sure that students understand the concepts of producers and consumers in reference to the plants and animals of the tundra.

PERFORMANCE OBJECTIVES 3–2

1. Describe the climatic conditions of the tundra.
2. Identify the organisms that survive in the tundra.
3. Define permafrost.

SCIENCE TERM 3–2

permafrost p. G75

3–3 FOREST BIOMES

THEMATIC FOCUS

The purpose of this section is to introduce students to the three major forest biomes. The characteristics of the coniferous forest, temperate deciduous forest, and the tropical rain forest biomes are described.

The themes that can be focused on in this section are energy and unity and diversity.

*Energy: As you discuss the forest biomes, point out the importance of energy from the sun on the plants that can grow in the biome. Stress that in the coniferous forest and the tropical rain forest, the lack of energy from the sun inhibits growth on the forest floor.

*Unity and diversity: Explain the conditions that promote the wide diversity of life in the tropical rain forest. Help students understand that climatic factors affect the number and diversity of organisms that grow in each forest biome.

PERFORMANCE OBJECTIVES 3–3

1. Identify the Earth's major forest biomes.
2. Compare climate and major types of life in the three major forest biomes.

SCIENCE TERMS 3–3

conifer p. G77
taiga p. G78
canopy p. G81

3–4 GRASSLAND BIOMES
THEMATIC FOCUS

The purpose of this section is to introduce the characteristics of the grassland biomes. The section closes by discussing the impact of the conversion of grasslands to farms and ranches.

The themes that can be focused on in this section are patterns of change and scale and structure.

*Patterns of change: Discuss how the conversion of the grasslands to use in farming and ranching has affected grassland organisms. All animals have less and less land for use. Plowing and overgrazing can lead to erosion that affects plant growth.

Scale and structure: Emphasize that as grasslands are converted to farms and ranches, the grasslands are disappearing. The structure of the grasslands as a habitat for organisms also changes.

PERFORMANCE OBJECTIVES 3–4
1. Describe the characteristics of a grassland biome.
2. Identify three factors that limit tree growth in grasslands.
3. Give examples of plant eaters and meat eaters in grasslands.

3–5 DESERT BIOMES
THEMATIC FOCUS

The purpose of this section is to introduce the characteristics of deserts. The major focus is on the adaptation of organisms to the climate. The section also compares hot deserts and cold deserts.

The themes that can be focused on in this section are evolution and unity and diversity.

*Evolution: When discussing the organisms of the desert, stress the adaptations that animals and plants have evolved that help them survive. Help students identify examples of these adaptations and how they help the organisms survive.

*Unity and diversity: Stress the remarkable differences in the ways organisms have adapted to the conditions in a desert biome. Each organism in its own way has acquired special behavioral or physical characteristics.

PERFORMANCE OBJECTIVES 3–5
1. Describe climatic conditions associated with desert biomes.
2. Name two ways that desert plants are adapted to arid conditions.
3. Describe several ways that desert animals are adapted to live in arid conditions.

3–6 WATER BIOMES
THEMATIC FOCUS

The purpose of this section is to introduce the characteristics of the two major water biomes, focusing on the organisms each biome supports. The section closes with a discussion of estuaries that exhibit characteristics of both water biomes.

The themes that can be focused on in this lesson are energy and systems and interactions.

*Energy: Emphasize that most organisms in water biomes depend on sunlight as a source of energy. Point out that this source is unavailable in the deep ocean. Creatures that survive in the deep ocean rely on heat from the Earth's interior.

*Systems and interactions: When discussing the food sources of the organisms in the marine biome, stress the fact that most animals depend directly or indirectly on phytoplankton for food.

PERFORMANCE OBJECTIVES 3–6
1. Identify the two major water biomes.
2. List several factors that affect marine organisms.
3. List several factors that influence organisms in freshwater biomes.

SCIENCE TERMS 3–6
marine biome p. G88
phytoplankton p. G88
freshwater biome p. G90
estuary p. G91

Discovery *Learning*

TEACHER DEMONSTRATIONS MODELING
Demonstrating Dispersal

Place a marble in the center of a shallow baking pan. Tell the class the marble represents a seed. Challenge students to think of ways you can make the seed disperse, or move.
• **How can this seed be moved?** (Accept all logical responses.)

Demonstrate different ways of moving the marble. Use a fan to blow air at it. Pour a pitcher of water over it. Pick it up and move it to a different location.
• **How can seeds be dispersed?** (Students should suggest, by being carried by the wind, water, or animals.)

Identifying Grassland Animals

Prepare a picture display of a few animals that are adapted to similar lifestyles in North American and African grassland biomes. As students examine the display, ask them to list the names of the animals and whether they think they live in North America or Africa.

Conduct a discussion focusing on the similarities among the animals from the different biomes. Point out that they are adapted to similar conditions and have similar characteristics.
• **What similar characteristics to escape their predators do the grazing animals have?** (Answers depend on pictures, but may focus on speed, protection of herds, or horns or antlers.)
• **In what ways are the large meat-eating animals alike?** (Accept all logical answers. Be sure students understand that the large carnivores are skillful hunters and have a keen sense of smell.)

CHAPTER 3
Exploring Earth's Biomes

INTEGRATING SCIENCE

This life science chapter provides you with numerous opportunities to integrate other areas of science as well as other disciplines into your curriculum. Blue-numbered annotations on the student page and integration notes on the teacher wraparound pages alert you to areas of possible integration.

In this chapter you can integrate earth science and meteorology (pp. 71, 85), earth science and geology (p. 71), life science and evolution (p. 72), earth science and maps (p. 74), life science and plants (p. 77), language arts (pp. 83, 91), earth science and oceanography (p. 88).

SCIENCE, TECHNOLOGY, AND SOCIETY/COOPERATIVE LEARNING

Economic, social, political, and environmental pressures threaten the existence of all land biomes. Growing population exerts pressure to develop once untouched areas. Resources are used for economic growth. The result can be the destruction of biomes. Tropical rain forests provide a prime example of the pressures facing the Earth's biomes. People have cut into the rain forests to make more land available for farming and ranching. The main resource of the rain forest is harvested to meet the demand for wood. Teak and other forest trees are made into furniture and other goods for export.

INTRODUCING CHAPTER 3

DISCOVERY LEARNING

▶ *Activity Book*

You may want to begin your teaching of the chapter by using the Chapter 3 Discovery Activity from your *Activity Book*. Using this activity, students will discover that organisms and climate are characteristic of different environments.

USING THE TEXTBOOK

Have students observe the photo on page G68.
• **What do you think is happening in the picture?** (Students might suggest the lions are scanning the grasslands in search of prey.)
• **In what kind of environment do the lions live?** (Students might identify the environment as grasslands or plains.)
• **What other animals would you expect to see in this environment?** (Accept all logical answers. Students may name animals such as antelopes that the lion preys on.)

Point out to students that lions live in the open plains in Africa. Have the students read the chapter introduction. Have students identify the different animals that live on the African plains. Tell students that these animals interact with one another and rely on the environment for their food sources.
• **What do zebras and gazelles eat?** (Plants, grasses.)

Exploring Earth's Biomes

Night falls quickly on the vast Serengeti Plain of East Africa, as if a black velvet curtain has suddenly been drawn over the land. The scattered acacia trees and the great herds of zebras, wildebeests, and gazelles that graze on the Plain during the day disappear in the sudden darkness.

Safe in camp, you sit in your tent and listen to the mysterious sounds of the night. Nearby, a family of zebras snorts and stomps, startled perhaps by the rumble of distant thunder. The wildebeests, or gnus, stir and shuffle as they settle down for the night. And then the lions begin to roar. The wild music of the lions sends chills down your spine.

Lions, zebras, wildebeests, and gazelles do not live everywhere in Africa. They inhabit only the open plains, or savannas, with few or no trees and plenty of grass. Different animals live in the steamy jungles, which have many trees but not much grass. As you will discover in the pages that follow, animal and plant populations are not the same from place to place. They vary because different areas of the Earth have different climates. Climate conditions play a large role in determining where organisms make their homes.

Journal *Activity*

You and Your World Perhaps you have camped in a state or national park, spent the night in a tent in your own backyard, or imagined what it would be like to camp out. In your journal, describe your experiences, whether they are actual or imagined.

◄ *Alert and watchful, a group of lionesses scan the grassy African plain for their prey.*

G ■ 69

Some countries have designed large-scale relocation programs to reduce overcrowding or to equalize the distribution of land. These programs have had devastating effects on the rain forest. They have also affected the cultures of the original rain-forest inhabitants. These people's traditional way of life may be lost, and they are exposed to new and often deadly diseases brought in by newcomers. Building projects designed to promote the development of Third World countries also have sped up the destruction of the rain forests.

The entire world has a stake in what happens to the rain forests. Deforestation has disrupted the carbon dioxide–oxygen cycle, which in turn affects the global climate. Species of plants and animals whose value is still unknown are destroyed. Therefore, the conservation and preservation of the rain forest and other biomes are a worldwide responsibility.

Cooperative learning: Using preassigned lab groups or randomly selected teams, have groups complete one of the following assignments.
- Prepare a three-minute segment for a television news magazine focusing on the plight of the rain forest. Groups should write scripts and prepare visuals for their segments.
- Illustrate a biome before and after the removal of a natural resource, for example, oil or timber, from the biome.

See Cooperative Learning in the *Teacher's Desk Reference.*

JOURNAL ACTIVITY

You may want to use the Journal Activity as the basis of a class discussion. As students discuss their camping experiences, help them identify ways that they can protect the environment, such as by cleaning up their litter and staying on designated trails. Students should be instructed to keep their Journal Activity in their portfolio.

- **Why do you think they live on the African plains?** (They feed on its grasses.)
- **What do lions eat?** (Other animals, meat.)
- **Why do you think the lion lives on the African plains?** (It feeds on the grazing animals there.)

Point out that the grasslands are only one type of environment in which animals and plants live.

- **Where do you think deer live?** (Students might suggest the woods or the forest.)

- **Where do polar bears live?** (Accept such responses as in the Arctic or in Alaska.)
- **Where would you expect to see a cactus?** (The desert.)

Help students conclude that different environments support different types of animals and plants.

3–1 Biogeography

MULTICULTURAL OPPORTUNITY 3–1

Many anthropologists believe that cultures developed by way of migration. Approximately 30,000 years ago, when Siberia and Alaska were connected by a land bridge, humans migrated from the regions of Asia and spread south across the Canadian plains. Encourage interested students to explore further these theories of cultural dispersion.

ESL STRATEGY 3–1

Tell students that in English, as perhaps in their native languages, many words are derived from ancient Greek. Go over the meanings of the following word roots and affixes.

bio: life
geo: earth
eco: habitat, environment
graphy: description
logy: study

Ask students what they think the section heading Biogeography means. Ask them to deduce meanings for biology, biography, geography, geology, ecology. Are there other words they know that use the Greek roots and affixes?

3–1 Biogeography

You are an explorer. In this chapter, you are going on a trip around the world. Your trip will take you from the cold, barren lands surrounding the North Pole to the dense jungles near the equator—and even into the depths of the oceans. As you travel, you will discover many strange and wonderful plants and animals. You will find that the kinds of plants and animals change as you move from place to place on your journey around the world.

The study of where plants and animals live throughout the world (their distribution) is called **biogeography.** Biogeographers, then, are interested in ecology, or the study of the relationships among plants, animals, and their environment.

The kinds of animals that live in an area depend largely on the kinds of plants that grow there. Do you know why? Animals rely on plants as one source of food. For example, zebras eat mostly grass. They would have a difficult time finding enough food in a jungle, where grass is scarce. But grassy plains are a good habitat, or living place, for zebras. Plains are also a good habitat for lions. Why? Lions are meat eaters (carnivores) that hunt plant eaters (herbivores), such as zebras, for food.

Figure 3–1 *The gray-headed albatross makes its nest out of mud and grass on small wind-swept islands in the Southern Hemisphere (bottom left). Meerkats live in Africa's Kalahari desert (top). In what kind of African habitat would you expect to find a lowland gorilla (bottom right)?* ❶

TEACHING STRATEGY 3–1

FOCUS/MOTIVATION

Prepare ahead of time by collecting several pictures of plants associated with different biomes. For example, you might collect and display pictures of palm trees along a beach, grasses on a prairie, trees in a coniferous forest, and cacti in a desert. When displaying the pictures, challenge students to identify characteristics of the environments in which the plants would grow.

• **Are the plants shown likely to grow in the same area?** (Answers may vary. Lead students to suggest that the plants naturally grow in different areas.)

• **What factors determine where these plants grow?** (Answers may vary. Students should suggest that climate is a major factor.)

• **Would the same or different animals be found in the different areas?** (Lead students to suggest that the type of animals in an area depends on the plants growing there.)

CONTENT DEVELOPMENT

As you introduce the concept of biogeography, help students identify the interrelationship of biology, the study of life and of geography, and the study of Earth's surface and features. Introduce the term *biogeographers* and have students predict the kinds of topics these scientists would study. You might offer the following suggestions: animals that live in an area, plants that live in an area, the climate and other characteristics of an area, ani-

In turn, the plant life in an area is determined mainly by climate. Climate describes the average conditions of temperature and precipitation (rain, snow, sleet, hail) in an area over a long period of time. Trees grow tall and dense in warm, rainy climates, especially if the days are long and there is plenty of sunlight throughout the year. Fewer trees grow in cold, dry climates, where the short days of winter arrive early and stay late.

Dispersal of Plants and Animals

In addition to studying where plants and animals live, biogeographers also study why plants and animals spread into different areas of the world. The movement of living things from one place to another is called **dispersal.** Plants and animals disperse in many ways. For example, about 50 million years ago, horses evolved in North America. During prehistoric times, the sea level dropped and a land bridge formed between Alaska and Siberia, which is in Asia. Horses soon moved westward across this natural land bridge into Asia. Over many thousands of years, horses dispersed all across northern Asia and into Europe.

Sometimes plants and animals disperse with help—from water, wind, and even people. Certain lizards, for example, have spread from island to island on floating branches. Some seeds, such as coconuts, also reach new places by floating on water. Certain microorganisms, the spores of fungi, dandelion seeds, baby spiders, and many other small, light organisms may be carried by the wind to new places.

Figure 3–2 *Some organisms disperse with the help of water, wind, and other living things. The dispersal of coconuts (top) and lizards (bottom right) may be assisted by water. What helps the dispersal of dandelion seeds (bottom left)?* ❷

G ■ 71

mals' use of the environment, dispersal of plants and animals. Have students read the section to confirm their predictions.

● ● ● ● **Integration** ● ● ● ●

Use the text copy on climate to integrate meteorology into your lesson.

Use the information about the land bridge between Alaska and Siberia to integrate geology into your lesson.

NATIONAL PARK SYSTEM

In 1872, Congress created Yellowstone National Park and established the National Park System. The system is operated by the National Park Service, a part of the Department of Interior. Today the park system includes national recreational sites, monuments, historical parks, preserves, battlefields, and cemeteries.

ECOLOGY NOTE

HABITAT INVADERS

Sometimes by trying to solve ecological problems, people create new ones. About 70 years ago in parts of the Southwest, people planted the tamarisk tree to help stop erosion. Today the tamarisk tree is the dominant plant on over 80,000 hectares. In some areas, it has pushed out native trees and threatens several species of birds that nest in the native trees.

CAREERS

Park Ranger

As you drive up to your campsite in Yosemite National Park, a **park ranger** is there to greet you. The ranger gives you a list of the guidelines you must follow while you are in the park. She also reminds you not to pick any plants growing in the park or feed any of the wild animals you might see around your camp.

Park rangers are responsible for enforcing the rules and regulations in state and national parks. They protect the plants and animals that live in the park and are also available to help visitors. A park ranger must have a college degree in forestry, park management, or some other related field.

If you are interested in ecology and enjoy working outdoors, you might want to consider a career as a park ranger. For more information, write to the National Park Service, United States Department of the Interior, Washington, DC 21240.

Often animals are brought to new homes by other animals. Fish eggs may be carried on the feet of ducks and other water birds. Insects may hitch a ride in the fur of mammals. You may be familiar with this form of dispersal if your pet dog or cat brings fleas into your home!

People have also been responsible for the dispersal of plants and animals. About one hundred years ago, a bird lover released some European birds called starlings in New York City. From New York, the starlings quickly spread across the country. Today, starlings are so common that some people consider them pests.

During the 1800s, ships bound for the Hawaiian Islands carried water for their crews in large barrels. Before the ships left their home ports, mosquitoes laid eggs in the water. The eggs hatched during the voyage. When the ships landed in Hawaii, they introduced mosquitoes to the islands. Unfortunately, the mosquitoes carried an organism that causes a serious bird disease called avian malaria. When the mosquitoes bit the Hawaiian birds, they transmitted the organism, causing the death of many birds.

Not all plants and animals carried to new homes by people are harmful. When European explorers came to the Americas they found the Native Americans growing corn, tomatoes, and squash. These plants were taken by the explorers to many parts of the world, where they are now important crops. Water buffaloes from southern Asia were brought to Europe and South America, where they became useful work animals.

Barriers

After the prehistoric horses traveled from North America to Asia, the sea level rose again and covered the land bridge they had crossed. The sea became a natural fence, or barrier, that kept the horses from moving back and forth between the two ① continents. Eventually, horses became extinct (died out) in North America. Horses were unknown to Native Americans until European explorers arrived with them about 500 years ago.

Water is one of many natural barriers that can prevent plants and animals from dispersing. However,

---

3–1 (continued)

FOCUS/MOTIVATION

To introduce the concept of barriers, create a barrier blocking access to one corner or section of the classroom. Ask students to suggest ways that they could overcome the barrier and gain access to the corner. Students might suggest climbing over the barrier, going around it, or crawling under it. They might also suggest removing the barrier.

• **Why can't you get into this corner of the room?** (It is blocked by a barrier.)
• **Is this a permanent barrier? Why?** (No, it can be removed.)
• **What are some examples of permanent barriers?** (Answers may vary. Students may suggest buildings, dams, mountains.)

CONTENT DEVELOPMENT

Refer students to the discussion of barriers.
• **How is a barrier like a fence?** (It prevents organisms from moving beyond it.)

• **What are some examples of natural barriers?** (Oceans, lakes, rivers, mountains, and valleys.)
• **How is an ecological barrier different from a physical barrier?** (An ecological barrier exists when ecological conditions such as soil type or water availability do not meet the needs of a particular organism.)
• **Can you think of barriers that stop people from moving?** (Answers will vary. In modern times, however, few barriers exist. Some students may suggest political restrictions on travel.)

what may be a barrier for one kind of animal may not be for others. For example, water is a highway for fishes. Other natural barriers include deep valleys and high mountains.

Objects built by people may also be barriers. For example, suppose that a dam on a river acts as a barrier to salmon. Adult salmon cannot swim up the river to reach the places where they lay their eggs. Young salmon cannot reach the ocean, the place where they grow into adults. How do you think the dam will affect the salmon's ability to survive and reproduce? What will eventually happen to the salmon? ①

Natural barriers can also be ecological. This means that they have to do with an organism's relationship to its environment—both the living and the nonliving parts. When a habitat (living place) does not meet the needs of certain plants and animals, it is an ecological barrier. The Virginia opossum has spread from the South into the northeastern United States. During cold winters, opossums in northern states suffer from frostbite on their hairless ears and tails. It is a sign that they have met an ecological barrier—a cold climate—that probably will keep them from moving much farther north.

Biomes of the World

The climate and the organisms living in an area give that area its special character. A grassland environment, for example, is quite different from a forest environment. Of course, sometimes it is a bit difficult to tell where one environment ends and another begins. In East Africa many grasslands are savannas—flat plains dotted with trees. When are there enough trees on a savanna to make it a forest and not a grassland? Settling such questions is a task for biogeographers.

To bring some order to the variety of environments on our planet, scientists have grouped environments with similar climates and ecological communities into divisions called **biomes.** Biome divisions are merely a classification system to help scientists describe the natural world. As you might expect, not all scientists divide the world into the same numbers and kinds of biomes. However, as a

Figure 3–3 *During their annual migration, salmon are able to swim and jump up small, natural waterfalls (bottom). But they cannot jump over artificial dams many meters high. Fish ladders—which look like large, low staircases covered by water—help the salmon get over dams (top).*

G ■ 73

3-2 Tundra Biomes

Many cultures have adapted to living in cold climates. Ask students to research the Alaskan Inuit. How do they live? How has their way of life been adapted to living in a cold climate? The oldest recorded Inuit culture appears to date back approximately 3000 years.

You might also discuss what kinds of changes the culture has undergone and why. For example, houses once made of sod and driftwood timber are now built with wooden frames; summer tupeks once made of skins have been replaced by canvas tents, and so on. Ask students to research and find additional examples.

ESL STRATEGY 3-2

Descriptions often involve the use of modifiers. Explain that a modifier is a word, phrase, or clause that describes or modifies another word. Adjectives are used to modify nouns or pronouns. Have students identify adjectives in the description of the tundra biome. Which adjectives are used to describe the tundra's climate, the plants, the animals, the soil, the water?

After completing this preparatory activity, ask students to write a short paragraph describing the tundra biome.

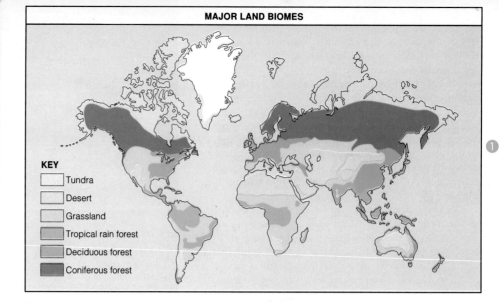

MAJOR LAND BIOMES

KEY
- Tundra
- Desert
- Grassland
- Tropical rain forest
- Deciduous forest
- Coniferous forest

Figure 3-4 *This map shows the distribution of biomes throughout the world. The white area on Greenland is an ice desert. In which biome do you live?* ❶

rule, at least six land biomes are accepted by most scientists. **The six major land biomes are tundras, coniferous forests, deciduous forests, tropical rain forests, grasslands, and deserts.** In your exploration of the Earth's biomes, you will visit each one of these areas and discover something about the plants and animals that live there.

3-1 Section Review

1. Describe three ways in which plants and animals may disperse from one place to another. How do barriers prevent plants and animals from dispersing? Give two examples.
2. What are the six major land biomes?
3. How do scientists classify biomes?
4. What is biogeography?

Critical Thinking—*Relating Concepts*
5. In some places where there are dams on a river, people have built structures called "fish ladders." How do you think a fish ladder helps the fishes get over a dam?

3-1 (continued)

CONTENT DEVELOPMENT

● ● ● ● **Integration** ● ● ● ●

Use the map of major land biomes to integrate map study into your lesson.

INDEPENDENT PRACTICE

Section Review 3-1
1. With help from wind, moving water, or other organisms. Barriers prevent movement back and forth or provide conditions that make it impossible for organisms to thrive. Mountains are physical barriers, climate is an ecological barrier, and dams are barriers built by people.
2. Tundra, coniferous forest, deciduous forest, tropical rain forest, grassland,

and desert.
3. By climate and ecological community.
4. Study of where plants and animals live throughout the world (in other words, their distribution).
5. By providing steps that fish can swim or jump up to reach their spawning areas.

REINFORCEMENT/RETEACHING

Monitor students' responses to the Section Review questions. If they appear to have difficulty understanding any of the concepts, review the material with them.

CLOSURE

▶ *Review and Reinforcement Guide*

At this point have students complete Section 3-1 in their *Review and Reinforcement Guide.*

TEACHING STRATEGY 3-2

FOCUS/MOTIVATION

Have students imagine that they are going to take a trip to the tundra during

3-2 Tundra Biomes

The first stop on your journey through the Earth's biomes is the tundra. A tundra biome circles the Arctic Ocean all around the North Pole. You set up camp near the ocean in Canada's Northwest Territories. It is winter, and despite your heavy clothing, the wind cuts to the bone. **The climate of a tundra biome is very cold and dry.** A tundra is, in fact, like a cold desert. The temperature rarely rises above freezing (0°C). And during most years, less than 25 centimeters of rain and snow fall on the tundra.

Most water on the tundra is locked in ice within the soil. Even in spring and summer (which last a total of only three months!) the soil stays permanently frozen up to about a finger's length of the surface. The permanently frozen soil is called **permafrost.** Permafrost, along with the fierce tundra winds, prevents large trees from rooting. The few trees that do grow on the tundra are dwarf willows and birches less than knee high.

Among the most common tundra plants are lichens. Actually, lichens consist of fungi and algae growing together. Lichens cover the rocks and bare ground like a carpet. They are the main food of caribou, a type of reindeer. During winter, the caribou search out places where the snow is thinnest so they can find lichens easily. By the time the snow is

Guide for Reading

Focus on this question as you read.

▶ *What is the climate of a tundra biome?*

Figure 3–5 *For part of the year, the tundra is dotted with shallow pools of water. The water cannot sink into the soil because of the permafrost layer. The permafrost is one reason tundra plants, such as the dwarf willow, do not grow very large. The thick, shaggy coats of musk oxen help them survive the long, cold tundra winters.*

ANNOTATION KEY

Answers

❶ Answers depend on where students live. Because definitive boundaries are not provided, accept all reasonable answers. (Interpreting a map)

Integration

❶ Earth Science: Maps. See *Exploring Planet Earth,* Chapter 4.

G ■ 75

the winter. Have them describe what weather conditions they would expect.
• **What kind of gear would you need to take along if you were to set up camp in the tundra during the winter?** (Accept all logical answers. Students should indicate that warm clothing and shelter that could withstand extreme cold would be essential.)

Ask students to study the large picture.
• **Does the picture show the tundra during the winter or the summer? How do you know?** (Students should notice the standing water and growing plants that are present during the brief summer.)

CONTENT DEVELOPMENT

Emphasize that during the tundra's short summer, the ground is very soggy. The entire tundra becomes a complex of small lakes, ponds, and marshes.
• **Why does the tundra become soggy in the summer?** (The permafrost below the thawed surface does not allow melted snow to soak into the ground.)
• **Why are large numbers of mosquitoes present during the summer?** (The many pools of still water that dot the tundra are ideal breeding grounds for mosquitoes.)
• **Why do so many migrating birds nest on the tundra?** (The population explosion of insects during spring and summer on the tundra provide an ample supply of food for the birds and their young. In addition, nesting in a remote area separates the migratory birds from the predators and competitors that live in their winter range. You can think of the birds as migrating in to take advantage of the benefits of the tundra and migrating out to avoid the disadvantages of the tundra [the harsh winters].)
• **Is there a relationship between the birds and the weasels and arctic foxes on the tundra?** (Yes, the weasels and foxes feed on the young birds in the nests.)

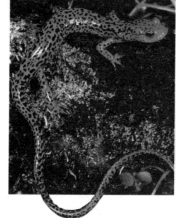

ACTIVITY
DISCOVERING
COMPARING FOREST BIOMES

Discovery Learning

Skills: Making comparisons, identifying characteristics

Materials: Posterboard, crayons, scissors, old magazines, tape

Suggest that students draw lines to divide their posters into thirds. They should plan the layout of the poster before they begin drawing or taping pictures into place. Have students research the information to determine the appropriate biomes of organisms they are not sure where to place. If students prepared charts as suggested in the Content Development section on page G77, they can refer to them for this activity.

Although answers will depend on students' posters, students should note that some organisms can live in more than one biome. Aspens can live in coniferous or deciduous forests, and broad-winged hawks can be found in tropical rain forests as well as in deciduous forests.

BACKGROUND INFORMATION
FOREST LAYERS

A deciduous forest may have up to five layers of plant growth. The tallest trees make up the canopy. Under the canopy is a layer of shorter trees called the understory. Then comes a shrub layer made up of short, branching, woody plants. An herb layer consists of grasses, ferns, and wildflowers. The final layer is the ground layer, which is made up of such material as mosses, fungi, and leaf litter.

Figure 3–11 *The red fox makes its home in deciduous forests. Salamanders, such as this long-tailed salamander, are also residents of deciduous forests.*

ACTIVITY

Comparing Forest Biomes

Divide a piece of posterboard into three sections. In each section, create a scene from each of the three forest biomes. You can use crayons to draw the scenes, cut out photographs from magazines, or use any other materials you find helpful. Label each forest scene. Be sure that each forest scene illustrates plants and animals found in that biome.

- Are any of the plants or animals found in more than one biome?

By the side of a rushing stream, you spy a print in the mud. It looks almost like the print of a small human hand. But you know the print was made by a raccoon searching for frogs during the night. Thrushes, woodpeckers, and blue jays flit back and forth between the trees. The ruffled grouse, a relative of the spruce grouse, rests in a tangle of bushes and watches cautiously as you walk by. Under a rotting log, you find a spotted salamander—jet black with big yellow spots. A black snake slithers away as it senses your approach.

By winter, many of the birds have migrated south. (Do you know why?) Snakes and frogs hibernate through the winter. Raccoons, grown fat in autumn, spend the coldest months sleeping in their dens, from which they may emerge during warm spells. The trees in winter are bare, and their branches rattle in the wind. With the coming of spring, however, the leaves will bud and the birds will return. The deciduous forests will come to life once again. But now you are ready to continue your journey.

Tropical Rain Forests

Your travels now bring you farther south—all the way to the Amazon River of South America. You camp there in a tropical rain forest. Tropical rain forest biomes are also found in central Africa, southern Asia, Hawaii, and even a bit of Australia.

Setting up your tent beneath the dripping trees, you discover that the rain forest is rightly named. In fact, it rains almost every day. Tropical rain forests get at least 200 centimeters of rain yearly. The climate is like summer year round, so plants can grow for all 12 months of the year.

3–3 (continued)

REINFORCEMENT/RETEACHING

Suggest that students name animals that live in the deciduous forests. Have students obtain a field guide to animal tracks and find out what the prints look like. They might make drawings for a bulletin board titled Animal Tracks in the Deciduous Forest. They can make drawings of raccoon and deer prints as well as of traces of other animals from the biome. They

might also display pictures of the animals next to the tracks.

CONTENT DEVELOPMENT

The word *jungle* is often used interchangeably with the term *tropical rain forest*. Emphasize that in reality the jungle is one small area of the rain forest, usually near edges of lakes and rivers. Here the thick, tangled vegetation associated with jungles is able to grow because sunlight can reach the forest floor. In most areas of a typical rain forest, the floor is often

After only a few minutes, your clothes are soaked with dampness and perspiration. The air is muggy and still, although not as hot as you expected. The temperature in the tropical rain forest, or jungle, is hardly ever higher than the temperature on a scorching summer day in Chicago or New York City. Why? The answer is overhead, where the tops of the trees meet to form a green roof, or **canopy**, 35 meters or more above the ground. According to explorer and zoologist Ivan Sanderson, the light below the canopy "is strange, dim, and green." Only along river banks and in places where people or fires have made clearings in the trees does enough sunlight get through the canopy to allow plants to grow on the forest floor.

Most plant life in a rain forest grows in the sunlit canopy. Woody vines called lianas—some thicker than your leg and more than 50 meters long—snake along the branches. You can see orchids and ferns perched on the branches and in the hollows of trees. Tropical rain forests have more varied plant life than any other land biome. The jungle you are exploring has more than 40,000 plant species!

Animal life in the rain forest is also marvelously varied. However, many of the jungle's creatures are out of your sight. High atop the tallest trees, poking here and there above the canopy, sit harpy eagles. Their keen eyes search the canopy below for monkeys and other prey. The canopy is full of parrots, toucans, and hundreds of other colorful birds. At night, bats flit among the trees.

Wild cats called ocelots and 3-meter-long snakes called boa constrictors hunt birds and monkeys in the shorter trees that grow just below the canopy. Standing quietly, you are careful not to startle the tapirs feeding on the ground among the trees. You cannot see the Amazon's big cat, the jaguar, which is very secretive. But as you continue to explore, you think you hear one roaring far off in the jungle. Underfoot, the soil is full of small creatures—centipedes, spiders, ants, and beetles.

Figure 3–12 Tropical rain forests are home to more types of living things than all other biomes combined. The large, unusual flowers of a Heliconia plant are just one of the strange and beautiful things you might see in a tropical rain forest.

Activity Bank
Cutting Down the Rain, p.148

G ■ 81

ACTIVITY
THINKING

SAVING THE RAIN FORESTS

Skills: Analyzing information, synthesizing information

Assign to teams the pro or con position on the topic. Tell teams that members are to work cooperatively to develop a position paper on the topic. Each team should select one member to present the position paper. Allow each team up to three minutes for presentation of the paper. Explain that after the presentations, each team member will be asked to select a point raised by the other team and provide a response to the point. Teams will alternate with one another in refuting their points. After the debate most students should agree that the destruction of the rain forest will impact their lives.

Integration: Use this Activity to integrate language arts into your lesson.

Figure 3–13 *The rain forest is home to many animals. The enormous claws of the tamandua help it climb trees and tear open the nests of ants and termites on which it feeds (left). The velvet worm lives among the fallen leaves on the forest floor (right).*

Figure 3–14 *Tropical rain forests are being destroyed at an alarmingly rapid rate. What happens to the other residents of the forest when the trees are cut down and burned?* ❶

As you make your way back to camp, you hear a strange sound that you cannot identify at first. Then you realize what it is: the ugly noise of a chain saw ripping through the trunk of a giant tree. The most dangerous animal in the jungle is at work! A few seconds later you hear a dull thud as the tree—which has been home to so many birds, monkeys, insects, and frogs—comes crashing to the ground. And you remember that every day an area of tropical rain forest bigger than the city of Chicago is cut down. At that rate, all the rain forests will be gone by the year 2081. Sadly, you prepare to leave the Amazon rain forest, wondering how much of it will be left when you return.

---

1. What are the three forest biomes? How are they different from one another?
2. What are conifers? What are deciduous trees? Give an example of each.
3. What keeps sunlight from reaching the floor of a tropical rain forest?

Connection—*You and Your World*

4. You probably know that many people in the United States, as well as in other countries, are trying to find ways to save the rain forests. Why do you think the rain forests are being cut down? Why do you think people feel it is important to stop the destruction of the rain forests? Do you think that the rain forests should be saved? Why or why not?

3-4 Grassland Biomes

From the Amazon rain forest, you travel across the Atlantic Ocean until you reach the grasslands of East Africa. **In a grassland biome, between 25 and 75 centimeters of rain fall yearly.** As you might expect from its name, grasses are the main group of plants in a grassland biome. Africa has the largest grasslands in the world, although other large grasslands are found in North America, central Asia, South America, and near the coasts of Australia. Grasslands with a few scattered trees, such as those in Africa, are known as savannas.

Your camp is in a field of grass occasionally dotted with thorny trees called acacias. There are few trees in the grasslands because of the low rainfall. Wildfires, which often rage over the grasslands, also prevent widespread tree growth. And people often set fire to the grasslands on purpose to control the spread of trees.

The animals that roam the grasslands also keep trees from spreading by eating new shoots before they grow too large. As you watch a herd of elephants tearing up acacia trees and feeding on

ACTIVITY THINKING

Saving the Rain Forests

Organize two teams to debate the following statement: "The destruction of the rain forests will not affect my life."

Debate

Guide for Reading

Focus on this question as you read.

▶ What is the climate of a grassland biome?

Activity Bank

Grandeur in the Grass, p.149

G ■ 83

3-4 Grassland Biomes

MULTICULTURAL OPPORTUNITY 3-4

Encourage students to research various African cultures in which people reside in a grassland environment. How is their lifestyle influenced by where they live? A particularly interesting study and a way to connect this section would be to research the people of the Sahel region, an area that has quickly moved from productive land to desert over the past few years.

ESL STRATEGY 3-4

Have students use complete sentences to
1. name the five locations on the Earth where grasslands are found.
2. give three reasons why few trees are found in this biome.
3. give the name used for grasslands where a few scattered trees grow.

CONTENT DEVELOPMENT

Grasslands are generally located at the same latitudes as deciduous forests, but they usually are in the middle of continents in regions that receive too little annual rainfall to support tree growth. While grasses are the predominant species, other species thrive there too. Clover, dandelions, wild strawberries, and many other low-growing herbaceous plants grow during the spring and summer, but during late summer and fall, tall grasses take over.

TEACHING STRATEGY 3-4

FOCUS/MOTIVATION

Use a wall map of the Earth's major land biomes or the map on page G74 to take students on an imaginary journey to the grasslands of Africa. Have students trace the route from the tropical rain forests in South America across the Atlantic Ocean to the grasslands in East Africa.

• **Where else in the world are there grasslands?** (North America, South America, Asia, and Australia.)

Mention that different names are used for grasslands. In North America, they are called prairies. In South America, Asia, and Africa, they are called respectively pampas, steppes, and veldts. Strictly speaking, the term *savanna* refers to a grassland that has just enough rainfall to support a sparse growth of scrubby trees.

HISTORICAL NOTE

DISAPPEARING BUFFALO

Millions of buffalo, the American bison, roamed the Great Plains, or North American grasslands, in the 1800s. They were the source of food and shelter for the Plains Indians. By 1903, only 34 of these magnificent creatures were left. For sport or money, American hunters had killed the buffalo, often randomly shooting into herds from moving trains. Today the buffalo have made a comeback, thanks to the efforts of conservationists and laws.

their leaves, you realize that even large trees are not safe.

Grasses, however, can survive trampling and low rainfall, and still grow thickly. That is why grasslands can feed the vast herds of large herbivores, such as the zebras and antelope you see grazing around you. These animals, in turn, are food for lions, African wild dogs, and cheetahs.

Many mice, rats, and other small animals also inhabit the grasslands, eating seeds, sprouts, and insects. Snakes prowl among the grasses, hunting these creatures. As you walk about your camp in the evening, you take care not to step on a puff adder or other poisonous snake as it searches for prey.

The smaller animals, including snakes, are the prey of the sharp-eyed hawks and eagles that continually sail over the savannas or perch in the acacias. In the distance, vultures circle in the sky, ready to feed on the remains of a zebra killed by lions.

Like the grasslands of North America and many other parts of the world, much of the African savannas has been turned into farms and ranches. And here, as in other parts of the world, overgrazing and overplanting may eventually destroy the grasslands. As you begin the last stage of your journey through the Earth's biomes, you reflect that your next stop—the Sahara Desert—was once a grassland!

Figure 3–15 *The grasslands of Africa are home to many different kinds of organisms, including acacia trees, giraffes, grasses, antelope, zebras, and ostriches. What other organisms would you expect to see in an African grasslands biome?* 1

84 ■ G

3–4 (continued)

INDEPENDENT PRACTICE

▶ *Activity Book*

Students who need practice on the concept of habitat should complete the chapter activity Designing a Habitat.

INDEPENDENT PRACTICE

Section Review 3–4

1. Between 25 and 75 centimeters.
2. Africa.

3. Low annual rainfall, animals, fire.
4. They will lose their grazing lands and eventually die out. They will lose their food source and will also die out.

REINFORCEMENT/RETEACHING

Review students' responses to the Section Review questions. Reteach any material that is still unclear, based on the students' responses.

CLOSURE

▶ *Review and Reinforcement Guide*

Students may now complete Section 3–4 in their *Review and Reinforcement Guide*.

TEACHING STRATEGY 3–5

FOCUS/MOTIVATION

Collect and display pictures of North American deserts taken during different seasons of the year. Label the season by

3–4 Section Review

1. How much rain does a grassland biome receive each year?
2. Where is the largest grassland biome found?
3. What three factors prevent trees from overrunning grasslands?

Critical Thinking—*Making Predictions*
4. If all the savannas in Africa are turned into farms and ranches, what effect will this have on the large herbivores that now live on the savannas? How will this affect the carnivores that prey on them?

3–5 Desert Biomes

North of the savannas, the grasslands of Africa become increasingly dry. Eventually you come to the Sahara Desert, which covers almost all of North Africa. In fact, the Sahara is about as big as the entire United States! And it is getting bigger, expanding into the grasslands to the south. **A desert biome is an area that receives less than 25 centimeters of rainfall a year.** Other desert biomes are found in western North America, western Asia, the center of Australia, and along the west coast of South America.

Guide for Reading

Focus on these questions as you read.

▶ *What is the climate of a desert biome?*

▶ *What is the difference between a hot desert and a cold desert?*

Figure 3–16 *The Sahara, in northern Africa, is a hot desert (left). Its average annual temperature is about 29.5°C. The Atacama Desert in South America is a cold desert (right). Its average annual temperature is about 17°C.*

3–5 Desert Biomes

MULTICULTURAL OPPORTUNITY 3–5

Ask students to investigate the Native Americans of New Mexico and Arizona, who live in a region that has many of the characteristics of a desert. How has their way of life developed to allow them to adapt to the difficult conditions of their environment? Students may find it interesting to examine how their ceremonial life is intimately tied to available resources. For example, the Papagos of southwestern Arizona practice the Nawait ceremony in celebration of the fruit gathered from the saguaro cactus and of the promise of rain so crucial to their desert existence.

ESL STRATEGY 3–5

Have students use complete sentences to
1. describe the location of the Sahara and tell where other deserts are located. (Students may use a globe to reinforce their oral descriptions.)
2. give the requirements for a land area to be classified as desert.
3. name hot and cold deserts.
4. explain how desert animals survive on little water.

the pictures. Discuss with students the different appearance of the desert at different times of the year.

● ● ● ● **Integration** ● ● ● ●

Use the pictures and discussion of climate to integrate meteorology into your lesson.

CONTENT DEVELOPMENT

Point out that the Earth's deserts are increasing in size mainly because of land misuse. For example, in heavily populated countries in Africa and Asia, tree cutting and overgrazing at the margins of desert have left the land unprotected. As a result the deserts have gradually spread.

REINFORCEMENT/RETEACHING

▶ *Activity Book*

Students who need additional experience in locating and identifying the major land biomes should complete the chapter activity Land Biomes of the Earth.

FACTS AND FIGURES

DEATH VALLEY

The lowest point in the United States is Death Valley in the California desert. It is 80 meters below sea level.

ACTIVITY
DISCOVERING

A DESERT TERRARIUM

Discovery Learning

Skills: Making observations, making predictions

Materials: Wide-mouth jar, sand, several small desert plants, water, screening

Through this simple activity, students can gain firsthand experience with desert plants. Students might record the height of their plants when they first plant them and then periodically note any growth. They should observe that the plants experience little or no growth over several months.

Students will express varied opinions about the effect of overwatering the desert plants. At first, the plants will absorb excess water. Eventually, they will no longer be able to absorb the water and may rot and die.

3–5 (continued)

ENRICHMENT

▶ *Activity Book*

Students can extend their understanding of the relationship of climate to biomes by completing the chapter activity Name That Biome!

INDEPENDENT PRACTICE

▶ *Activity Book*

Students can reinforce their understanding of the plants and animals characteristic of a biome by completing the chapter activity Science Views From Around the World.

ACTIVITY
DISCOVERING

A Desert Terrarium

Use a wide-mouthed jar to build a small desert terrarium. Add 2 to 5 cm of sand to the bottom of the jar. Plant a few small cacti and other desert plants in the sand. **Note:** *Do not put any animals in your terrarium because it is too small for them.* Cover the mouth of the jar with a piece of screening such as that used in screen doors. Place the jar where it will get plenty of sunlight and heat. Water your desert terrarium no more than once a month.

■ What do you think would happen to the plants in your terrarium if you watered them every day?

Although most people think of a desert as always being hot, a desert can actually be hot or cold. The Sahara is a hot desert—scorching by day, chilly at night. In a cold desert, such as the Gobi Desert in northern China or the Atacama Desert along the west coast of South America, there is also a great difference between daytime and nighttime temperatures. But in a cold desert, daytime temperatures during the winter may be below freezing (0°C)!

Freezing is the last thing you need to worry about as you walk through the burning sands of the Sahara Desert. You cannot help but notice that the plants in the desert are adapted to the lack of rainfall. Many have widespread roots that are close to the surface. This enables the roots to absorb water quickly, before it evaporates. Like the cactus plants of the North American deserts, the aloe plants of the African deserts have thick, fleshy stems that help them store water. After a rainfall, the stem of an aloe plant swells to almost 3 meters in diameter. You may be familiar with aloe as an ingredient in many soaps and hand lotions. Aloe is extremely useful in soothing skin irritations and minor burns (including sunburn).

Even though you look hard, you see few animals in the Sahara. But they are there. By day, lizards and small rodents often escape the heat in underground burrows. Here the temperature may be as much as

Figure 3–17 *The orange and yellow flowers of an aloe plant (left) and the grass and trees of an oasis (right) contrast sharply with the bleak desert that surrounds them.*

CONTENT DEVELOPMENT

Ecologists often classify desert plants by the strategies they use to survive droughts. Drought-resisters such as cacti store water in their stems. Drought-endurers such as the creosote bush have evolved leaves that prevent the loss of water. Drought-escapers such as the mesquite have developed long taproots to obtain moisture.

ENRICHMENT

▶ *Activity Book*

Students who are particularly interested in the features of the cactus should complete the chapter activity Cactus Adaptations.

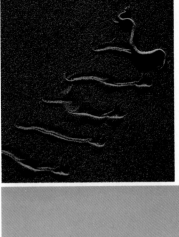

30°C cooler than at the surface. Night brings the animals to the surface searching for food.

Like the plants, desert animals must live on as little water as possible. Most of the water used by desert animals comes from the seeds and stems of plants, which are about 50 percent water. The most famous desert animals—camels—can live without water if there are enough plants available for them to eat. In fact, camels can get along without water for up to 10 days! During this time, they live off the water stored in the body fat in their humps. And like other desert animals, camels lose almost no water in their wastes. Only in these ways can they survive in a world where rain hardly ever falls.

As your trek across the dry Sahara comes to an end, you realize you have completed your journey through the Earth's major land biomes. That means you are now ready to explore the largest biome on Earth—the oceans.

Figure 3–18 *Certain animals have evolved in ways that help them to survive in the harsh conditions of desert biomes. The chameleon holds its body as far from the ground as possible as it tiptoes along (top left). The sidewinding movement of the adder is also an adaptation that minimizes contact with the hot sand (top right). What are some of the adaptations camels have for surviving in the desert (bottom)?* ❶

3–5 Section Review

1. Describe the main characteristics of a desert biome.
2. What is the difference between a hot desert and a cold desert?
3. In what ways are desert plants and animals adapted to the lack of rainfall? Give two examples of each.

Critical Thinking—*Making Inferences*

4. Why do you think there are no tall trees in the desert?

G ■ 87

3-6 Water Biomes

MULTICULTURAL OPPORTUNITY 3-6

Encourage students to research the lifestyles of Pacific islanders. The people of the Hawaiian Islands, for example, have a rich cultural heritage.

How has their environment influenced their way of life?

ESL STRATEGY 3-6

Make sure students understand that there are two parts to the water biome and that the Earth's largest biome is the marine biome. Help them create a study chart to show the differences between marine and freshwater biomes. Have them include the following data in the chart.

Data: lakes and ponds, near shore, marine, still water, perch, freshwater, phytoplankton, near surface, oceans, trout, lobsters, streams and rivers, deep water, running water, tuna, clams, shallow water.

FACTS AND FIGURES

PACIFIC OCEAN DEPTHS

The Pacific Ocean is the world's largest ocean, covering about 165,760,000 square kilometers. Although its average depth is 4028 meters, the Pacific has its greatest known depth (10,918 meters) at Mindanao Deep.

Figure 3–19 *Starfish, flowerlike sea anemones, and seaweed are some of the marine organisms that live at the edge of the sea.*

Figure 3–20 *The enormous seaweed known as kelp forms vast marine "forests," which are often home to the playful sea otter.*

3–6 Water Biomes

Your trip around the world would not be complete without a visit to the water biomes. After all, most of the Earth's surface is covered with water. **The two major water biomes are the marine biome and the freshwater biome.**

The Marine Biome

The **marine biome,** or ocean biome, covers about 70 percent of the Earth. Organisms that live in this biome have adaptations that allow them to survive in salt water. Other factors that affect ocean organisms are sunlight, temperature, water pressure, and water movement. The oceans can be divided into different zones, or areas, based on these factors. Each of these zones contains organisms that are adapted to conditions in that zone.

You begin your exploration of the ocean near the shore. Most marine organisms live near the surface or near the shore. Animals that live near the shore are alternately covered and uncovered by the tides. Many of the animals burrow into the sand while others attach themselves to rocks to keep from being washed out to sea. Strolling along the shore you find clams, barnacles, and sea stars in shallow tidepools.

Past the low-tide line, algae and microscopic plants called **phytoplankton** live near the surface of the ocean where they can receive the most sunlight. They use the sunlight to produce food. Almost all the animals in the ocean depend either directly or

TEACHING STRATEGY 3-6

FOCUS/MOTIVATION

Direct students' attention to the pictures on pages G88 and G89. Encourage them to identify the organisms shown in the pictures. Ask them to generalize about the diversity of life in the water biomes.

CONTENT DEVELOPMENT

Explain that sunlight, temperature, water pressure, and water movement interact to establish three distinct zones of life in the ocean. Use a chalkboard diagram to illustrate each zone. The shoreline region where high and low tides occur is the intertidal zone. Extending from it along the continental shelf is the neritic zone.

Here light penetrates to the relatively shallow bottom. The greatest concentration of marine organisms is found here. The oceanic zone is the vast ocean beyond the continental shelf. Most organisms are near the surface of this zone. Near the floor of the zone, high water pressure, cold temperatures, and total darkness exist. Only a few organisms are adapted to life here.

indirectly on these plants for food. In shallow water, you find lobsters and crabs crawling along the bottom. In deeper water, marine animals in a variety of shapes and sizes swim through the open ocean. These animals include many types of fishes, such as tuna and swordfish, as well as dolphins, whales, and other marine mammals. (Yes, dolphins and whales are mammals like you. They are not fishes!) Large sea birds, such as albatrosses, spend most of their lives in the skies above the open ocean.

At one time, scientists thought that the deepest parts of the ocean had no life at all. The deep ocean is an area of cold temperatures, high pressures, and complete darkness. Now, however, scientists have discovered that some of the strangest marine organisms live in the deep ocean. Many of them have unusual adaptations for survival in this dark environment. For example, some deep-sea fishes and squid actually have organs that are capable of producing light. In 1974, scientists discovered previously unknown organisms—giant tube worms, blind crabs, and huge clams—clustered around hot-water vents on the ocean floor. These strange creatures do not rely on energy from the sun to survive. Instead, they use chemicals from deep inside the Earth.

Figure 3–21 *Many marine animals are creatures of the open sea. The albatross spends most of its life soaring above the waves (center). The sailfish may use its long bill to kill or injure prey (top right). Dolphins are not fish, but mammals (left). Deep-sea fishes are monstrous in appearance, but not really in size (bottom).*

G ■ 89

FACTS AND FIGURES

SODIUM CHLORIDE

Sodium chloride is the most abundant salt in the ocean biome. It makes up almost 78 percent of all the salt in the ocean.

INTEGRATION

SOCIAL STUDIES

The water biomes provide a large variety of life that is a food source for humans. In fact, fishing is one of the oldest occupations of people. Some of the methods fishers use today have been in existence for thousands of years. Other methods rely on modern science and technology. Fishers use sonar, radar, electronic devices, and information from satellites to help them increase catches.

Encourage students to investigate the importance of fishing to the economies of the Philippines and the Gulf states of the United States.

HISTORICAL NOTE

H.M.S. *CHALLENGER*

Beginning in 1872, the *Challenger* began an epic expedition to study the oceans. Exploring the Atlantic, Pacific, and southern oceans, the scientists aboard the *Challenger* gathered information about the physical, chemical, and biological characteristics of the ocean. The scientists were pioneers in oceanography.

CONTENT DEVELOPMENT

● ● ● ● **Integration** ● ● ● ●

Use the discussion of marine properties to integrate oceanography into your lesson.

ENRICHMENT

Emphasize the importance of plankton to marine biomes. Explain that in addition to phytoplankton, other plant and animal plankton exist. One phytoplankton is the diatom. Animal plankton include jellyfish, eggs, and some tiny shrimplike animals. Most plankton move by drifting on ocean currents and tides. In the open ocean, plankton can live at depths of nearly 200 meters

Figure 3–22 *The young mayfly lives in fast-moving freshwater streams. Although young mayflies live in aquatic habitats, adult mayflies are winged creatures of the air.*

The Freshwater Biome

From the depths of the oceans, you move on to the Earth's other water biome. The **freshwater biome** includes both still water and running water. Lakes and ponds are still water. Streams and rivers are running water.

As in the marine biome, there are a number of factors that affect freshwater life. These factors are temperature, sunlight, the amount of oxygen and food available, and the speed at which the water moves. These factors determine which organisms live in a freshwater environment.

Walking along a fast-moving stream, you find that the organisms in the stream have special structures that keep them from being swept away. Many plants have strong roots that anchor them to the stream bottom. Others have stems that bend easily with the moving water. Mosses cling to rocks in the stream. And the young of some insects have suckerlike structures on their bodies that help them to attach themselves to rocks or other objects in the stream. Fishes such as trout have streamlined bodies for swimming in the fast-moving water.

Leaving the stream, you next visit a small lake. Here such common freshwater plants as waterlilies and cattails grow around the shore of the lake, while

Figure 3–23 *Frogs (bottom right) and grebes (top) live in still freshwater habitats (bottom left). Although excellent swimmers, grebes can barely walk on land. How does building a floating nest of reeds, such as the one shown here, help grebes survive?* ❶

---

algae and duckweed float on the surface. In the middle of the lake, a fish—perhaps a yellow perch or a bluegill—breaks the surface. A water snake glides silently by. You notice the bulging eyes of a frog staring out at you from among the duckweed. You cannot see the microscopic plants and animals that are a part of any freshwater biome. You do catch a glimpse of a family of ducks and a shy raccoon, however. These animals visit freshwater biomes to feed or nest. What other animals might you see in a freshwater biome? ❷

Estuaries

After leaving the lake, you move on to the last stop on your journey, the Chesapeake Bay on the eastern coast of the United States. Now you are at an **estuary** (EHS-tyoo-air-ee)—the boundary between a freshwater biome and a marine biome. The Chesapeake Bay is the largest estuary in the United States. Estuaries include salt marshes, lagoons, mangrove swamps, and the mouths of rivers that empty into an ocean. Estuaries are areas that contain a mixture of fresh water and salt water. Some scientists think that estuaries make up a separate biome, while others consider them as ecosystems.

Because estuaries are usually shallow, sunlight can reach all levels of the water. Marsh grasses, algae, and other kinds of plants live in estuaries and provide food for a variety of fishes, crabs, oysters, and

ACTIVITY READING

Life Near a Trout Stream

Many writers have been influenced by nature. Sean O'Faolain (1900–1991) was born in Ireland and often wrote stories about life in the Irish countryside. You might enjoy reading his short story "The Trout." ❶

Figure 3–24 *Estuaries include salt marshes (left) and mangrove swamps (right). The spreading roots of the mangrove tree help to keep the plant from falling over.*

G ■ 91

NUTRIENTS IN FRESHWATER BIOMES

One problem that occurs in water biomes is that nutrients tend to sink to the bottom of the water where plants and animals cannot use them. Fortunately, nature has ways of bringing these nutrients back to the surface.

In deep lakes, the spring thaw combines with strong winds to mix lake water thoroughly. In this way, bottom water is brought to the surface. In a time that is called the spring turnover, all nutrients and sunlight are available in abundance. The result is a seasonal growth, or bloom, of phytoplankton in the spring. Some lakes also have a big turnover in the fall; these lakes may have a fall plankton bloom as well.

---

shrimp. Estuaries are especially important as "nurseries" for many different types of young fishes and other animals before they head out to the open ocean. Many sea birds also nest in estuaries.

An estuary such as the Chesapeake Bay is very fertile. Because the Bay produces so many crabs, oysters, and fishes, it is an important part of the economy in Virginia and Maryland. Many people also find the Bay a pleasant area in which to live or spend their leisure time.

As you look back on your trip through the Earth's biomes, you wonder what will become of estuaries—and of forests, deserts, and grasslands—in the future. Can people enjoy the Earth's wild places without destroying them? What can you do to help protect the Earth's biomes?

Figure 3–25 *Chesapeake Bay, like other estuaries, is an extremely fertile habitat. Blue crabs and other kinds of seafood are abundant in the Bay. Why is important to protect the Bay and other estuaries from pollution and overuse?* ❶

3–6 Section Review

1. Describe the two major water biomes.
2. Compare the factors that affect marine life with the factors that affect freshwater life.
3. Why are there no green plants on the bottom of the ocean?
4. Why are estuaries important?

Connection—*You and Your World*
5. What effect might population growth in the area around the Chesapeake Bay have on the ecology of the Bay? How might this affect the area's economy? What do you think can be done to protect the Bay?

3–6 (continued)

INDEPENDENT PRACTICE

▶ *Activity Book*

Students who need more practice in identifying freshwater organisms and their interactions should complete the chapter activity A Water Environment.

GUIDED PRACTICE

Skill Development

Skill: Making inferences

In 1971, a hydroelectric project was begun in Canada that includes building dams and diverting rivers. The La Grande River near James Bay was one of the rivers dammed. One unexpected impact of the damming has been the release of mercury into the food chain of the area.
- **Could the mercury affect fish in the water?** (Yes, it contaminates the fish.)
- **Should the contaminated fish be eaten by humans?** (No, it is harmful to humans.)
- **What might happen to people who relied on fishing to support themselves?** (They would no longer be able to fish and would have to change occupations or move to a different location.)

INDEPENDENT PRACTICE

Section Review 3–6

1. Marine biomes cover 70 percent of the Earth and contain salt. Freshwater biomes include still water, such as lakes and ponds, and running water, such as rivers and streams.

2. Ocean factors include sunlight, temperature, water pressure, water movement, and salt content. Freshwater factors include temperature, sunlight, the amount of oxygen and food available,

CONNECTIONS

Fish Farming

What do you think of when you hear the word farm? You may think of neat rows of corn, chickens scratching in a barnyard, or cows grazing in a meadow. But do you ever think of fishes?

Fish farming, or aquaculture, has become a booming business in the United States. Americans are increasingly concerned about their *health* and are eating more fish and less meat. Today, about one fourth of all the fish and other kinds of seafood served in restaurants or sold in supermarkets has been farmed rather than caught in a lake or stream.

The most popular fish being farmed in the United States is catfish. Part of the appeal of catfish is the popularity of Cajun food from Louisiana—blackened catfish is a favorite dish in this culture. The second most popular fish is trout, which was the first fish to be widely farmed in the United States. Trout farmers have combined aquaculture with new breeding techniques to create "efficient" fishes that mature in 10 months rather than in the natural 18. Trout farmers hope to soon breed fishes that mature even faster.

Fish farming is done both outdoors and indoors. Outdoor farming may be done in special ponds or in portions of the ocean that have been sectioned into pens. Indoor fish farming takes place in large tanks that look like giant aquariums. Indoor fish farmers are even able to raise tilapia, a popular tropical fish that is native to the Nile River in Egypt.

Other kinds of seafood farmed in the United States include shrimp and salmon. Salmon are farmed mainly in Washington State and Maine, where they are raised in floating pens in saltwater bays. Shrimp are farmed mostly in Texas, in ponds in the Rio Grande Valley. Fish farming may become even more widespread as more people realize that fish is a healthful and tasty alternative to red meat.

CONNECTIONS
FISH FARMING

Students may be interested in why fish is a healthy food choice. Explain that fish is high in protein, low in calories, and in many cases, low in fat and cholesterol. Explain that some seafood, especially shellfish such as lobster and shrimp, are high in sodium and should be avoided by people on low sodium diets.

Help students understand the concepts behind aquaculture. A comparison to grain or vegetable farming may help students better understand aquaculture. Also, students might contrast fish farming to fishing as methods of supplying fish. Ask them to consider which method is more efficient.

If you are teaching thematically, you may want to use the Connections feature to reinforce the themes of patterns of change or systems and interactions.

and the speed at which the water moves.
3. Plants are green through the process of photosynthesis, which requires sunlight.
4. Estuaries are fertile sources of food.
5. Accept all logical answers. It could deplete resources of the bay. The economy could suffer if fishing is no longer a profitable occupation. The bay can be protected through laws limiting use of its resources and through strict zoning laws.

REINFORCEMENT/RETEACHING

Monitor students' responses to the Section Review questions. If they appear to have difficulty with any of the questions, review the appropriate material in the lesson.

CLOSURE

▶ *Review and Reinforcement Guide*

At this point have students complete Section 3–6 of their *Review and Reinforcement Guide.*

Laboratory Investigation

BUILDING A BIOME

BEFORE THE LAB

1. Divide the class into groups of four to six students per group and assign each group one of the biomes listed in the Procedure.
2. Several days before the investigation, ask students to bring in 2-liter cardboard milk or juice cartons.
3. Gather all materials needed at least one day prior to the investigation. You will need considerable quantities of sandy soil and potting soil. Large bags of cactus and regular potting soils are available from nurseries and garden stores.
4. Plan for enough space near windows or under artificial lights to expose the biomes to the amount of light prescribed.

PRE-LAB DISCUSSION

Have students read the complete laboratory procedure.
• **What is the purpose of the laboratory investigation?** (To determine how well certain plants grow in different biomes.)
• **Do you think the three kinds of seeds will grow equally well in each biome?** (Answers will vary, but accept any plausible hypotheses.)
• **What two variables will be different in each mini-biome?** (Water and light.)
• **What additional variable will the desert biome have?** (Sandy soil.)
• **Will temperature be a factor to consider in this investigation?** (Yes, if some biomes are placed in direct sunlight for extended periods.)
• **What kinds of observations will we make to decide which seeds grow best?** (Answers will vary. Students may suggest such factors as stem length, color, and evidence of wilting.)

Laboratory Investigation

Building a Biome

Problem

How do different plants grow in different biomes?

Materials (per group)

2-L cardboard milk carton	scissors
sandy soil or potting soil	lamp
5 lima bean seeds	index card
30 rye grass seeds	tape
10 impatiens seeds	stapler
clear plastic wrap	

Procedure

1. Your teacher will assign your group one of the following biomes: desert, grassland, deciduous forest, rain forest.
2. Cut away one side of a milk carton. Poke a few small holes in the opposite side for drainage. Staple the spout closed.
3. Fill the carton with soil to within 3 cm of the top. **Note:** *If your group has been assigned the desert biome, use sandy soil.*
4. At one end of the carton, plant impatiens seeds. In the middle of the carton, plant lima bean seeds. Scatter rye grass seeds on the soil at the other end of the carton.
5. On an index card, identify your group, the seeds planted, and the type of biome. Tape the card to the carton.
6. Water the seeds well. Cover the open part of the carton with plastic wrap.
7. Put the carton in a warm place where it will remain undisturbed. Observe daily.
8. After the seeds have sprouted, follow the instructions for your group's biome:
   Desert: Let the soil dry to a depth of 2.5 cm; 5 to 6 hours of light per day.
   Grassland: Let the surface dry, then add water; 5 to 6 hours of light per day.
   Deciduous forest: Let the surface dry, then add water; 1 to 2 hours of light per day.
   Rain forest: Keep the soil surface wet; no direct light.
9. Observe the development of the plants in the biomes of all the groups.

Observations

1. After the seeds have grown for a week, describe the growth in each biome.
2. In which biome did most of the seeds grow best?
3. Where did the rye grass seeds grow best? The lima beans? The impatiens?
4. Which plants grew well in more than one biome?
5. How do lima beans react to little light?

Analysis and Conclusions

1. Explain why the plants grew differently in each biome.
2. Why did the seeds need water when they were planted?
3. What was the variable in this experiment?
4. **On Your Own** Predict how the impatiens, lima bean, and rye grass seeds would grow in tundra and coniferous forest biomes. Design an experiment to test your prediction.

TEACHING STRATEGY

1. Have the teams follow the directions carefully as they work in the laboratory.
2. To help students draw logical conclusions, you might suggest that they compare just one factor, such as height of each kind of plant, in the different biomes.
3. Place a chart for recording and comparing students' observations on the chalkboard.

DISCOVERY STRATEGIES

Discuss how the investigation relates to the chapter ideas by asking open questions similar to the following.
• **Can such plants grow well in more than one biome?** (Yes, they should grow well in the deciduous-forest and grassland biomes.)
• **In which biomes do you predict the seeds will not grow very well?** (In the coniferous-forest and desert biomes because of the lack of water in both and the limited light in the coniferous forest.)

Study Guide

Summarizing Key Concepts

3–1 Biogeography

▲ Biogeography is the study of where plants and animals live throughout the world.

▲ Biomes are divisions based on similar climate, plants, and animals.

▲ The major land biomes are tundras, coniferous forests, deciduous forests, tropical rain forests, grasslands, and deserts.

3–2 Tundra Biomes

▲ Tundra biomes are very cold and dry.

▲ Most of the water on the tundra is permanently frozen in the soil as permafrost.

3–3 Forest Biomes

▲ The three major forest biomes are coniferous forests, deciduous forests, and tropical rain forests.

▲ Trees in a coniferous forest are conifers, which produce seeds in cones.

▲ Deciduous trees shed their leaves in the autumn and grow new leaves in the spring.

▲ Tropical rain forests have more varieties of plants and animals than any other land biome.

3–4 Grassland Biomes

▲ Grassland biomes receive between 25 and 75 centimeters of rain yearly.

▲ Low rainfall, fires, and grazing animals prevent the widespread growth of trees on grasslands.

3–5 Desert Biomes

▲ Deserts receive less than 25 centimeters of rain yearly.

▲ Deserts can be either hot or cold.

▲ Plants and animals in a desert are adapted to the lack of rainfall.

3–6 Water Biomes

▲ The two major water biomes are the marine biome and the freshwater biome.

▲ The marine, or ocean, biome covers about 70 percent of the Earth.

▲ The freshwater biome includes both still water (lakes and ponds) and running water (streams and rivers).

▲ An estuary is an area that contains a mixture of fresh water and salt water.

Reviewing Key Terms

Define each term in a complete sentence.

3–1 Biogeography
biogeography
dispersal
biome

3–2 Tundra Biomes
permafrost

3–3 Forest Biomes
conifer
taiga
canopy

3–6 Water Biomes
marine biome
phytoplankton
freshwater biome
estuary

G ■ 95

---

4. Accept all reasonable answers, but point out that none of these plants is native to the tundra or coniferous-forest biomes.

GOING FURTHER: ENRICHMENT

Part 1

Challenge students to design experiments to actually test how impatiens, lima beans, and rye seeds will grow in tundra and coniferous-forest biomes. To achieve the lower temperatures needed to simulate these biomes, the plant containers could be placed under an appropriate amount of light in an unheated garage at certain times of the year. If you have a refrigerator available for your science classes, the plants could be placed there, and light could be provided by a lamp in the refrigerator.

Part 2

Some students may be interested in setting up a freshwater biome. They can set up a miniature pond biome in a 2-liter jar with a lid. The bottom should be covered with some coarse gravel with a centimeter or two of clean sand over it. A few sprigs of *Elodea* can be rooted in the sand. After water is added, it should stand for a few days. Then three or four small guppies and a few snails can be added. If the biome is properly balanced, it will be self-sufficient. Have students watch for changes in their mini-pond over a period of time.

• **What part of your investigation simulates characteristics of the biomes?** (Amount of water and light and for the desert biome, the soil type.)

OBSERVATIONS

1. Seeds probably sprouted most rapidly in the deciduous and rain-forest biomes because of the amount of water used.

2. Young plants grew best in the deciduous-forest and grassland biomes.

3. Rye and beans should have grown best in the grassland biome and the impatiens in the deciduous-forest biome.

4. All plants should have grown fairly well in more than one biome.

5. They should have grown tall, spindly, and pale.

ANALYSIS AND CONCLUSIONS

1. Plants have different light, water, and soil needs.

2. They needed water to sprout.

3. Different amounts of water and light were variables. For the desert biome, the type of soil was also a variable.

Chapter Review

ALTERNATIVE ASSESSMENT

The *Prentice Hall Science* program includes a variety of testing components and methodologies. Aside from the Chapter Review questions, you may opt to use the Chapter Test or the Computer Test Bank Test in your *Test Book* for assessment of important facts and concepts. In addition, Performance-Based Tests are included in your *Test Book*. These Performance-Based Tests are designed to test science-process skills, rather than factual-content recall. Since they are not content dependent, Performance-Based Tests can be distributed after students complete a chapter or after they complete the entire textbook.

CONTENT REVIEW

Multiple Choice
1. d
2. b
3. d
4. b
5. c
6. c
7. a
8. c

True or False
1. F, land bridge
2. F, freshwater
3. T
4. F, deciduous trees
5. F, in the sunlit canopy

Concept Mapping
Row 1: Plants
Row 2: Wind, Water

CONCEPT MASTERY

1. Barriers can prevent plants and animals from dispersing. Ecological barriers—for example, cold weather—may not meet an animal's needs. Natural barriers, like high mountains, may make it impossible for animals to move from their environment. Objects made by people—for example, dams—can prevent animals from getting from place to place for breeding or other purposes.
2. Climate is the main factor in determining the type of plants and animals that can adapt to an area. As such, it is a main factor in determining biome characteristics.

Content Review

Multiple Choice

Choose the letter of the answer that best completes each statement.

1. The freshwater biome includes all of the following except
   a. lakes.   b. streams.
   c. ponds.   d. oceans.
2. The forest biome that reaches farthest north is the
   a. rain forest.   b. coniferous forest.
   c. deciduous forest.   d. savanna.
3. You would probably expect to find caribou living in a
   a. rain forest biome.
   b. grassland biome.
   c. desert biome.
   d. tundra biome.
4. All of the following are examples of estuaries except
   a. mangrove swamps.
   b. rivers.
   c. salt marshes.
   d. lagoons.
5. Anything that prevents plants and animals from moving from place to place is called a
   a. biome.   b. habitat.
   c. barrier.   d. community.
6. Most living things in the marine biome are found near the shore or
   a. in fast-moving streams.
   b. in the deep ocean.
   c. near the ocean surface.
   d. in small ponds.
7. Not many trees grow in a grassland biome because of low rainfall, fires, and
   a. animals.
   b. freezing temperatures.
   c. high winds.
   d. floods.
8. The greatest variety of plant and animal species is found in a(an)
   a. desert.   b. estuary.
   c. rain forest.   d. taiga.

True or False

If the statement is true, write "true." If it is false, change the underlined word or words to make the statement true.

1. Horses dispersed from North America into Asia by crossing a <u>mountain range</u> between Alaska and Siberia.
2. Lakes and ponds are part of the <u>marine</u> biome.
3. A climate that is too cold for an organism to survive is an example of an <u>ecological barrier</u>.
4. Trees that shed their leaves in autumn are called <u>conifers</u>.
5. Most of the plant life in a tropical rain forest can be found growing <u>on the forest floor</u>.

Concept Mapping

Complete the following concept map for Section 3–1. Refer to pages G6–G7 to construct a concept map for the entire chapter.

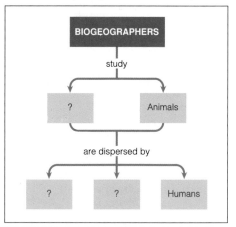

3. The term *biome* is one used by scientists to group various regions into logical segments. Biomes are a way to classify the Earth into different groups. Some scientists identify more regions as biomes than others do by giving the biomes more specific characteristics.
4. Descriptions should reflect information in the chapter about climate, location, and plants and animals.
5. The main factor is salt content. Marine organisms, for the most part, cannot survive in fresh water.

6. The organisms must adapt to the lack of light, high water pressure, and cold temperatures.

CRITICAL THINKING AND PROBLEM SOLVING

1. Biomes are general classifications. There are some areas that do not fit neatly into any one classification. Also, biomes do not have clear boundaries; instead they overlap.

Concept Mastery

Discuss each of the following in a brief paragraph.

1. How do barriers prevent plants and animals from spreading into new areas? Give three examples.
2. Why is climate an important factor in dividing the Earth into biomes?
3. Why do you think it is difficult for scientists to agree on the number and kinds of biomes?

4. Briefly describe each of the six major land biomes.
5. Why are most organisms that live in a marine biome unable to survive in a freshwater biome?
6. What kinds of adaptations are needed by organisms living in the deepest parts of the ocean?

Critical Thinking and Problem Solving

Use the skills you have developed in this chapter to answer each of the following.

1. **Making generalizations** Why is it difficult to tell exactly where one biome ends and another begins?
2. **Relating cause and effect** In which biome would you expect to find the animals shown below? What effect do they have on their environment?

3. **Relating facts** A tropical rain forest has a greater variety of species than any other biome. What characteristics of a tropical rain forest could account for this?
4. **Making predictions** What do you think would happen to the lions and other carnivores on the African savannas if a disease killed all the herbivores, such as zebras and wildebeests?
5. **Making inferences** What characteristics would you expect animals that remain on the tundra all year instead of moving south for the winter to have?
6. **Relating concepts** An estuary is an area where fresh water and salt water meet. Explain why it is difficult for scientists to classify estuaries as either freshwater or marine biomes.
7. **Using the writing process** Imagine that you are a reporter for your local newspaper. You have been assigned to interview a rancher in South America who wants to clear an area of tropical rain forest in order to provide grazing land for cattle. Write out a list of questions that you will ask the rancher in your interview.

You might want to assign some of the Concept Mastery and Critical Thinking and Problem Solving questions as homework and have students include their responses to unassigned questions in their portfolio. Students should be encouraged to include both the question and the answer in their portfolio.

ISSUES IN SCIENCE

The following issues can be used as springboards for discussion or given as writing assignments.

1. Because of its location, the tundra has been disturbed less by humans than has any other biome. Scientists have discovered that the North American tundra is rich in fossil fuels and other mineral resources. With modern technology, it is possible now to remove these resources economically. Many environmental scientists are fearful, however, that the tundra will be permanently destroyed if these resources are removed. What is your opinion and why?

2. As the human population grows and demand for space and resources increases, the natural habitats of many animals decreases. The vast spaces required by many animals—for example, the leopard in the African grasslands—have been reduced greatly, resulting in smaller habitats. An effect of this habitat reduction is smaller populations, which can lead to loss of gene diversity and to increased infant mortality.

Many zoos now house, breed, and often return endangered species to their natural environment. The San Diego Zoo, for example, returned a few endangered California condors to the natural environment. Some people believe zoos are prisons for animals, which spend their lives bored and unoccupied and die prematurely. Others argue that the zoos are helping to preserve species and provide education for people about nature. What do you think and why? Do zoos help or hurt animals?

---

2. Elephants are found in the grassland biome. Through their grazing, they help prevent trees from growing in the grassland.

3. Mild temperatures and abundant rainfall make the rain forest a suitable habitat for a great variety of species.

4. Lions and other carnivores would have to find other animals to prey on, or the size of their population would decrease.

5. These animals would need to have some adaptations that would protect them from the cold, such as thick fur. They also

would have to be able to survive without much water because the tundra has little rainfall and the water freezes in winter.

6. Because an estuary has some characteristics of both major water biomes, one would expect organisms from both biomes to inhabit an estuary. There is no real distinct area in which the estuary could be called marine or freshwater.

7. Students' questions should show an understanding of the effects of the destruction of the tropical rain forests on the environment.

Chapter 4   WILDLIFE CONSERVATION

SECTION	HANDS-ON ACTIVITIES
4–1 Identifying Problems pages G100–G115 Multicultural Opportunity 4–1, p. G100 ESL Strategy 4–1, p. G100	**Student Edition** ACTIVITY (Doing): A Picture Says a Thousand Words, p. G101 LABORATORY INVESTIGATION: A Miniature World, p. G124 **Teacher Edition** Observing an Ecosystem, p. G98d
4–2 Seeking Solutions pages G115–G123 Multicultural Opportunity 4–2, p. G115 ESL Strategy 4–2, p. G115	**Student Edition** ACTIVITY BANK: Paper Route, p. G151 **Laboratory Manual** Weather and Whooping Cranes, p. G39 **Activity Book** ACTIVITY: And Then There Were None, p. G123 **Product Testing Activities** Testing Orange Juice Testing Disposable Cups Testing Food Wraps **Teacher Edition** Endangered Species, p. G98d
Chapter Review pages G124–G127	

OUTSIDE TEACHER RESOURCES

Books
National Wildlife Federation Staff, *Endangered Animals,* National Wildlife Federation.

Pringle, Laurence. *The Animal Rights Controversy,* Harcourt.

Audiovisuals
Ecology: Interrelationships in Nature, filmstrips, SVE

Endangered Species, computer software, SVE

Vanishing From the Earth, filmstrips, National Geographic

OTHER ACTIVITIES	MEDIA AND TECHNOLOGY
Student Edition ACTIVITY (Reading): The Green Literary Scene, p. G107 ACTIVITY (Reading): Once, a Once-ler..., p. G109 **Activity Book** CHAPTER DISCOVERY: Changing Environments, p. 115 **Review and Reinforcement Guide** Section 4–1, p. G35	**English/Spanish Audiotapes** Section 4–1
Student Edition ACTIVITY (Writing): It's the Law, p. G119 ACTIVITY (Writing): Dare to Care, p. G122 ACTIVITY (Writing): Taking Action, p. G122 **Activity Book** ACTIVITY: The Honeybee Connection, p. G121 ACTIVITY: Put It in Writing, p. G125 ACTIVITY: Make a New Start, p. G127 ACTIVITY: Out, Dammed Spot! p. G129 ACTIVITY: It's a Jungle Out There, p. G133 **Review and Reinforcement Guide** Section 4–2, p. G37	**Prentice Hall Science Integrated Media** It's All Happening at the Zoo Ecotourism Can We Save the Tigers? **English/Spanish Audiotapes** Section 4–2
Test Book Chapter Test, p. G71 Performance-Based Tests, p. G91	**Test Book** Computer Test Bank Test, p. G77

*All materials in the Chapter Planning Guide Grid are available as part of the Prentice Hall Science Learning System.

CHAPTER OVERVIEW

Wildlife conservation is a formidable problem facing the world today. Since life began on Earth millions of species have appeared, survived for a time, and then passed out of existence. But in the past 300 years or so, human activities have greatly increased the rate of extinction.

Plants and animals that are in danger of becoming extinct are said to be endangered. Their numbers increase daily, and a number of factors contribute to this increase: intentional killing, destroying habitats, changing communities, and accidental killing. Deforestation, desertification, wetlands destruction, and pollution are often the result of human activity entered into without much thought of potential consequences.

The methods used to preserve and protect endangered species, manage populations of wild organisms, and ensure the wise use of living resources are forms of wildlife conservation. The enactment of fishing and hunting laws and the preservation of existing habitats are two specific methods used. But wildlife conservation is not a simple task. A solution to one problem may precipitate a bigger problem. The more we can learn about the wildlife that surrounds us, the better able we will be to solve the problems of wildlife conservation.

4–1 IDENTIFYING PROBLEMS
THEMATIC FOCUS

The purpose of this section is to introduce the student to the terms *extinct* and *endangered* and to discuss factors such as intentional killing, destruction of habitats, changing communities, and accidental killings, all of which contribute to the extinction of wildlife. The main thrust of the section, however, is to point out to students reasons why wildlife conservation is necessary, not only to the endangered species themselves, but ultimately to the survival of the human species.

The themes that can be focused on in this section are evolution, patterns of change, and unity and diversity. All of these themes, as they relate to wildlife conservation, are interrelated by the commonality that human activities have become a primary cause of wildlife extinction.

*Evolution: Stress the fact that extinction is a natural part of the Earth's history but that human activities can change environments faster than organisms can adapt to these changes. You may wish to point out that evolution can be described as a change through time, but it is also a study of the patterns and processes that shape these changes. Human activities may be responsible for changes we might prefer to avoid.

*Patterns of change: Point out that manifestations of change are common in the wildlife world. Behavior—and even the appearance—of certain species changes with the seasons. Crossbreeding can sometimes produce new species. Frequently, changes we see are cyclical, but there are times when unexpected changes cause permanent damage. Human activities can cause animals to become endangered or extinct. These activities have greatly increased the rate of extinction. As habitats are destroyed, species become rarer. Human activities have in the past, and most likely will in the future, cause irreversible changes. In the past, many of the changes were regrettably harmful. Perhaps our increasing knowledge of wildlife will effect changes in the future that will improve the lot of the organisms around us.

*Unity and diversity: Humans harm wildlife and wildlife habitats through many activities that are motivated by different things. A dam is built to prevent annual flooding, and the lake created changes the entire ecosystem of the region. In any region, there is a diversity of organisms. A change in the population of one species can have a major effect on the population of another species. The chain seems endless. The creation of a better world for humans as well as for wildlife depends on fostering a respect for the diversity on our planet.

PERFORMANCE OBJECTIVES 4–1

1. Discuss the reasons for the extinction of organisms.
2. Explain why people should try to save endangered species.

SCIENCE TERMS 4–1
extinct p. G100
endangered p. G101
deforestation p. G104
desertification p. G107
exotic species p. G109

4–2 SEEKING SOLUTIONS
THEMATIC FOCUS

The purpose of this section is to introduce students to the concept of wildlife conservation and to familiarize them with a number of options available to accomplish this task. All methods used to preserve and protect endangered species, manage populations of wild organisms, and ensure the wise use of living resources are forms of wildlife conservation.

The themes that can be focused on in this section are patterns of change, systems and interactions, scale and structure, and stability.

*Patterns of change: Stress the fact that change need not be irreversible. If human activity can destroy natural habitats, it can also preserve them. It is also possible to reclaim environments that have been polluted or have been otherwise corrupted. Although it is true that as habitats are destroyed species become rarer, other means of increasing the population of endangered species are available.

*Systems and interactions: Point out that exotic species often interfere with the interactions of native communities. On the other hand, some species can be intro-

OTHER ACTIVITIES	MEDIA AND TECHNOLOGY
Student Edition ACTIVITY (Reading): The Green Literary Scene, p. G107 ACTIVITY (Reading): Once, a Once-ler..., p. G109 **Activity Book** CHAPTER DISCOVERY: Changing Environments, p. 115 **Review and Reinforcement Guide** Section 4–1, p. G35	**English/Spanish Audiotapes** Section 4–1
Student Edition ACTIVITY (Writing): It's the Law, p. G119 ACTIVITY (Writing): Dare to Care, p. G122 ACTIVITY (Writing): Taking Action, p. G122 **Activity Book** ACTIVITY: The Honeybee Connection, p. G121 ACTIVITY: Put It in Writing, p. G125 ACTIVITY: Make a New Start, p. G127 ACTIVITY: Out, Dammed Spot! p. G129 ACTIVITY: It's a Jungle Out There, p. G133 **Review and Reinforcement Guide** Section 4–2, p. G37	**Prentice Hall Science Integrated Media** It's All Happening at the Zoo Ecotourism Can We Save the Tigers? **English/Spanish Audiotapes** Section 4–2
Test Book Chapter Test, p. G71 Performance-Based Tests, p. G91	**Test Book** Computer Test Bank Test, p. G77

*All materials in the Chapter Planning Guide Grid are available as part of the Prentice Hall Science Learning System.

CHAPTER OVERVIEW

Wildlife conservation is a formidable problem facing the world today. Since life began on Earth millions of species have appeared, survived for a time, and then passed out of existence. But in the past 300 years or so, human activities have greatly increased the rate of extinction.

Plants and animals that are in danger of becoming extinct are said to be endangered. Their numbers increase daily, and a number of factors contribute to this increase: intentional killing, destroying habitats, changing communities, and accidental killing. Deforestation, desertification, wetlands destruction, and pollution are often the result of human activity entered into without much thought of potential consequences.

The methods used to preserve and protect endangered species, manage populations of wild organisms, and ensure the wise use of living resources are forms of wildlife conservation. The enactment of fishing and hunting laws and the preservation of existing habitats are two specific methods used. But wildlife conservation is not a simple task. A solution to one problem may precipitate a bigger problem. The more we can learn about the wildlife that surrounds us, the better able we will be to solve the problems of wildlife conservation.

4–1 IDENTIFYING PROBLEMS
THEMATIC FOCUS

The purpose of this section is to introduce the student to the terms *extinct* and *endangered* and to discuss factors such as intentional killing, destruction of habitats, changing communities, and accidental killings, all of which contribute to the extinction of wildlife. The main thrust of the section, however, is to point out to students reasons why wildlife conservation is necessary, not only to the endangered species themselves, but ultimately to the survival of the human species.

The themes that can be focused on in this section are evolution, patterns of change, and unity and diversity. All of these themes, as they relate to wildlife conservation, are interrelated by the commonality that human activities have become a primary cause of wildlife extinction.

*Evolution: Stress the fact that extinction is a natural part of the Earth's history but that human activities can change environments faster than organisms can adapt to these changes. You may wish to point out that evolution can be described as a change through time, but it is also a study of the patterns and processes that shape these changes. Human activities may be responsible for changes we might prefer to avoid.

*Patterns of change: Point out that manifestations of change are common in the wildlife world. Behavior—and even the appearance—of certain species changes with the seasons. Crossbreeding can sometimes produce new species. Frequently, changes we see are cyclical, but there are times when unexpected changes cause permanent damage. Human activities can cause animals to become endangered or extinct. These activities have greatly increased the rate of extinction. As habitats are destroyed, species become rarer. Human activities have in the past, and most likely will in the future, cause irreversible changes. In the past, many of the changes were regrettably harmful. Perhaps our increasing knowledge of wildlife will effect changes in the future that will improve the lot of the organisms around us.

*Unity and diversity: Humans harm wildlife and wildlife habitats through many activities that are motivated by different things. A dam is built to prevent annual flooding, and the lake created changes the entire ecosystem of the region. In any region, there is a diversity of organisms. A change in the population of one species can have a major effect on the population of another species. The chain seems endless. The creation of a better world for humans as well as for wildlife depends on fostering a respect for the diversity on our planet.

PERFORMANCE OBJECTIVES 4–1
1. **Discuss the reasons for the extinction of organisms.**
2. **Explain why people should try to save endangered species.**

SCIENCE TERMS 4–1
extinct p. G100
endangered p. G101
deforestation p. G104
desertification p. G107
exotic species p. G109

4–2 SEEKING SOLUTIONS
THEMATIC FOCUS

The purpose of this section is to introduce students to the concept of wildlife conservation and to familiarize them with a number of options available to accomplish this task. All methods used to preserve and protect endangered species, manage populations of wild organisms, and ensure the wise use of living resources are forms of wildlife conservation.

The themes that can be focused on in this section are patterns of change, systems and interactions, scale and structure, and stability.

*Patterns of change: Stress the fact that change need not be irreversible. If human activity can destroy natural habitats, it can also preserve them. It is also possible to reclaim environments that have been polluted or have been otherwise corrupted. Although it is true that as habitats are destroyed species become rarer, other means of increasing the population of endangered species are available.

*Systems and interactions: Point out that exotic species often interfere with the interactions of native communities. On the other hand, some species can be introduced into a habitat without disruption of the existing conditions. Careful research can provide alternate methods of saving endangered species. Overpopulation by one species can sometimes be controlled by the introduction of a predator into the environment. The ecologist, however, must be careful to maintain a balance when this type of action is taken.

Scale and structure: Stress the fact that habitat destruction can affect the environment on local, regional, and global levels. Recall that the burning of one area of a forest causes acid rain that damages other areas of the forest, but the damage does not stop there. Loose soil, no longer held in place by plant roots, can be washed into lakes and rivers, damaging freshwater biomes. Eventually, muddy rivers can carry the dirt to the ocean, harming the marine biomes. By refraining from this type of deforestation, we can prevent the entire chain reaction. Unfortunately, good conservation practices in one area do not seem to spread to others as fast as poor ones do. Often, special conservation action must be taken at each step along the chain to repair the damage.

Stability: Point out that when human activity or natural phenomena affect the stability of a habitat, the results are often unpredictable. A decrease in the snail population can have a disastrous effect on the population of migrating birds that are only temporary visitors to an area. Also, wildlife conservation helps to preserve genetic diversity. Although many domesticated animals and plants are valued for the purity of their strain, that very purity can also mean that they are equally susceptible to the same diseases. An outbreak of a particular disease could destroy an entire strain. When organisms exhibit diverse genetic structure, they also exhibit different susceptibilities to specific dangers. Finally, it is important to stress that conservation preserves resources for future use.

PERFORMANCE OBJECTIVES 4–2
1. Describe some conservation measures aimed at saving wildlife.

SCIENCE TERMS 4–2
wildlife conservation p. G116
captive breeding p. G118

Discovery *Learning*

TEACHER DEMONSTRATIONS MODELING
Observing an Ecosystem

Take your class on a short trip to a seashore, park, lake, or other natural area that is nearby. Have them take paper and pencils with them.

Tell students to observe the area and to list all the living organisms they can see. Then have them list organisms they believe to be present but cannot see, such as earthworms, microscopic organisms, and the like. Ask students to list all the nonliving factors that make up the area. These would include soil, sunlight, water, rocks, temperature, and elevation.

Finally, have students choose one of the organisms they have listed. For example, at the seashore a student might choose a seagull.

• **How do the nonliving factors that you have observed affect the life of the organism you have chosen?** (Answers will vary. For a seagull, possible answers include: The gull needs water to drink; the gull seems to be able to endure great spans in temperature because it is here in the summer and stays around even during the coldest days in winter.)

• **How does the organism you have chosen depend on other organisms in this environment?** (Answers will vary. Possible answers for a gull include: The gull feeds on fish and small living creatures in the area; the gull uses plant parts to build a nest.)

• **How do you think other organisms might depend on this organism?** (Possible answer: Large carnivores might eat the gull.)

• **Did you notice any endangered species on your trip?** (Answers will vary. In certain areas students might have been able to iden-

tify specific animals or plants that they know to be endangered. On a short excursion to any ecosystem, it is unlikely that students would observe an endangered species.)

Point out that students will be able to provide a more scientific explanation for their observations after completing the chapter.

Endangered Species

Prepare a collage of pictures of endangered species. You can limit the collage to animals and plants found primarily in the United States or you can choose interesting exotic species from around the world. Try to select animals and plants that would be of particular interest to your students. Display the collage for the class.

• **What organisms are pictured in the collage?** (Answers will vary depending on your choice of pictures. Students may not be able to specifically identify all the organisms. If they cannot, identify them as specifically as possible. For example, say: This is an American gray wolf. This is a prairie dog found in Utah.)

• **What do all these organisms have in common?** (They are all endangered species.)

• **What can you tell me about endangered species?** (Accept all logical answers. Answers might include: Their population is growing less and less each year. They are in danger of becoming extinct.)

• **Which of these organisms interest you the most?** (Answers will vary.)

Let the students vote for the organism that is of greatest interest to them and assign students to groups depending on their choice. Then have the members of each group research the particular organism chosen to discover what caused the organism to become endangered, what is being done to prevent its extinction, and the like.

Return to the collage in about a week when students have had time to research their organisms. Let them work in the same small groups to prepare a short report for the class. Have a spokesperson from each group deliver the report to the class.

CHAPTER 4
Wildlife Conservation

INTEGRATING SCIENCE

This biological science chapter provides you with numerous opportunities to integrate other areas of science, as well as other disciplines, into your curriculum. Blue-numbered annotations on the student page and integration notes on the teacher wraparound pages alert you to areas of possible integration.

In this chapter you can integrate life science and evolution (p. 100), fine arts (p. 101), life science and plants (p. 105), language arts (pp. 107, 109, 123), life science and human biology and health (p. 112), social studies (p. 113), and American government (p. 116)

SCIENCE, TECHNOLOGY, AND SOCIETY/COOPERATIVE LEARNING

In ancient times, zoos were used by kings as a symbol of their wealth and power; ancient Greeks used them as a means of studying wild animals and their behavior; and the Romans kept wild animals in zoos until they were needed in the deadly and bloody Coliseum fights.

But in more modern times, zoos have been a source of entertainment. People could go to zoos and see exotic animals that they would otherwise never have been able to see. Gradually, an increasingly sensitive public began to protest not only the conditions under which animals were confined, but the whole concept of collecting and confining animals in zoos. This backlash against zoos resulted in the evolution of the role of a zoo and the

INTRODUCING CHAPTER 4

DISCOVERY LEARNING

▶ *Activity Book*

You may want to begin your teaching of the chapter by using the Chapter 4 Discovery Activity from your *Activity Book.* Using this activity, students will discover that there are many causes for changes occurring in the environment.

USING THE TEXTBOOK

Have students observe the photo on page G98.
• **Why do you think a picture of a black rhino was used to open this chapter?** (Students might suggest that the black rhino is an endangered species.)
• **What feature of the black rhino is responsible for its becoming endangered?** (Some students may know that the rhino's horn is greatly valued in some cultures.)

Explain that a rhino horn is worth more than $24,000 in Yemen, where the horns are used to make the handles of a special kind of dagger. A rhino horn is worth more than $40,000 in China, where the horns are ground up to make folk remedies.
• **Do you know of any unusual methods being used to protect these animals?** (Some students may know that game wardens in parts of Africa dehorn the animals in order to protect them from poachers and hunters.)

Wildlife Conservation

Guide for Reading

After you read the following sections, you will be able to

4–1 Identifying Problems

■ Discuss the reasons for the extinction of organisms.

■ Explain why people should try to save endangered species.

4–2 Seeking Solutions

■ Describe some conservation measures aimed at saving wildlife.

As the noisy truck approaches, the rhinoceros begins to run away. But it is not fast enough. One of the people in the truck picks up a rifle, aims, and fires. The rhino stumbles and falls to the dusty ground of the African plain. The people drive up to the fallen rhino. One of them takes out a saw and begins to cut off the rhino's horns.

Rhino horns are nothing more than large curved cones made of the same substance as your fingernails. But in some parts of the world, people believe that rhino horns have magical properties. So the horns are worth more than their weight in gold.

Fortunately for this one rhinoceros, things are not always what they seem. The rhino was shot by a tranquilizer dart and is fast asleep. Its horns are being removed by skilled game wardens. Without its horns, the rhino looks rather strange—but it is now safe from illegal hunters. It is also still safe from other predators, because it is the rhino's size and not its horns that deters attacks.

Removing rhino horns is one of the more unusual ways of protecting wildlife. What are some other things that people do to help save rare organisms? Why do organisms become rare in the first place? Read on to find out the answers to these questions.

Journal *Activity*

You and Your World Explore your thoughts and feelings about dinosaurs and other organisms that have vanished from the Earth.

The black rhinoceros peers nearsightedly at an uncertain future. In the past 20 years, over 90 percent of Africa's black rhinoceroses have been killed for their horns.

G ■ 99

conditions under which animals were and are confined.

Today, zoos provide the least restrictive and most natural environment possible for each animal in their collections. The role of zoos has also changed—no longer just places of entertainment, they are important centers for education, research, and wildlife conservation.

As more and more organisms are placed on the endangered species list, the role of the zoos in wildlife conservation has become increasingly important. Captive breeding of endangered species may offer a species its only chance for survival. Reproductive techniques carried out by major zoos are increasing the number of many endangered species and are raising hopes that some of these organisms can even be returned to the wild.

Cooperative learning: Using preassigned lab groups or randomly selected teams, have groups complete one of the following assignments.

• Design a zoo habitat for the endangered species of their choice. The setting should be designed to accommodate a breeding pair or group and should contain all the features of the organism's natural habitat. The groups' final products could be in the form of a shoe-box diorama, a drawing, a mural, or some other preapproved creative format.

• Design a T-shirt that would make the general public more aware of an endangered species, the reason it has been placed on the endangered species list, and the possible ways to help save it.

See Cooperative Learning in the *Teacher's Desk Reference.*

JOURNAL ACTIVITY

You may wish to use the Journal Activity as the basis of a class discussion. As students discuss their thoughts and feelings about dinosaurs and other organisms that have vanished from the Earth, lead them to a discussion of the black rhinoceros in the chapter-opening photograph. Point out that they will understand more about endangered species after they have completed this chapter. Students should be instructed to keep their journal activity in their portfolio.

Assure students that the dehorning does not hurt the rhino. Although rhinos use their horns in territorial displays and sometimes in courtship behavior, the horns are not essential. Unlike the horns of cattle and antelopes, rhino horns do not have a bony core. Cutting off a rhino's horn is roughly equivalent to trimming a human's fingernails. Eventually, the horn grows back. In Namibia, the dehorning of the black rhinoceros seems to be having good results.

• **What do you predict about the future of the rhinoceros?** (Accept all logical answers. Students might suggest that people throughout the world are becoming more aware of the plight of these animals and are taking effective actions to alleviate the conditions. They may have heard of the Rhino Walks.)

4-1 Identifying Problems

MULTICULTURAL OPPORTUNITY 4-1

Interested students can research some of the medical drugs that are derived from plants and animals. Which of these are from plants and animals that are endangered? Ask students to consider the number of species becoming extinct every year and then draw conclusions about how many important medical drugs may be lost by the extinction of these species.

Students may fail to realize that not many years ago folk medicines were an important part of every family's health care. Have students share with the class any folk remedies that may be part of their family heritage.

ESL STRATEGY 4-1

Verify that students understand the meaning of *extinct* and *extinction*. Have them describe and illustrate ways in which humans have helped to increase the extinction rate of the Earth's living things. Ask them if they can identify any species native to their countries of origin that are now extinct or are endangered.

TEACHING STRATEGY 4-1

FOCUS/MOTIVATION

Have students make a list of every living thing, past and present, that they can think of in five minutes. You may wish to write this assignment on the chalkboard and have students start as soon as they arrive in your classroom. Have a volunteer read his or her list. Ask other students to name any organisms that they have on their lists that were not on the list that was read.

CONTENT DEVELOPMENT

Remind students that wildlife exists everywhere on the Earth.
• **Can you name some wildlife that might exist on the continent of North America?**

Guide for Reading

Focus on these questions as you read.
▶ *What is extinction? How do organisms become endangered or extinct?*
▶ *Why should people care about endangered species?*

Figure 4–1 *A 1990 reconstruction shows the dodo as a sleek bird with a small, dignified tail. This is quite a change from the obese, stupid bird with a silly feather-duster tail in John Tenniel's illustration for Lewis Carroll's* Alice in Wonderland.

4–1 Identifying Problems

Two thousand kilometers east of Africa, in the warm tropical waters of the Indian Ocean, lies the small island of Mauritius. This island is best known for the dodo—a large, fat, flightless bird that once lived there. You may know about the dodo from jokes or expressions such as "dumb as a dodo." But the real story of the dodo is not funny at all.

After Mauritius was discovered by Europeans in the early sixteenth century, ships began stopping there regularly to pick up fresh supplies of food and water. Huge numbers of dodos were killed by sailors for food and for sport. (A twentieth-century person might not think it sporting to walk up to a practically tame bird and hit it over the head!) Amazingly, the dodo was able to survive a hundred years of assault by sailors armed with clubs. But it was not able to survive thirty years of the first permanent human settlement on Mauritius.

The people who settled on Mauritius brought with them dogs, pigs, cats, monkeys, and rats. (The settlers probably did not intend to bring rats, but rats manage to accompany humans almost everywhere.) The pigs, cats, monkeys, and rats killed and ate the dodos' eggs and chicks. The dogs killed the adult birds. The settlers themselves killed all the dodos they could find, even though the birds were quite harmless and not worth eating. By 1680, dodos had become **extinct.** In other words, their species no longer existed.

The process by which a species passes out of existence is known as extinction. Extinction is a natural part of our planet's history. In fact, more than 99 percent of all the living things that have ever existed on Earth are now extinct. Since life began on Earth more than 3.5 billion years ago, countless species of microorganisms (microscopic organisms), fungi, plants, and animals have appeared, survived for a time, and then passed out of existence. For the last 600 million years, species have become extinct at the average rate of about one per year. But in the past three hundred years or so, human activities—such as hunting, farming, building cities, and cutting down forests—have greatly increased the rate of extinction.

(Rabbits, deer.)
• **What are some examples of wildlife on the continent of South America?** (Birds, mice.)
• **What kind of wildlife would you expect to find in Europe?** (Foxes, turtles.)
• **Can you name some wildlife that might exist on the continent of Asia? Of Africa?** (Camels, tigers; elephants, lions.)
• **What are some examples of wildlife on the continent of Australia? Of Antarctica?** (Kangaroos, koalas; penguins, seals.)

Explain that wildlife can be found in every place on the Earth. Wildlife can be found in the atmosphere above the Earth, wildlife can be found on the surface of the Earth, and wildlife can be found below the surface of the Earth, including in deep parts of the oceans.

● ● ● ● **Integration** ● ● ● ●

Use the discussion of extinction throughout history to integrate the concept of evolution to your lesson.

Experts estimate that the extinction rate is now several species per day. And unless current trends are stopped, the extinction rate could be up to several species per hour by the end of the century!

Human activities increase the rate of extinction because they change the environment too quickly for organisms to adapt. Adaptation occurs through the slow process of evolution. And in evolutionary terms, something that takes place over a period of hundreds—even thousands—of years occurs quickly. (Although humans are not responsible for all the quick changes that occur, natural events that cause sudden changes are few and far between.)

Let's return for a moment to the example of the dodo. Like organisms the world over, the dodo evolved in response to the challenges of its environment. These challenges did not include predators such as humans, dogs, cats, pigs, monkeys, and rats. When humans settled on Mauritius, they made a major change in the island's environment—in the blink of an evolutionary eye, humans added fierce predators to the island's ecosystems. Unable to change quickly enough to survive the challenge of the predators, the dodo became extinct. So did giant tortoises, owls, and many other native organisms.

When their environment changes for the worse, organisms become rarer and rarer. Organisms that are so rare that they are in danger of becoming extinct are said to be **endangered.** About 4500 kinds of animals and 20,000 kinds of plants are endangered. In addition, hundreds of species are not known well enough to be formally classified as endangered.

ACTIVITY DOING

A Picture Says a Thousand Words

Create a poster to help make other students aware of the problems of wildlife extinction. ❷

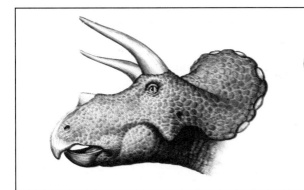

Figure 4–2 *Dinosaurs, such as* Triceratops, *became extinct millions of years ago. Bones that have turned to stone are all that remain (right). An artist's reconstruction shows what* Triceratops *might have looked like when it was alive (left).*

ACTIVITY DOING

A PICTURE SAYS A THOUSAND WORDS

Skills: Describing

Materials: Posterboard, water colors or acrylic paints, paint brushes

Students should create posters that show an awareness of the problems involved in wildlife extinction. Posters should be judged on the basis of content and artistic preparation. The best posters produced might be displayed throughout the school.

Integration: Use this Activity to integrate art into your science lesson.

• **Why would people want to have cattle instead of native animals?** (People can own cattle, but not wildlife. Cattle are sometimes considered to be a symbol of wealth.)

• **What animal is better adapted for the African grasslands, cattle or native plant-eating herbivores?** (The native herbivores tend to be healthier, to produce more protein, and to cause less damage to the range.)

Explain that the introduction of cattle is largely a cultural choice and one that is causing serious problems for many species of African wildlife.

• **Did a similar situation occur in the United States?** (Yes, cattle displaced the native bison in much of the central United States.)

ENRICHMENT

The largest game preserve in the world is the Etosha Reserve in Namibia. It totals almost 100,000 square kilometers, making this game preserve in southwest Africa larger than the country of Ireland.

CONTENT DEVELOPMENT

Unregulated commercial hunting was only one of several reasons for the extinction of the passenger pigeon. Other reasons include the spread of a disease in some very large colonies, very low reproductive rate (one egg per nest), and the clearing of land that used to be pigeon-breeding grounds for farms. Some people believe the extinction of the passenger pigeon was due to excessive commercial hunting. There were many factors, however, that led to the demise of the passenger pigeon.

Inform students that many African animals are becoming endangered because of the introduction of cattle. Cattle compete with native wildlife for limited grass.

According to dictionary definitions, the term *wildlife* refers to wild animals, particularly vertebrates, that are hunted by humans. In practice, the term has a much broader meaning, particularly when it is being used by ecologists and environmentalists. In an environmental context, the term *wildlife* is often used to refer to all the organisms in a wild community, particularly the larger multicellular ones—animals, plants, and fungi. This textbook uses the broader meaning of the term because it is more intuitively obvious to students (wildlife means wild life) and because the broader meaning seems to be becoming the more common usage of the term.

More than 300 species of plants in the United States have become extinct since the Europeans first came to the Americas. Worldwide, a tenth of the plants known to science are in danger of extinction.

Figure 4–3 *The Texas blind salamander (top right), sifaka (bottom right), aye-aye (top left), and Knowlton cactus (bottom left) are all endangered species. The aye-aye is in particular trouble because people consider it to be bad luck and kill it on sight. What does it mean to say a species is endangered?* ❶

The human activities that cause species to become endangered or extinct are many. They also are the results of a variety of motives. In this textbook, we have chosen to divide the human activities that threaten wildlife into two broad categories based on their main purpose. The first category includes human activities whose main purpose is to kill specific kinds of wildlife. We have called this category "intentional killing." The second category includes activities that are not specifically directed at killing wildlife. These activities may kill as many or more living things as purposeful killing, but their main purpose is not the death of organisms. Such activities include cutting down forests, introducing foreign species, and running over animals in boat or car accidents.

Intentional Killing

The rhinoceros you read about in the chapter opener belongs to a species that numbered about 65,000 in 1970 and about 3000 in 1991. Almost all

---

4–1 (continued)

REINFORCEMENT/RETEACHING

Make sure students understand the difference between extinction and endangered. The process by which a species passes out of existence is known as extinction. Organisms that are rare and in danger of becoming extinct are endangered.

CONTENT DEVELOPMENT

Conservationists warn that 1 million of the Earth's 10 million wild species may disappear before the year 2000. Most of these species of plants and invertebrates are found in the tropics; many of them will never be classified. People are sympathetic to the plight of endangered ani-

mals, but ecologically speaking, endangered plants are more important.

GUIDED PRACTICE

Skills Development

Skill: Hypothesizing

Uncontrolled, intentional killing can have a devastating effect on a species. Yet each year the state of Wisconsin issues several hundred thousand deer-hunting permits to people. Have students propose reasons for these deer-killing permits,

knowing that intentional killing can cause the extinction or endangerment of a species.

ENRICHMENT

In 1987, a 7.5-kilometer-long toad tunnel was built in England to avoid the killing of more than 20 tons of toads each year. Most of the toads had been killed by cars as the toads attempted to cross busy country roads during mating season.

of the rhinos that died during that 21-year period were killed by poachers (illegal hunters). A poacher is able to sell a rhino horn for about $200. This may not seem like a lot of money. But in the poorest countries of Africa, the average person makes only about $200 a year—which may not be enough to obtain necessities such as food and shelter. Can you see why it is not always easy to stop overhunting of wild animals? ❷

Rhinos have been overhunted for their horns, which are used to make dagger handles in Yemen and folk remedies in Asia. Other animals have been overhunted for other reasons. Some—such as wolves and bald eagles—were shot, poisoned, and trapped because they were believed to prey on humans and livestock. Others—sun bears, fruit bats, whales, and sea turtles, to name a few—are killed for gourmet food. Still others are killed to fulfill the demands of fashion. Elephants are shot for their tusks, which are used to make ivory jewelry and trinkets. The endangered hawksbill turtle is hunted for its shell, which is used to make jewelry, and for its meat. Snow leopards, sea otters, and wild chinchillas are among the many animals that became endangered because their beautiful skins were in great demand for coats, hats, and other fur products. A fad for shoes, handbags, and other leather goods made from the tough, bumpy skins of American alligators came very close to killing off the species. Snowy egrets were nearly hunted into extinction for their lovely feathers, which were used to decorate hats.

Figure 4–4 *The sun bear gets its common and scientific names from the sun-colored crescent on its chest. It is endangered due to habitat destruction, the fur and pet trades, and its grilled paws being regarded as a delicacy. The snow leopard has been hunted to the brink of extinction for its fur. The passenger pigeon was once the most numerous bird. But during the 1800s, it was slaughtered by the millions. The last passenger pigeon died in a zoo in 1914.*

G ■ 103

BACKGROUND INFORMATION
DESERTIFICATION

Poor management of soil in some areas of the world has resulted in the desertification of more than 90 million hectares of grassland. When a grassland is overgrazed by cattle and/or sheep in an attempt to produce more food, it becomes a desert. The land's nutrients are no longer replaced, erosion increases, plants die, and animals and insects move elsewhere. Ironically, the solution to this problem is grazing, but controlled grazing. In controlled grazing, large herds of cattle or sheep are allowed to graze in a pasture while another pasture is left untouched. This method has many beneficial effects: The animals' hooves break up the soil so that plants can root; the animals' trampling breaks off dead plant growth and provides nutrients for seedlings; and areas that are grazed are then given time to recover. Applying controlled grazing can help to meet the world's demand for food and can prevent a grassland from becoming a desert.

GUIDED PRACTICE

Skills Development

Skill: Drawing conclusions

Divide the class into teams of four to six students. Have each team list five reasons why dinosaurs may have become an extinct species.

• **Which of the five causes you listed might have had the greatest effect on possibly saving dinosaurs?** (Answers may vary.)

• **Which of the five causes you listed might have had the least effect on possibly saving dinosaurs?** (Answers may vary.)

• **Why do you think that dinosaurs became an extinct species?** (Answers may vary.)

GUIDED PRACTICE

Skills Development

Skill: Applying concepts

Have students discuss reasons why they do or do not feel that the Earth represents a fragile environment for living things.

Figure 4–5 *The beautiful golden-brown wood of the Hawaiian koa tree was once used extensively. Now the vast koa forests are gone.*

Figure 4–6 *This tropical forest was drowned by the construction of a dam in Brazil. Although quite useful to humans, dams destroy habitats up river, down river, and within the river itself.*

Up to this point, you have been reading about ways in which uncontrolled killing can lead to animal species becoming endangered. Uncontrolled killing can also cause the downfall of plant species. In Australia, for example, there were once huge forests of red cedar trees. The largest red cedar trees were cut down for their wood, which was used to make furniture. Soon there were no trees large enough to harvest for their wood. But the destruction did not stop there. Because cattle cannot eat red cedar trees, ranchers made a special effort to destroy all the red cedar trees they could find as they cleared away forests to make room for pastures. Now only a few trees remain.

Destroying Habitats

The examples you just read about involve living things that became endangered because they were (or are) being killed on purpose. However, far more species are in trouble because of the destruction of their habitats. (Recall from Chapter 1 that a habitat is the place where an organism lives and obtains the resources it needs to survive.) As you now read about habitat destruction, keep in mind that these are but a few of the many examples. Habitats have been damaged or destroyed, and continue to be damaged or destroyed, in every one of the biomes you learned about in Chapter 3.

DEFORESTATION People cut down forests to obtain wood or to clear land for farms, factories, shopping malls, office buildings, and homes. The removal of forests is known as **deforestation.** History shows that deforestation has been going on for a long time and has occurred in most of the countries of the world.

When Europeans first arrived in the New World, forests covered most of the eastern half of the United States. Almost all the original forest was cleared to make room for farms and towns and to harvest timber. When the old forests were destroyed, the plants and animals that had evolved to live in those environments had no place to go. Some, such as the ivory-billed woodpecker and eastern bison, became extinct. Others, such as the Oconee bells shown in

Figure 4–8 on page 106, are found in only a few places and are rare or endangered.

Today, forests in the western part of the United States are being cut. Many people are concerned that some of the rare species of the Pacific Northwest and Alaska—such as the spotted owl, Pacific yew, and American marten—will become extinct as their habitat shrinks.

The deforestation of greatest concern to people around the world is occurring in the tropical rain forests of Latin America, Africa, and Asia. Each year, an area of tropical rain forest the size of Washington state disappears. About 40 percent of the Earth's tropical rain forests are already gone, and the rate of deforestation is increasing. Some tropical forest is destroyed as hardwood trees—such as teak and mahogany—are harvested. Much more is cut and burned to make room for farms and cattle pastures. The newly cleared land is productive at first. But most of the land stops producing enough food or grass within four to eight years. New areas of forest must be cut in order to feed people and livestock. And as the forest shrinks, the plants, animals, and other organisms that live in, on, or among the trees disappear.

Figure 4–7 *Large areas of forest in the western United States— including Washington (top left) and Alaska (bottom left)—are being cut down. But the deforestation of greatest concern to most people is taking place in the tropics (right). Why are people more concerned about tropical forests?* ⬤

G ■ 105

oak, and maple. Because of the destruction of forests, fewer hardwood trees are available for harvest. Many sawmills today cut a very thin layer of hardwood from a log (much as you would peel an orange) and then glue this layer over less-expensive, abundant wood to give the appearance that the wood is solid hardwood when it really is not. This thin layer of wood is called veneer. You may have some veneered furniture in your home or in your classroom.

Figure 4–8 *Deforestation affects more than trees. What will happen to the two-toed sloth (top right), margay (bottom right), toad and black orchid (top left), cottontop tamarin (center left), and Oconee bells (bottom left) if their forest homes are destroyed?* ❷

In Chapter 1, you learned that all ecosystems are interconnected. As you might expect, deforestation causes a great deal of damage to nearby ecosystems. For example, the burning of one area of forest in West Africa causes acid rain that damages other areas of the forest. Deforestation also hurts more distant ecosystems. When hills are stripped of their covering of trees, dirt that is usually held in place by plant roots can be washed into lakes and rivers, damaging freshwater biomes. Eventually, muddy rivers carry their load of dirt to the ocean. The excess dirt can then harm marine biomes. Ultimately, deforestation affects ecosystems all over the world. For example, when forests are cleared by burning, carbon dioxide is released into the air. This increases the amount of carbon dioxide in the air. Can you predict how deforestation affects the carbon and oxygen cycles all over the Earth? ❶

DESERTIFICATION What do you think of when you hear the word desert? You may think of cactus plants and roadrunners. Or you may think of camels and shifting sand dunes. You probably do not think of grassy fields and grazing herds of goats, sheep, and cattle. Yet when too many animals graze in an area, grassland may be transformed into a desert. The

4–1 (continued)

CONTENT DEVELOPMENT

Trees and forests occupy an important place in our environment. During photosynthesis, trees use carbon dioxide and release oxygen. Trees provide habitat for much wildlife. Trees also are harvested, and hundreds of products are created from them. The maple syrup you may use for breakfast is derived from trees. Even the latex used to make "rubber" gloves and paint is derived from trees.

Trees also have an impact on the climate of an area.

• **How do you think the climate of an area might change if a large forest were cut down?** (Answers will vary. Some factors to consider include: the loss of tree cover would cause a rise in temperature; the loss of trees causes a decrease in transpiration, which results in less precipitation and a drier climate; and wind would blow more strongly through the area because there would be no trees to act as windbreaks.)

GUIDED PRACTICE

Skills Development

Skills: Making observations, drawing conclusions

At this point have students complete the in-text Chapter 4 Laboratory Investigation, A Miniature World. Students will gain insight into the effects of an imbalance in an ecosystem.

process in which desertlike conditions are created where there had been none in the recent past is known as **desertification** (dih-zert-uh-fih-KAY-shuhn).

A little desertification occurs naturally at the places where deserts meet other biomes. If rainfall is plentiful for several years, the desert may shrink a bit; if rainfall is scarce, the desert may expand a bit. In recent years, however, more and more desertification has occurred as the result of human actions such as growing crops, raising livestock, and cutting down forests.

Unlike the natural deserts that you learned about in Chapter 3, deserts made by human actions are barren and lifeless. Sometimes, desert organisms move into a new desert and make it their home. Once in a while, the area may gradually return to its former state if there is enough rain and if the grazing animals are kept away. Too often, however, the newly made desert remains an empty wasteland.

ACTIVITY READING

The Green Literary Scene

"Knowledge is power," so the saying goes. A good knowledge of environmental issues will help to give you the power to change things for the better. Here are a few books to help you get started: *Going Green: A Kid's Handbook to Saving the Planet,* by John Elkington, Julia Hailes, Douglas Hill, and Joel Makower; *A Kid's Guide to How to Save the Planet,* by Billy Goodman; and *The Population Explosion,* by Paul Ehrlich and Anne Ehrlich. ❶

Figure 4–9 *Overgrazing is one of the factors that transformed green pastures into barren desert in northeast Africa. What is the process of making a desert called?* ❸

G ■ 107

ENDANGERED SPECIES

According to the United States Department of the Interior in 1990, the following are among the world's endangered species of animals. Some are endangered throughout their range; others, in only the part of their range listed here.

Common Name	Range
American crocodile	United States (FL)
Asiatic lion	Turkey to India
Bald eagle	Contiguous United States, Canada
Cheetah	Africa to India
California condor	United States (CA, OR)
Elephant	Africa, Asia
Florida panther	Southeastern United States
Gila trout	United States (AZ, NM)
Gorilla	Africa
Grizzly bear	Contiguous United States
Houston toad	United States (TX)
Humpback whale	Oceans
Leopard	Africa, Asia
Mission blue butterfly	United States (CA)
Mountain zebra	South Africa
Oahu tree snail	United States (HI)
Orangutan	Borneo, Sumatra
Rhinoceros	Africa, Asia
Tiger	Asia

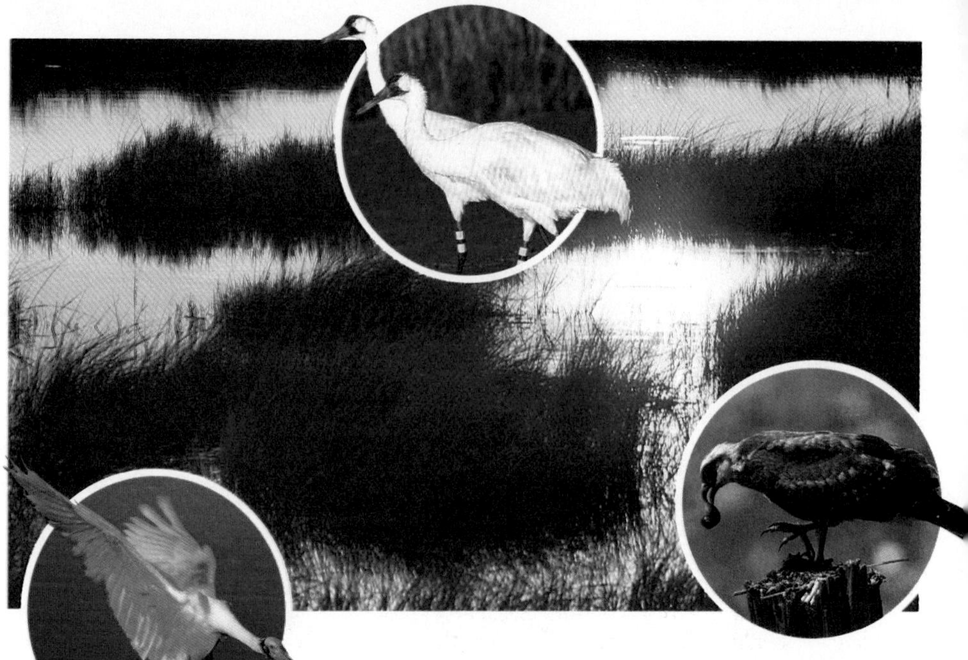

Figure 4–10 *Wetlands, such as this marsh in the Louisiana bayous, are home to many creatures. The survival of organisms such as the roseate spoonbill (left), whooping crane (center), and Everglades kite (right) is made uncertain by continued wetlands destruction.*

WETLANDS DESTRUCTION Wetlands are exactly what their name suggests—wet lands, such as swamps, marshes, and bogs. At one time, wetlands were considered nothing more than ugly breeding grounds for mosquitoes. Now people realize that wetlands are extremely valuable ecosystems. They are temporary homes for migrating waterbirds, and permanent homes for minks, alligators, mangroves, Venus' flytraps, frogs, turtles, and many other organisms. Wetlands are also the source of nutrients for many ocean biomes near the shore.

Unfortunately, about half the Earth's wetlands have been drained, filled in, or destroyed by pollution. The effects of wetlands destruction are far reaching. For example, farmers in southern Florida are draining marshes to grow more crops. The marshes contain snails eaten by small hawklike birds known as Everglades kites. As the marshes vanish, so does the kites' food supply. The rest of the story should be familiar to you by now. Yes, the Everglades kite is close to extinction. What are some other possible effects of continued wetlands destruction on the organisms that live there? How might this destruction affect fishing and duck hunting? ❶

108 ■ G

4-1 (continued)

CONTENT DEVELOPMENT

Distinguish between surface water (lakes, rivers, and reservoirs), groundwater (water that is below the surface of the Earth and protected from the sun), and wetlands (swamps, marshes, sloughs, and bogs). Not long ago, the area of our wetlands measured twice as large as the area we have today.

• **Why is it important to protect our wetlands?** (Protection would help to decrease the chance that wetland inhabitants would become endangered or extinct.)

• **How can we help to protect our remaining wetlands?** (People can actively campaign at the local, state, and federal government levels to help enact laws that restrict the use of wetland areas.)

GUIDED PRACTICE

Skills Development

Skill: Relating cause and effect

Divide the class into teams of four to six students. Each team should assume that it is a management group in charge of protecting and maintaining several wetland areas. Teams should debate the idea of creating a series of nature trails in a wetland area that has no existing trails and is not accessible to the general public. After weighing advantages and disadvantages

POLLUTION As you can see in Figure 4–11, pollution can be a threat to living things. Pollution comes in all shapes and sizes. Birds and useful insects may be poisoned when crops are sprayed with chemicals meant to kill pests. Acid rain can kill water plants, deform fish, and prevent fish eggs from developing. Birds, sea turtles, fishes, and other animals can become hopelessly tangled in bits of discarded plastic fishing lines and fishing nets. Can you think of other ways in which pollution harms wildlife? ❷

Figure 4–11 *Because synthetic substances such as plastics break down extremely slowly, they can be dangerous to wildlife for a long time. This seal tangled in nylon net survived its ordeal. Most entangled organisms are not so lucky.*

Changing Communities

The sad story of the dodo illustrates what can happen when foreign species are introduced to an organism's environment. Species that are released into a place where they had not previously existed are known as **exotic species.** Don't be confused by this use of the word exotic—exotic species may not be strangely beautiful or different in a way that makes them striking or fascinating. Many exotic species are quite ordinary—the pigeon that you might see pecking at crumbs in a city park is an exotic species.

Exotic species may directly interact with the native species. This interaction may take the form of competition or predation—some examples of which you shall now read about.

If you are from the South, you are probably familiar with the kudzu vine. This vine, imported from Japan to feed sheep and goats, grows extremely rapidly all over everything in sight, including other plants. Kudzu competes with native plants for light, water, and nutrients. Eventually, the kudzu vine causes the death of the plants it has grown over by preventing them from getting enough light.

Exotic predators have been the downfall of many species, including the dodo. Pigs, rats, mongooses, cats, and dogs have each at some time been the main cause of extinction of at least two species of birds. Herbivores, which can be thought of as predators of plants, can also bring about the extinction of their prey. In Hawaii, goats and cattle have eaten several types of plants into extinction.

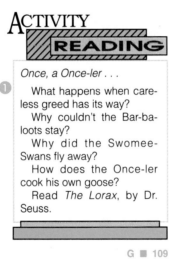

ACTIVITY
READING

Once, a Once-ler . . . ❶

What happens when careless greed has its way?

Why couldn't the Bar-ba-loots stay?

Why did the Swomee-Swans fly away?

How does the Once-ler cook his own goose?

Read *The Lorax,* by Dr. Seuss.

G ■ 109

DOLPHINS

There are few things as delightful and impressive as trained dolphins leaping, somersaulting, and showing off the other behaviors they have learned. Swimming with wild dolphins in the ocean or with captive dolphins in a special pool is a thrilling and unforgettable experience for a human. The popularity of dolphins has helped make people aware of threats to wild dolphins such as ocean pollution, tuna fishing, and drift-net fishing. This awareness has helped to bring about changes that protect wild dolphins. But the popularity of dolphins also has its bad side. There is now a great demand for captive dolphins. If they are given excellent care, many animals live longer in captivity than they do in the wild, but dolphins do not. Although dolphins have a life expectancy of 30 to 50 years in the wild, about 50 percent of captured dolphins die within two years, and the rest live an average of 5.8 years. Is it right to sacrifice a few hundred dolphins to help ensure the survival of thousands of others? Would people continue to care about dolphins if there were not so many captive dolphins?

Figure 4–12 *Exotic species can be the downfall of organisms. Kudzu vines have completely covered these trees in North Carolina (top left). The brown tree snake has killed off most of the birds of Guam (top right). The Indian mongoose, brought to Hawaii and the Caribbean islands to kill rats, found that native birds were more to its taste (bottom).*

Have you ever arranged dominoes in a long line and then tapped the first one? If so, you might have observed that as the first domino fell, it knocked over the second domino, which knocked over the third, and so on. In a similar way, when one species is killed, other species may be brought down with it. By interfering with the normal interactions in a community, exotic species can act like a finger tapping the first domino in a line. Thus exotic species can cause native organisms to become endangered or extinct even if the exotic species do not interact directly with them. When the goats and cattle ate the Hawaiian plants into extinction, they indirectly caused the extinction of certain native birds that fed on the plants. The extinction of the birds in turn caused the extinction of other kinds of plants, which depended on the birds to pollinate them.

Accidental Killing

Imagine an enormous gray animal with the round, fat body and front flippers of a porpoise, a paddlelike tail, beady eyes, and a rather "cute" face. This strange-looking creature is the manatee, an endangered aquatic animal that lives in rivers in Florida. It is a peaceful, slow-moving animal that spends its time near the surface of the water, grazing on floating plants. Unfortunately for the manatee, people have discovered that its habitat is ideal for whizzing around in motorboats. A collision with a motorboat's sharp, whirling propeller can badly injure or even kill a manatee. In the first six months

4–1 (continued)

CONTENT DEVELOPMENT

Sometimes the needs of plants, animals, and people are in conflict. The activities of people can result in the accidental loss of plant and animal life. Discuss the questions below with your class and record their responses on the chalkboard.
• **List several activities of people that can result in accidental loss of plant life.** (Careless use of fire, new construction.)
• **List several activities of people that can result in accidental loss of animal life.** (Driving an automobile, tree cutting.)
Sometimes naturally occurring events can result in the accidental loss of plant and animal life.
• **List several naturally occurring activities that can result in accidental loss of plant life.** (Lightning, forest fires.)
• **List several naturally occurring activities that can result in accidental loss of animal life.** (Violent storms, drought.)
Ask students to consider which of the activities listed on the chalkboard are easily fixed and which ones are not. Discuss reasons why some of the activities might be relatively easy or difficult to change.

ENRICHMENT

Commercial fishing fleets sometimes use methods to catch fish that not only catch the desired fish but other kinds of fish as well, resulting in some accidental killing. For example, a fishing fleet may catch dolphins even though they are trying to catch great numbers of tuna. The commercial fishing industry is working toward developing better methods that will reduce the probability of accidental killing.

Figure 4–13 *Government agents confiscated these parrots before the smuggler had a chance to sell the survivors. Trained whales and dolphins have helped to make people concerned about wild whales and dolphins. However, this benefit is not without its price. Most dolphins do not survive more than two years in captivity.*

of 1990, more than 10 percent of Florida's manatees died. About one third of these deaths are known to have been caused by collisions with motorboats.

Very young children sometimes have to be warned not to hug the family pet too tightly, least they "love it to death." Strange as it may seem, some apparently harmless activities meant to increase people's appreciation for nature may pose a threat to the Earth's living things. People are loving wildlife to death!

Many people enjoy growing strange and beautiful plants in their gardens and homes. But some plants—certain kinds of cactuses, orchids, and tulips, for example—are collected from the wild. Overcollection has made a number of species rare or endangered in their natural habitat.

Owning unusual pets—such as parrots, monkeys, and saltwater fish—may help people feel closer to nature. But potential owners should be aware that some "pet" animals are taken from the wild. This unwise and selfish practice can also be extremely cruel and wasteful. For example, baby parrots can be captured by cutting down the trees that contain their nests. As you can imagine, very few baby birds survive the crash to the forest floor. For every 100 parrots taken from the wild, only about 10 survive long enough to be sold.

Figure 4–14 *Recently, two new laws were put into effect. One limits the number of tourists who can visit the Galapagos Islands each year (bottom). The other prohibits whale-watching tours from getting close to the whales (top). Why were these laws enacted?* ①

BACKGROUND INFORMATION
GENE BULLETS

A revolutionary type of gun is being used by scientists to blast genetic material into plant cells, producing permanent changes in mature organisms. This special "shotgun" uses gunpowder to drive a nylon "bullet" covered with thousands of microscopic tungsten particles. Each tungsten particle is coated with RNA or DNA.

A steel plate stops the nylon projectile but allows the minute, genetically coated tungsten particles to pass through and enter mature plant cells. The cells are not harmed because of the high velocity of the tungsten bullets. Once inside the cells, the inserted DNA or RNA aids in the manufacture of new proteins. Particle bombardment has an advantage over most other methods of gene transfer because it affects many cells at once. What possible uses for gene implantation by particle bombardment can you foresee?

HISTORICAL NOTE
CORN BLIGHT

In 1970, a virulent form of southern corn disease spread from Texas to Minnesota, destroying 1 billion dollars' worth of corn. Research later discovered that 80 percent of the corn in the United States had a gene that made it susceptible to the blight.

Figure 4–15 *Some modern medicines come from unusual wildlife sources, including snake venom and the rosy periwinkle plant.*

You have just learned about the many ways in which wildlife is threatened by human activities. And perhaps you're thinking "So what? What does all this mean to me? How can it possibly affect my life—today, tomorrow, in the years to come?"

Well, we could start off by giving you the least selfish reason for caring about the fate of wildlife: Wildlife is important because it is beautiful, worthwhile, and has just as much right to be in the world as humans do. But many people are unwilling to accept this as the only reason. So let's take a look at some of the practical reasons for saving wildlife.

ECONOMIC AND SCIENTIFIC VALUE Many products that we use every day and would probably not want to do without are harvested from wild sources. Such valuable products include latex (a rubbery substance used to make balloons, surgical gloves, paint, and other items), wood, and most kinds of seafood.

Many medicines are derived from chemicals extracted from wildlife. Some unusual sources of modern medicines include molds, snake venom, catfish slime, and sponges. Plants too are sources for medicine. In fact, about one fourth of the medicines used today come from plants. One plant that is particularly valuable for its medicinal uses is the rosy periwinkle. Medicines made from this plant are used to treat childhood leukemia (a type of cancer). At one time, only about 1 out of 5 patients with childhood leukemia survived. Now patients are treated with medicines made from the rosy periwinkle and about 19 out of 20 survive. Interestingly, the rosy periwinkle was nearly wiped out when its habitat in the rain forests of Madagascar was destroyed. Can you now explain why medical professionals should be concerned about deforestation? ❶

Wild plants and animals are not only sources of useful products, they are also living banks of information. By studying them, humans can learn about the process of evolution, about the way the body works, and about the nature of behavior. And that's just the beginning!

GENETIC DIVERSITY One of the most important scientific reasons wildlife is valuable to humans is that it possesses most of the "library" of genetic

---

4–1 (continued)

CONTENT DEVELOPMENT

When a plant becomes extinct, some people may believe that that plant no longer has any scientific value. To some degree, that is correct. If scientists can discover a fossil of that plant, however, they can learn many things about that plant even though it may have become extinct and disappeared many years ago.
• **What is a fossil?** (An imprint or remains of a plant or animal from the past.)

GUIDED PRACTICE

Skills Development
Skill: Drawing conclusions

Wildlife is not valuable to scientists simply because it provides fossils.
• **What do you think a scientist does with the past and present records of plants and animals?** (These records will be used to model and predict the future.)
• **How can understanding the past of a plant or animal be of benefit to us in the years to come?** (Answers will vary.)

● ● ● ● **Integration** ● ● ● ●

You can use the discussion of medicines from plants to integrate health into your lesson.

Use the discussion of Figure 4–17 to integrate the concept of genetic diversity to social studies.

information that exists on Earth. This library is made up of units of heredity known as genes. You can think of genes as being extremely short, simple directions. The thousands upon thousands of genes that an organism has work together to determine the characteristics of that organism—what it is, what it looks like, how its body works, and so on.

There are many species of wild animals and plants and the individuals in each species are usually quite different from one another. Thus wild animals and plants have an enormous diversity of genes. This is not the case with domesticated animals and crop plants. Each species of these organisms is made up of a number of varieties, or breeds. Each individual in a particular variety is practically the same as any other individual. For example, a Holstein cow has pretty much the same genes as any other Holstein cow, and a corn plant is almost identical to all the other corn plants in a field. While this sameness has many advantages, it also means that the organisms react to diseases in exactly the same way. What, you might wonder, is the danger in that?

Suppose a terrible plant disease strikes a corn field. All the corn plants respond to the disease in the same way—they all die. Can you guess what happens when the disease is transmitted to a neighboring field that is planted with the same kind of corn? And what happens when the disease spreads to all the other corn farms in the area, which are also planted with the same kind of corn? That's right— all the corn dies. And the people who were depending on that corn to feed themselves and their livestock are in big trouble.

Now suppose the same plant disease spreads to a grassy hillside in which some wild relatives of corn are growing. Some of these wild relatives will die from the disease, just as all the corn plants did. But some may have genes that help them to resist the disease. These surviving plants can pass on their genes, including ones for disease resistance, to their offspring. And if scientists know about the genes for disease resistance, they can use techniques of plant breeding or genetic engineering to transfer the genes to domesticated corn plants. The result is the production of corn plants that are resistant to the disease.

Figure 4–16 *One Holstein cow looks very much like any other Holstein cow. How does this fact relate to the concept of genetic diversity?* ②

Figure 4–17 *In the past, scientists tried to convince South American villagers to "modernize" their agricultural practices. Now,* ② *scientists are encouraging them to grow their traditional crops, thus maintaining precious genetic diversity and preserving the villagers' culture.*

G ■ 113

son should rank when compared to the existing four reasons.

4-2 Seeking Solutions

MULTICULTURAL OPPORTUNITY 4-2

Have students work in small groups to identify an environmental problem in their community that they can help solve. Ask them to develop an action plan of what they can do and encourage them to follow it through. Have them work out a timetable for conducting their activities and for reporting results to the class. Follow up by having students identify environmental problems in other parts of the world and by proposing solutions.

ESL STRATEGY 4-2

Have students unscramble the following letters to spell correctly some terms used in this section. When the words have been identified, students should select a matching definition for each word from the list below.

diwefill	(wildlife)
vatcipe derebnig	(captive breeding)
eylccer	(recycle)
tabitahs	(habitats)

1. a way to save endangered species
2. where organisms live and obtain their food
3. the opposite of domestic animals
4. the change of waste to a reusable form

4-1 (continued)

INDEPENDENT PRACTICE

Section Review 4-1

1. The total disappearance of an organism from the biosphere. Organisms become extinct for many reasons; among them are major changes in climate, genetic flaws, destruction of habitats, pollution, intentional killing, and disease.
2. There are many; among them are destruction of habitats, pollution, intentional killing, and destruction of forests for expansion.
3. Human activity has greatly increased the rate of extinction.
4. Deforestation is the removal of forests; desertification is the process in which desertlike conditions are created where there

---

Figure 4–18 *The veterinarians (animal doctors) are doing a checkup on a young whooping crane. This is just one way people can help to preserve the web of life. What are some other ways?* ❶

Finally, imagine the following situation. Long before the outbreak of the corn disease, the hillside is completely cleared of its wild plants and then planted with crops or grass good for livestock. Because of the destruction of their habitat, the wild relatives of corn become extinct. Their genes are lost forever. What do you think will happen when the corn disease strikes? Will scientists be able to develop a disease-resistant variety of corn? Perhaps they will; perhaps they won't. But certainly, their job has become a good deal harder.

PRESERVING THE WEB The most selfish reason for caring about the fate of wildlife is also possibly the most compelling. Wildlife is necessary for the continued survival of the human species. In Chapter 1, you learned that Earth's environment can be thought of as a giant spider web. Each thread of the web represents an interaction between a living thing and its living and nonliving surroundings. What happens if too many strands of a spider's web are broken? As Chief Seattle (leader of the American Indian tribes of the Puget Sound area and the person for whom the city of Seattle, Washington is named) noted over a hundred years ago, "Man did not weave the web of life, he is merely a strand in it. Whatever he does to the web he does to himself."

4–1 Section Review

1. What is extinction? How do organisms become extinct?
2. What are some human activities that cause organisms to become endangered or extinct?
3. How do human activities affect the rate of extinction?
4. What are deforestation and desertification?
5. Why should people be concerned about wildlife?

Critical Thinking—*Making Generalizations*
6. Think about the extinct and endangered organisms you have learned about in this section and elsewhere. What sort of characteristics make it more likely for an organism to become extinct or endangered?

---

had not been any in the recent past.
5. Answers will vary. There are many reasons; for example, prevention of extinction, sources of medicines, sources of food, the sheer beauty of many animals, and the protection of the web of life.
6. Answers will vary. Possible answers include low reproductive rate; small numbers; limited range; not tolerant of humans; perceived as useless or dangerous; tastes good; has valuable fur, shell, ivory, horns, or other body parts; evolved in absence of significant predators, parasites,

or competitors; narrow niche; genetic homogeneity; slow-moving; strong instinct for herding or flocking; strong instinct for defending territory or young.

REINFORCEMENT/RETEACHING

Monitor students' responses to the Section Review questions. If they appear to have difficulty understanding any of the concepts, review this material with them.

PROBLEM ??? Solving

Oh, Dear. Deer!

"They ate my prize-winning roses!"

"They ate *my* vegetable garden."

"Did you try planting onions?"

"They ate those, too."

"They killed all the apple trees at the farm down the road last winter. Chewed off the bark."

"I heard one attacked a pickup truck a ways down the road."

"I wouldn't doubt it. The males go crazy in the autumn. Too many hormones or something."

"So much for Bambi."

Many towns in the northeastern United States are under attack—and by of all things, deer! The wolves and mountain lions that preyed on deer and thereby kept their number in check have long been gone from the area, killed off by previous generations of humans. As farms are turned into wooded suburbs, the deer population has skyrocketed.

The imaginary town of Deerfield is desperately searching for a solution to its deer problem. At the moment, the most popular proposal involves importing dingoes, which are wild dogs native to Australia. It is hoped that the dingoes will bring the deer population down.

Discovering Points of View

How do you think each of the following townspeople feels about this solution? What alternative solutions might each person propose? Why?

    an ecologist
    a hunter
    a sheep farmer
    an animal control officer (dog catcher)
    a veterinarian (animal doctor)
    an animal-rights activist
    a parent with small children
    a chemical manufacturer
    an apple farmer
    an electrician

4–2 Seeking Solutions

As you have learned in the previous section, human actions can harm Earth's living things. But fortunately for all of us, human actions can also protect them. **The methods used to preserve and protect endangered species, manage populations of wild organisms, and ensure the wise use of living resources are forms of wildlife conservation.** Conservation is the intelligent handling of resources (living

G ■ 115

Guide for Reading

Focus on these questions as you read.

▶ *What is wildlife conservation?*

▶ *What are some methods of wildlife conservation?*

A company owns a piece of tropical rain forest in Peru. This piece of rain forest is relatively small, about the area of two football fields. If the company cuts down the forest, it can sell the wood for about $1000. This amount of profit will look pretty good on the financial report for the week. But the company is concerned about its long-term profits as well as its short-term ones. Will cutting down the forest be the most profitable activity over the course of months and years? A study of the situation quickly shows that cutting down the forest is the wrong thing to do. If the forest is left standing, it will produce fruit, nuts, and latex worth at least $7000 every year. Do you think the company will settle for a one-time profit of $1000 when it can have a profit of $7000 every year? Of course not!

Have students determine the profit the company will make from the unharmed forest in 10 years and in 20 years. (The company will make $70,000 in 10 years and $140,000 in 20 years.)

4–2 (continued)

CONTENT DEVELOPMENT

Remind students that the definition of habitat is the place in which an organism lives. The backyard of the home or apartment where each student lives is a habitat. Have each student create a list of fifteen plants and animals that use the students' backyards as their habitat, or homes. The animals included on each list should live in, not be a visitor to, each backyard.

Upon completion, have each student make a parallel list that identifies fifteen plants or animals that frequently or occasionally visit the backyard habitat.
• **What kinds of things could you do to increase the number of residents of and visitors to your backyard habitat?** (Plant an additional variety of foliage.)
• **What kinds of things could you do to decrease the number of residents of and visitors to your backyard habitat?** (Possible answers include using herbicides or pesticides and digging out plants.)

CAREERS

Conservationist

The people who see to it that the use of natural resources causes the least possible harm to the environment are called **conservationists.**

There are many positions in the field of conservation. One might work as a soil scientist, range manager, or wildlife manager, to name a few. A conservationist might be involved in water and land management, improving habitats, surveys, or research. People who become conservationists have an interest in nature and have a desire to be part of a program that cares for natural resources. For more information about this rewarding field, write to the Forest Service, U.S. Department of Agriculture, PO Box 2417, Washington, DC 20013.

and nonliving) so that they provide the greatest possible benefit for the longest possible time. Conservation allows us to use part of a resource now and at the same time preserve a sufficient supply of the resource for the future. The conservation of Earth's plants, animals, and other living things is known as **wildlife conservation.**

Setting Limits

The fate of the dodo and other extinct species has taught us a sad lesson: People cannot be allowed to kill as many living things as they wish. Enough individuals must be left so that a species can maintain its numbers through reproduction. But how can this be achieved? One way of setting limits on the numbers of living things killed is by enacting hunting and fishing laws. Such laws specify how many animals a hunter or fisher is allowed to take from the wild. They may also place restrictions on the species, size, and sex of the animals captured. In addition, hunting and fishing laws specify at which times the animals can be hunted. For example, it is illegal to hunt ducks in the spring and summer, when they are breeding and raising their young.

Unfortunately, these kinds of limits are sometimes not enough. Louisiana's population of American alligators continued to decline rapidly even after the state enacted a law limiting the hunting season to sixty days and allowing each hunter to take only six alligators of a certain size. It was not long before the alligator was in danger of extinction throughout its habitat in the swamps of the southern United States. By 1970, it was necessary to ban alligator hunting in the United States.

Of course, laws need to be enforced if they are to work. And enforcement is often a difficult and dangerous task. Game wardens in the United States, Kenya, Brazil, and elsewhere have been killed in the line of duty. But when the laws are allowed to work, species can be brought back from the edge of extinction. One success story involves the American alligator you just read about. Under protection, the alligators have increased significantly in number. In many areas, they are no longer considered endangered and so they can once again be hunted for

INDEPENDENT PRACTICE

▶ *Activity Book*

Students who need practice on the concept of preserving habitats should complete the chapter activity Out, Dammed Spot!

CONTENT DEVELOPMENT

Explain to students that sometimes habitats overlap. If the organisms do not eat the same food, however, there is usually no problem. For example, a squirrel inhabits the inside of a hollow tree trunk and gets its food from among the leaves on the ground. These leaves may be the habitat of a land snail. But since the snail is not looking for the same food as the squirrel is, this overlapping of habitats causes little interaction between the two animals.

● ● ● ● **Integration** ● ● ● ●

Use the discussion of hunting and fishing laws to integrate the concept of conservation to American government.

their hides. As long as hunters continue to obey the laws, alligators will never again become endangered from overhunting.

Preserving Habitats

You have just arrived at the most important exhibit in the zoo—a parking meter. You cannot believe your eyes. A parking meter? Parking meters belong on streets and in parking lots, not in zoos! What's going on here?

A sign on the parking meter explains it all. The money that people put into the parking meter will be used to purchase land in the tropics. As you hunt through your pockets for change, you recall that habitat destruction has caused more species to become extinct or endangered than overhunting has. Thus, preserving habitats is the most important method of conserving wildlife. Now you agree: It makes sense for the parking meter to be considered the most important exhibit in the zoo.

Have you ever been to Yosemite or any other national park in the United States? If you have, you are probably aware of how hard the National Park Service works to keep the parks as close to their natural state as possible. This helps to preserve wildlife habitats. A few rare or endangered organisms—such as silversword plants, Attwater's greater prairie chicken, and American crocodiles—are found almost entirely in national parks or wildlife refuges. Many

Figure 4–19 *National and international laws protect rare and endangered species. Laws limit the number of American alligators and colobus monkeys that can be killed. Laws also protect the endangered* Rafflesia arnoldi *plant, which has the world's largest flower—more than 90 cm across and 6.8 kg in mass. Unfortunately, the flower smells like rotting meat.*

Figure 4–20 *The parking meter exhibit in the San Francisco Zoo collects donations of spare change. The donations are used to buy and protect wildlife habitats.*

ANNOTATION KEY

Integration
❶ American Government

FACTS AND FIGURES
OVERHARVESTING AND POPULATION DECLINE

The Peruvian anchoveta accounted for as much as 17 percent of the world's harvest of marine fishes in the late 1960s. But harvesting strategies were designed without scientific data on the number and size of sustainable populations. For this reason, and because of other factors, anchoveta yields declined dramatically in the early 1970s.

BACKGROUND INFORMATION
DENSITY DEPENDENCE

The population of a species is said to be density dependent if its size is strongly influenced by the size of the previous generation. The population size of one generation in relation to its resources determines the birth and death rates and thus the size of the next generation.

For density-dependent species, population size is related to the carrying capacity of the environment, the maximum number of organisms that can be supported by a given habitat. Carrying capacity is determined by factors such as available space and food supply, or a maximum sustainable rate of exploitation. If the maximum rate is exceeded, the population declines—sometimes to the point of becoming endangered.

Although there is disagreement among ecologists whether most species are density dependent or not, the effects of exceeding the maximum rate of exploitation are undeniably clear.

GUIDED PRACTICE

Skills Development

Skills: Making predictions, observing

Divide the class into teams of four to six students. Each team should:
1. Choose a nest-building animal and describe the nest that it might build.
2. Draw a picture of the nest.
3. Create a list of materials needed to build the nest.
4. Build a model of the nest using the same materials that the animal would use, whenever possible.
5. Predict what would happen if the materials that your animal uses to build its nest were not available.
6. What materials might be substituted?

ENRICHMENT

Birds are said to have an eye for color. Some bird nests examined by scientists have included decorations like bottle caps and foil from discarded gum wrappers!

WHOOPING CRANES

While one person attracts the parent birds' attention, a biologist skillfully removes one of the two eggs in the whooping cranes' nest and places it in a special box that is warm and padded. Once the egg is safely put away, the biologist places a plastic egg in the nest and sneaks away. The whooping cranes return to their nest and inspect the eggs. Then the female crane settles back on the eggs, not noticing that one of them is a clever fake.

Although whooping cranes lay two eggs each year, the parents can raise only one chick. By stealing one of the eggs, the biologist has a chance to save a chick from certain death. If all goes well, the pair of whooping cranes will have produced two chicks instead of just one. The rate at which the cranes reproduce will have been doubled.

HISTORICAL NOTE

WHERE THE BUFFALO ROAM

After the American bison almost disappeared from the wild, bison from the Bronz Zoo in New York City were sent west and freed on the range.

4–2 (continued)

CONTENT DEVELOPMENT

Setting aside lands to preserve habitat is not a new idea. For many years people have been working to set aside land for the preservation of habitat. This effort to set aside land, however, is not free of controversy. As the nation's dependence on fossil fuel for oil increases, so does its demands. Many estimates maintain that there are significant deposits of oil located under some of the nation's national parks.

• **Considering that people in the United States have a heavy dependence on oil and that significant oil deposits may be found underneath some of the nation's national parks, should Americans erect machinery on the surface of these parks and drill for oil? Why or why not?** (A possible answer might be yes—we should work to decrease our reliance on foreign

countries for oil. Another possible answer might be no—even careful planning will result in some change of the original habitat, thereby defeating an extremely important function of the national park system.)

ENRICHMENT

The Alaskan pipeline stretches from the northern expanses of Alaska to the south, carrying crude oil destined for more southern ports and for processing. Because the pipeline is so long, much of

the native wildlife has difficulty crossing it. The pipeline is elevated in spots to allow safe and free passage of native wildlife.

REINFORCEMENT/RETEACHING

▶ *Activity Book*

Students who need extra practice on the concept of preserving habitats should complete the chapter activity The Honeybee Connection.

---

other countries also have set up parks and preserves that cannot be developed by industry. In 1976, for instance, Costa Rican officials set aside over 500 square kilometers of rain forest as a preserve. Here many rare plants and animals live and thrive.

Habitats also need to be preserved in places other than national parks and wildlife refuges. The zoo's parking meter is one way of raising funds for habitat preservation outside of government reserves. By buying land, conservation organizations ensure that the land will remain in its natural state. After all, the people who own the land are the ones who make the decisions about what will happen to it.

Raising Reproductive Rates

Sometimes preserving habitats is not enough. To save highly endangered species from extinction, it may be necessary to raise their reproductive rate, or get individuals to produce more offspring. How can this be done?

Reproductive rates are sometimes raised through **captive breeding,** or causing animals in zoos to have offspring. For some species that have vanished from the wild, such as the California condor, captive breeding is the only way of saving the species.

Recently, advanced techniques originally invented for use in humans and cattle have been applied to captive breeding programs. As you can see in Figure 4–22, the results of these techniques are often a bit startling. A "test-tube baby" animal may look quite different from its host mother. But the host mother is usually quite content to care for "her" baby. Test-tube baby techniques allow an endangered-species

Figure 4–21 *National parks preserve places of natural beauty and wonder. They also protect the wildlife that lives in these places. Yosemite National Park in California is a temperate forest habitat (top). What kind of habitats are found in Everglades National Park in Florida (bottom left) and in Zion National Park in Utah (bottom right)?* ❶

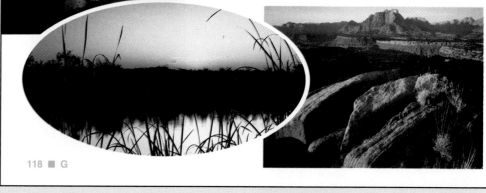

Figure 4–22 *Because California condors are nearly extinct, it is too risky to allow the real parents to bring up baby. To avoid confusing the condor chick, its keepers use a realistic hand puppet to feed and groom it. Although the test-tube baby bongo does not look much like its eland host mother, the eland takes good care of "her" baby.*

female to produce many more offspring during her lifetime than would otherwise be possible.

Other advanced techniques in reproductive biology allow individuals to produce offspring long after their lifetimes are completed. Scientists are currently developing ways of storing plant seeds and freezing animal sperm, eggs, and embryos so that they can survive in "suspended animation" for many years.

In some cases, captive breeding has been so successful that it has become possible to return animals to their natural habitats. Captive lion tamarin monkeys have been trained to live in the wild, then released into the rain forests of Brazil. In time, the offspring of these monkeys will breed with wild monkeys, thus adding some much-needed genetic diversity to the population. The Arabian oryx, a graceful antelope with long horns, became extinct in the wild in 1972. But because of captive breeding programs started 10 years before in the United States, the oryx was not lost forever to the deserts of the Arabian Peninsula. In the early 1980s, a small herd of formerly captive oryx were released in the country of Oman. Guarded day and night by rangers, the oryxes have thrived. Now, 10 years after their return, there are more than 100 oryx, over three fourths of which have known no home except the deserts of Oman.

ACTIVITY

It's the Law

The legal protection of living things goes above the state level. One of the most important federal laws (laws that affect the entire United States) is the Endangered Species Act. One of the most important international laws is CITES (Convention on International Trade in Endangered Species of Fauna and Flora).

Using references available in the library, prepare a report on one of these laws.

ACTIVITY WRITING
IT'S THE LAW

The Endangered Species Act of 1973 says that it is illegal for endangered species to be "killed, hunted, collected, harassed, harmed, pursued, shot, trapped, wounded, or captured." CITES restricts or prohibits trade in endangered species.

Check each report for accuracy. Make sure that each student has chosen only one of the laws and that he or she has described the law correctly. You may want to alert the language arts or government teacher of this assignment and have one of those teachers grade the reports as well.

Integration: Use this Activity to integrate language arts and government into your science lesson.

ing programs. Pigeon populations in large cities can become so large that they become a nuisance, so peregrine falcons have been introduced to the habitat. The falcons not only hunt pigeons for prey, they also have sometimes nested and produced offspring on the window ledges.

REINFORCEMENT/RETEACHING

▶ *Activity Book*

Students who need more practice on the concept of preserving habitats should complete the chapter activity And Then There Were None.

GUIDED PRACTICE

▶ *Laboratory Manual*

Using the investigation called Weather and Whooping Cranes, students will gain a better understanding of climatic effects on wildlife.

GUIDED PRACTICE

Skills Development

Skill: Making predictions

Divide the class into teams of four to six students.

• **If drilling for oil were allowed in the national park system, predict the environmental impact this drilling might have on the existing plant life of the habitat.** (Machinery sometimes breaks, and an oil or chemical spill in an area might not only damage or kill plants, but the residue might

be hazardous for many future years.)

• **Predict the environmental impact this drilling might have on the existing animal life of the habitat.** (The activity and noise associated with machines might cause animals to relocate farther away from the commotion, resulting in increased competition with existing species of that new habitat.)

CONTENT DEVELOPMENT

Several major cities have introduced their own type of informal captive breed-

CONNECTIONS

Computer Dating for Wildlife

In spite of many cartoons to the contrary, computer dating does not involve machines having a romantic candlelit dinner for two. Computer dating is actually a way of using *computers* to match up potentially compatible people so they can get together socially. For humans, computer dating is a way of meeting people with similar interests. With luck, a person will make new friends and establish new relationships.

For wildlife, computer dating is not a matter of matching up individuals with similar hobbies and outlooks on life. Its purpose is to match up individuals that are as dissimilar as possible in terms of their genes. This helps maintain the genetic diversity of the species. And genetic diversity helps to ensure the continued survival of species, both in zoos and in the wild.

Here's an example of computer dating for wildlife in action. In 1986, 68 European zoos agreed to participate in an international captive breeding program for Siberian tigers. The zoos sent a list of ancestors—parents, grandparents, great-grandparents, and so on—for each of their tigers to an organization that coordinates captive breeding programs. There, information on the zoos' 207 tigers was entered into a computer. The scientists managing the captive breeding program used the computer to analyze the information. The computer's analysis helped the scientists decide which tigers should be bred, when they should be bred, and to which other tigers they should be bred. The scientists also came up with a plan for moving the tigers from one zoo to another in order to meet their computer-assigned dates. So thanks to computer dating, tigers are now off on busy—but romantic—journeys around Europe.

4–2 (continued)

CONTENT DEVELOPMENT

Point out to students that conservation is defined as the wise and careful use of resources. Conservation benefits the environment in two ways: First, it makes resources last longer; second, it reduces the pollution that is associated with obtaining and using resources.

Conserving the Earth's resources is a massive undertaking. It is a task that no one person could handle by himself or herself. When the size of a task is great, it is sometimes easy to think "There's noth-ing I can do." But there are various things each person can do.

• **List ten ways resources can be conserved in your everyday life.** (Such a list might include parents' making fewer car trips so that less gasoline will be used and less air pollution will result; using less electricity or heat at home; recycling glass and paper products at home and at school; buying fewer consumer goods that require the use of electricity; using less water when washing dishes or taking a shower; buying and using energy-efficient appliances.

INDEPENDENT PRACTICE

▶ *Activity Book*

Students who need practice on the concept of using people power to restore damaged ecosystems should complete the chapter activity Make a New Start.

ENRICHMENT

Minnesota, as well as other states, uses a simple idea to improve the environment for everyone. The idea is called Adopt a Highway. Here is how it works: A

Using People Power

Conserving the Earth's living resources is an awesome task. There are many complex social, political, and ethical issues that affect conservation measures—far too many to be discussed here. But achieving a balance between the needs of humans and the needs of wildlife is not impossible. Indeed, such a balance can ultimately benefit both humans and their fellow passengers on "Spaceship Earth."

In any conservation effort, it is important to keep human needs, attitudes, and desires in mind. When people understand environmental issues and realize how wildlife conservation benefits them, they become some of the best friends wildlife has.

The first step in getting people to support wildlife conservation is to make them aware that there is a problem. Sometimes this is done in spectacular ways: a concert or television special, perhaps. Or an environmental group may host a fair, a fund-raising walk or race, or other event. But the process of making people aware goes on constantly in quieter, less obvious ways. The next time you visit a zoo or park, read a magazine, or listen to an interview of a celebrity—such as Tom Cruise, Meryl Streep, Bette Midler, or Sting—pay attention. You may be

Figure 4–23 *Captive-bred animals—such as lion tamarins (top left), Arabian oryx (top right), and red wolves (bottom)—have been trained to live in the wild, and then released. In some cases, the animals' release has inspired governments to increase the size of the wildlife preserve in which the animals live.*

BACKGROUND INFORMATION
SPECIATION

Sometimes organisms from two different populations of the same species can no longer interbreed. The offspring are either sterile or die before they mature. What causes the genetic codes to become so different? The answer lies in an evolutionary process called speciation. Populations isolated from one another are affected over time by different selection pressures, which cause the populations to become increasingly different genetically. Eventually, the populations become genetically distinct and can no longer interbreed, even if they come to occupy the same geographic area again. Speciation is an important part of evolution. As one ecologist has written, "After all, if there were no means by which the tree of life could branch, the whole world might simply be covered with one highly evolved living slime."

group of people, such as a Lion's Club or a high school class, is assigned one or two miles of a local street or highway. The group assumes responsibility for removing litter on a regular basis from their adopted road. The program is designed not only to make the environment more attractive but also to raise the environmental awareness of its residents. It is hoped that if people know how it feels to pick up litter, they will think twice about becoming litterbugs.

GUIDED PRACTICE

Skills Development
Skill: Drawing conclusions

Divide the class into teams of four to six students per team. Write Things YOU Can Do to Help Save the Environment on the chalkboard, along with the following five activities: write an article for your school newspaper; write an editorial for your local newspaper; run a fund-raiser for the environment; clean up a park; and recycle.

• **Rank these five activities in order of effectiveness.** (Answers may vary.)

Allow students sufficient time to discuss and order the activities.
• **List five additional activities you could do to help save the environment.** (Answers may vary.)
• **Rerank these ten activities in order of effectiveness.** (Answers may vary.)

Expand the activity by encouraging students to show examples that relate to each of the activities in the list. For example, students who listed writing an editorial for a local newspaper near the top of their list could bring in examples of newspaper editorials. They could also write a sample editorial and share it with the class. Similarly, students could bring in photographs, articles, pamphlets, or other materials that relate to each activity.

Figure 4–24 *Making people aware of conservation issues is sometimes done in spectacular ways. The 1990 Earth Day festival in New York City's Central Park drew thousands of spectators and participants. By placing their bodies and their small boat between whaler's harpoons and whales, Greenpeace activists prevent the killing of whales.*

ACTIVITY WRITING

DARE TO CARE

Check each report for accuracy. If you do not require a formal bibliography, have students prepare a list of the sources they used for the report.

Integration: Use this Activity to integrate language arts skills into your science lesson.

FACTS AND FIGURES

EXTINCTION RATES

Until recently, few people concerned themselves about the extinction of plant and animal species. In the United States, people often do not even know the names of plants that vanished as the forests were cut, the marshes were drained, and the prairies were plowed. More documentation exists for large animals than for smaller animals and plants.

Between 1640 and 1850, while the human population increased from 545 million to 1171 million, about 40 species of warm-blooded animals became extinct. That is an extinction rate of one species every five years. Between 1850 and 1900, the human population rose to 1608 million and another 64 species of mammals and birds vanished, a rate of one species every nine and a half months.

ACTIVITY WRITING

Dare to Care

Conservation is not just for scientists. All kinds of people from all over the world work together to help save the Earth and its living things. Here are just a few people whose lives and actions have encouraged others to become involved in conservation issues.

George Adamson
Sunderlal Bahuguna
Rachel Carson
Jacques Cousteau
Kuki Gallman
Chico Mendes
Michael Werikhe

Write a brief report on the life and accomplishments of one of these people.

surprised at how many lessons about the environment are being taught.

In many cases, the interests of wildlife and those of the majority of people are not in conflict. Thus people do not have to be coaxed into liking conservation measures. They may already be aware of the problems and anxious to help. But what can ordinary people do?

Quite a lot, once they realize that their opinions matter and they can make a difference. In India, villagers have saved the forests near their homes by hugging the trees and getting in the way of loggers who want to cut the trees down. In Africa, farmers are learning new methods of growing their crops among the trees of the forest. In South America, many Amazon Indian tribes have united to form a powerful political group for rain forest preservation. And there are many, many other examples.

Every person, young or old, rich or poor, can help in the struggle to save Planet Earth. Even little things matter—the little efforts of a lot of people can make a big difference.

Here are a few simple things you can do to help save the Earth and its inhabitants.

- Recycle substances such as paper, steel, glass, and aluminum. This reduces the need for raw

---

4–2 (continued)

INDEPENDENT PRACTICE

▶ *Product Testing Activity*

Have students perform the product tests on orange juice, disposable cups, and food wraps from the Product Testing Activity worksheets. Have students relate the length of time it takes for various materials to decompose and the impact of this length of time on the environment in general and on the habitats of wildlife specifically.

CONTENT DEVELOPMENT

The thousands of spectators who have participated in Earth Day celebrations in Central Park in New York City for the past few years have expressed their concern for the environment. At the same time, they left behind hundreds of kilograms of garbage that needed to be cleaned up.

• Why is it valuable for people to participate in Earth Day celebrations? (Participation helps to increase their awareness of environmental concerns and focuses attention on the need for all people to contribute to the efforts to protect the environment.)

• Was littering by participants in Earth Day activities in keeping with the goals of Earth Day? (No, participants should have disposed of their litter properly to demonstrate their concern for the environment.)

materials and helps save habitats from deforestation and mining.

- Write to companies to make them aware of environmental issues. This inspires them to find ways to do less harm to the environment—and even to help it!
- Support companies that are environmentally aware. This encourages them to continue their good work. It may also motivate companies that are less aware to improve their ways.
- Refuse to buy exotic pets, tortoise shell, ivory, furs, and other products made from rare and endangered animals. Ultimately, this makes it less desirable for people to obtain or sell such things.
- Make an effort to think about the ways your actions affect the web of life. This may help you find alternatives that are just as useful to you and more beneficial to the Earth.
- Can you think of other ways to help wildlife and the environment?

Perhaps the most important things you can do to help the Earth and its living things are to learn as much as you can about wildlife and the environment and to share your knowledge with others. Like the Lorax in the famous book by Dr. Seuss, you can "speak for the trees" and the other wild things that "have no tongues" and cannot speak for themselves. You and other people can make your voice the voice of the Earth and its voiceless wildlife. With a good understanding of the past and the present, people can work together to make a better future.

4–2 Section Review

1. What is considered to be the most important method of conserving wildlife? Why?

Connection—*You and Your World*

2. Design a conservation program for the rare or endangered organism of your choice. Explain how your plan takes into consideration the different conservation methods and issues that you read about in Section 4–2.

Activity Bank

Paper Route, p.151

ACTIVITY WRITING

Taking Action

There are many organizations that are dedicated to preserving planet Earth and its inhabitants. Here are just a few of the larger organizations.

Audubon Society
Greenpeace
World Conservation Union (WCU), formerly International Union for the Conservation of Nature (IUCN)
National/International Wildlife Federation
Nature Conservancy
Sierra Club
Wilderness Society
World Wildlife Fund

Prepare a report on one of these groups. Your report should explain the purpose of the group and describe its activities.

❷

ACTIVITY WRITING

TAKING ACTION

Check each report for factual accuracy and for students' explanations of the purpose of the group and their descriptions of its activities.

Integration: Use this Activity to integrate language arts skills into your science lesson.

INTEGRATION
MATHEMATICS

The economics of conservation is difficult for some students to understand. Use a conserving light bulb as an example of how the initial cost of the bulb is higher than for an ordinary bulb but eventually the conserving light bulb saves both energy and money. For example, if a regular light bulb costs a dollar and a conserving light bulb costs three dollars but lasts four times as long and costs only one fourth as much to operate, the conserving bulb represents a good economic and social investment.

Help students plan an appropriate activity, for example, planting a tree or picking up litter on the school grounds, as a class Earth Day project.

INDEPENDENT PRACTICE

▶ *Activity Book*

Students who need practice writing about wildlife conservation should complete the chapter activity Put It in Writing.

INDEPENDENT PRACTICE

Section Review 4–2

1. Accept all logical responses. One possible candidate for the most important method of conserving wildlife might be education. An educated and knowledgeable human population would probably do more for wildlife conservation than any specific method designed to attack the problem.

2. Students' plans may focus on protecting plants or animals but should include many of the methods and issues discussed in this section.

REINFORCEMENT/RETEACHING

Monitor students' responses to the Section Review questions. If they appear to have difficulty understanding any of the concepts, reteach the material that is still unclear.

CLOSURE

▶ *Review and Reinforcement Guide*

At this point have students complete Section 4–2 in their *Review and Reinforcement Guide.*

Laboratory Investigation

A MINIATURE WORLD

BEFORE THE LAB

1. Divide the class into groups of three to six students.
2. Gather all materials at least one day prior to the investigation. You should have enough supplies to meet your class needs.
3. Jars should be at least 2 liters in size. Wash the jars thoroughly before using them. Use a lamp with a bulb of at least 60 watts. For the plants, use hortwort (*Ceratophyllum*), *Elodea,* or fanwort (*Cabomba*). Construction sand may be substituted for gravel. Wash sand or gravel thoroughly. To save electricity, you may wish to place the lamps on timers. The aquariums require at least sixteen hours of light per day.

PRE-LAB DISCUSSION

Have students read the complete laboratory procedure.

• **What is the purpose of the laboratory investigation?** (Possible answers: To create a self-sustaining ecosystem; to observe the interactions between plants and animals.)

• **Explain how the sealed jars are similar to the planet Earth.** (Once the jars are sealed, no organisms can enter or leave. The energy from the lamp has the same function as the sun's energy—to enable the plants to create food.)

• **Why must jars stand uncovered for at least 48 hours?** (To bring the water to room temperature, to dissolve air in the water, to allow various sediments to settle.)

Laboratory Investigation

A Miniature World

Problem

How do human activities affect the environment?

Materials *(per group)*

large jar with cover	4 aquatic plants
table lamp	8 small pond snails
2 guppies	clean gravel

Procedure 🧪 🐚

1. Place gravel 3 cm deep on the bottom of the jar.
2. Fill the jar with tap water to about 6 cm from the top.
3. Let the jar stand uncovered for at least 48 hours.
4. Using the accompanying diagram as a guide, place plants in the jar.
5. Place the snails and guppies in the jar.
6. Close the jar tightly.
7. Place the jar in a location away from windows and other areas in which temperature and light change greatly.
8. Place the table lamp next to the jar so that the light shines on the jar. The light bulb should be about 15 to 20 cm from the jar.
9. Within 4 to 5 days, the water in the jar should be slightly green in color. If the water does not have any color in it, move the lamp closer to the jar. **Note:** *The light bulb should not touch the jar.* If the water is bright green, move the lamp away from the jar. Adjust the position of the lamp as needed until the water stays a pale green in color.
10. Observe the jar every 2 to 3 days.

Observations

How did the jar change over time?

Analysis and Conclusions

1. Why is the lamp necessary?
2. How do the plants and animals in the jar interact?
3. What would happen to the miniature world inside the jar if people killed all the snails and fish?
4. Imagine that an exotic plant disease which killed all the plants was accidentally introduced to your jar. How would this affect the miniature world in the jar?
5. You could have found the answers to questions 3 and 4 by doing something to simulate these forms of environmental damage. Explain why you were not asked to do this.
6. **On Your Own** Design an experiment to test the effects of deforestation on your miniature world. What results would you expect to obtain from your experiment?

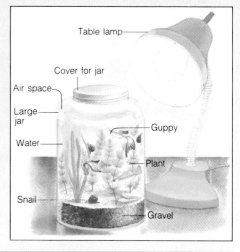

Labels: Table lamp; Cover for jar; Air space; Large jar; Water; Guppy; Plant; Snail; Gravel

---

TEACHING STRATEGY

1. Students may need assistance determining which ends of the plants should be placed in the gravel.
2. If the aquariums in the jar start to die or look unhealthy, unseal the jar and allow students to maintain it as a small aquarium that is not self-sustaining. Replant, refresh water, and remove dead animals as necessary. Have students speculate on what would have happened to the jar if it had been left alone. (Eventually, the plants, fish, and snails would all have died.)

DISCOVERY STRATEGIES

Discuss how the investigation relates to the chapter ideas by asking open questions similar to the following.

• **What would happen inside the jar if the water began to get too green?** (The color of the water shows that photosynthesis is taking place. If the plants start to grow too fast they might crowd out the animals.)

• **What do you think would happen if you were to put the jar in complete darkness?** (The plants would die because they could not make food, and the animals would die

Summarizing Key Concepts

4–1 Identifying Problems

▲ A species that no longer exists is said to be extinct. The process by which a species passes out of existence is known as extinction.

▲ Extinction is a natural part of Earth's history.

▲ In the past few hundred years, human activities have greatly increased the rate at which organisms become extinct.

▲ Organisms that are so rare that they are in danger of becoming extinct are said to be endangered.

▲ Some species become rare, endangered, or extinct because they are killed deliberately.

▲ Many species are threatened by the destruction of their habitats.

▲ The destruction of forests is known as deforestation. Deforestation harms both nearby and distant ecosystems.

▲ Although some desertification occurs naturally, most is caused by human activities.

▲ Pollution damages habitats and poses a threat to living things.

▲ Exotic, or non-native, species can upset the balance of interactions in an ecological community and cause native species to become endangered or extinct.

▲ Some activities meant to increase people's appreciation for the natural world may pose a threat to wildlife.

▲ Wildlife has economic and scientific value.

▲ The genetic diversity of wildlife provides keys for solving current and future problems.

▲ Because all living things are interdependent, wildlife is necessary for the continued survival of the human species.

4–2 Seeking Solutions

▲ Wildlife conservation is the wise management of Earth's living resources so that they can supply present and future needs.

▲ Preserving habitats is the most important method for conserving wildlife.

▲ In any conservation effort, it is important to keep human needs, attitudes, and desires in mind.

▲ Education is the first step in getting people to help with wildlife conservation.

▲ Captive breeding helps to raise reproductive rates and maintain genetic diversity.

▲ Wildlife conservation is not easy because it is closely linked to many complex social, political, and ethical issues.

▲ If everyone does a little bit to help conserve resources, wildlife and the environment will be helped a lot.

Reviewing Key Terms

Define each term in a complete sentence.

4–1 Identifying Problems
extinct
endangered
deforestation
desertification
exotic species

4–2 Seeking Solutions
wildlife conservation
captive breeding

G ■ 125

---

abling the plants to continue the process of photosynthesis.

3. Over time, the levels of carbon dioxide and oxygen would become unbalanced since the animals would not be able to return carbon dioxide to the water. Eventually, the plants would die.

4. Without plants to produce oxygen during photosynthesis, the animals in the jar would die.

5. It is not proper to kill living organisms in such an experiment.

6. Accept all logical experimental designs that include both a control and experimental setup. Students should infer that deforestation would result in less oxygen produced during photosynthesis and might result in the death of the animals.

GOING FURTHER: ENRICHMENT

Part 1

Have students investigate the differences between freshwater and saltwater aquariums.

• **What do the two environments have in common?** (They need light, about the same temperature range, and a balance of plant and animal life.)

• **What are some of the differences?** (The plants and animals in saltwater must be different from those used in freshwater.)

Part 2

Challenge students to design experiments that focus on specific harmful effects of deforestation, such as acid rain, siltation, or lack of shade. Explain to students that their experiments should not be designed to harm living things.

---

because of a lack of food and oxygen.)

• **Predict what would happen if you added ten more guppies.** (Overcrowding would result, and the system would not be able to support the guppy population. Many guppies might die.)

• **Why must care be taken to maintain a certain fish-to-water ratio in the jars?** (Decreasing the amount of water would also result in overcrowding.)

OBSERVATIONS

The water in the jar became slightly green. Accept all other valid observations.

ANALYSIS AND CONCLUSIONS

1. The lamp simulated sunlight.

2. Plants take carbon dioxide dissolved in the water and use it to make food during photosynthesis. During this process, plants give off oxygen. Both the plants and animals need oxygen to survive (to perform respiration). The animals release carbon dioxide back to the water, en-

Chapter Review

Chapter Review

ALTERNATIVE ASSESSMENT

The *Prentice Hall Science* program includes a variety of testing components and methodologies. Aside from the Chapter Review questions, you may opt to use the Chapter Test or the Computer Test Bank Test in your *Test Book* for assessment of important facts and concepts. In addition, Performance-Based Tests are included in your *Test Book*. These Performance-Based Tests are designed to test science process skills rather than factual content recall. Since they are not content dependent, Performance-Based Tests can be distributed after students complete a chapter or after they complete the entire textbook.

CONTENT REVIEW

Multiple Choice
1. b
2. d
3. d
4. d
5. b
6. a
7. b
8. c

True or False
1. T
2. F, extinct
3. F, Habitat preservation
4. F, ivory tusks
5. F, human activities
6. T
7. F, tropical rain forests of Latin America, Africa, and Asia
8. F, plays

Concept Mapping
Row 1: affect
Row 2: habitat destruction, endangered
Row 3: extinction

CONCEPT MASTERY

1. Understanding genetic diversity helps scientists produce new plants and animals that are resistant to disease. Unusual genetic varieties are also a source of new medicines and other products.
2. Possible answers include overhunting, overharvesting, deforestation, desertification, wetlands destruction, pollution, introduction of exotic species. Students

---

Content Review

Multiple Choice

Choose the letter of the answer that best completes each statement.

1. Which of the following is extinct?
   a. rhinoceros   c. snowy egret
   b. dodo   d. lion tamarin
2. The intelligent management of resources is known as
   a. desertification.   c. habitat restoration.
   b. recycling.   d. conservation.
3. Organisms can become endangered because of
   a. habitat destruction.
   b. interactions with exotic species.
   c. overhunting.
   d. all of these.
4. Wildlife is important because it is
   a. a source of valuable products.
   b. a source of genetic diversity.
   c. necessary for environmental balance.
   d. all of these.
5. The process by which a species passes out of existence is known as
   a. endangerment.
   b. extinction.
   c. deforestation.
   d. genetic diversification.
6. A species that is not native to an area is said to be
   a. exotic.   c. extinct.
   b. endangered.   d. endemic.
7. A species that is so rare that it is in danger of disappearing is said to be
   a. exotic.   c. extinct.
   b. endangered.   d. endemic.
8. The destruction of forests is known as
   a. desertification.   c. deforestation.
   b. timber harvesting.   d. defoliation.

True or False

If the statement is true, write "true." If it is false, change the underlined word or words to make the statement true.

1. Extinction <u>is</u> a natural part of Earth's history.
2. The dodo is a(an) <u>endangered</u> species.
3. <u>Enforcing hunting laws</u> is the most important method of wildlife conservation.
4. Elephants have become endangered because of the demand for their <u>meat</u>.
5. Most desertification occurs as the result of <u>natural processes</u>.
6. Wetlands are considered to be <u>extremely valuable</u> ecosystems.
7. The deforestation of greatest concern to people worldwide is occurring in the <u>coniferous forests of the United States</u>.
8. Education <u>does not play</u> an important part in wildlife conservation.

Concept Mapping

Complete the following concept map for Section 4–1. Refer to pages G6–G7 to construct a concept map for the entire chapter.

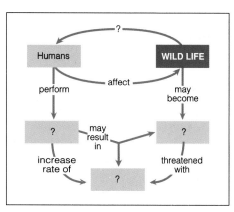

---

also may mention natural disasters such as forest fires, volcanic eruptions, and earthquakes.

3. A species is extinct when there are no longer any living members. Once it has become extinct, it is gone forever. An endangered species is at risk of becoming extinct. Sometimes it is possible to save endangered species.

4. Elephant tusks and the shells of hawksbill turtles are used for jewelry. Endangered fur-bearing animals include snow leopards, sea otters, and wild chinchillas.

Alligator skins were fashionable for shoes and handbags; snowy egret feathers were used to decorate hats.

5. Human activities can cause extinction through direct means or through indirect means. Some animals have been killed in such great numbers that their species are endangered. Indirectly, human activities threaten species by changing or destroying habitats. In areas where the human population increases quickly, wildlife habitats are often threatened.

6. By breeding endangered species in

Concept Mastery

Discuss each of the following in a brief paragraph.

1. Explain why it is important to preserve genetic diversity.
2. Discuss five ways in which habitats are damaged or destroyed.
3. What is the difference between the terms extinct and endangered?
4. Giving specific examples, explain how the demands of fashion have caused organisms to become endangered.
5. How do human activities affect the rate of extinction? Why do they have this effect?
6. How does captive breeding help animals in the wild?
7. What does the phrase "loving it to death" mean? How does this apply to the relationship between people and wildlife?
8. List four useful products that come from wildlife.

Critical Thinking and Problem Solving

Use the skills you have developed in this chapter to answer each of the following.

1. **Applying concepts** Suppose one of your friends wanted to buy a pet parrot. What sort of things do you think your friend should know before the parrot is purchased? Do you think buying a pet parrot is a good idea? Why or why not?
2. **Making predictions** In June 1990, Florida passed a law that requires motorboats to go at very slow speeds in certain waterways. In addition, motorboats have been completely banned from a few waterways. How do you think these new restrictions on motorboats will affect manatees?
3. **Relating cause and effect** About 200 years ago, Hawaii's forests were inhabited by 58 species of birds that were not found in any other place in the world. Of these 58 species, 22 are extinct and 20 are endangered. How might each of the following factors have contributed to the disappearance of these birds?
   a. Destruction of three fourths of Hawaii's forests
   b. Exotic species such as sheep, cattle, and rabbits
   c. Exotic species such as cats, rats, and mongooses

d. Exotic species such as pigeons, sparrows, and doves
e. Hunting

4. **Using the writing process** Write a short book for first-graders on one of the following topics: endangered species; species that became extinct because of human activities; a method of wildlife conservation. Illustrate your book with your own drawings and/or with pictures from magazines. (Remember to get permission before you cut up the magazines!)

G ■ 127

---

captivity, the species can be preserved from extinction. Animals and plants bred in captivity can sometimes be returned to their habitats to help create a population large enough to be self-sustaining.

7. "Loving it to death" might include overfeeding a pet or hugging a small animal too tightly. An attraction to or affection for endangered species should not tempt people to buy them for pets.

8. Possible answers include latex, medicines, wood, and most kinds of seafood.

CRITICAL THINKING AND PROBLEM SOLVING

1. The friend should check that the parrot is not a member of an endangered species and that it can live successfully in whatever environment is planned for it.

2. It is hoped that they will be saved from extinction.

3. **a.** Many species probably lived in the forests. When their habitats were destroyed, the birds became extinct.

b. Forest may have been cleared when sheep and cattle were introduced.

c. Cats, rats, and mongooses prey on birds.

d. Pigeons, sparrows, and doves may have competed with native birds for the same resources.

e. Overhunting can cause extinction.

4. Students' books should be scientifically accurate and consistent with chapter material despite the simplified presentation. Before beginning, they might read books written for first-grade students. They should note the simplified vocabulary, short sentences, and large number of illustrations.

KEEPING A PORTFOLIO

You might want to assign some of the Concept Mastery and Critical Thinking and Problem Solving questions as homework and have students include their responses to unassigned questions in their portfolio. Students should be encouraged to include both the questions and the answers in their portfolio.

ISSUES IN SCIENCE

The following issues can be used as a springboard for class debate or given as writing assignments.

1. Why spend millions of dollars trying to save endangered species when people are starving all over the world? Is this a valid argument? What are some of the ethical issues involved in saving endangered species when "people conservation" is so important?

2. Nuclear energy is said to be clean energy. Because nuclear plants do not burn anything to generate electricity, they do not cause air pollution. As a result, wildlife can coexist with nuclear plant sites. Nuclear plants do generate toxic wastes, however, that are difficult to dispose of properly and are harmful to people, animals, and plants. Do you think nuclear energy provides more advantages or disadvantages? Would you recommend the use of nuclear energy over other forms? Why or why not?

BIOSPHERE II:
A WORLD UNDER GLASS

Background Information

A biosphere is defined as an enclosed ecological system. As such, a biosphere must contain all the living things and nonliving materials necessary to maintain the lives of the organisms within the biosphere. Moreover, the materials necessary to successfully reproduce must be found within the biosphere. And finally, a source of energy that can be consumed must be present. In most biospheres, the sun is the ultimate source of energy and through photosynthesis food is produced to maintain the heterotrophs living in the biosphere.

There are several important goals that the builders of Biosphere II hope to achieve. The first is to gain a better understanding of the Earth's biosphere and the dynamics of the interactions that occur within such a biosphere. Another goal is to develop a means of providing refuge for endangered plants and animals—a goal that may become very important in future decades if pollution of the atmosphere and water does not abate. A third, but possibly most important goal, is to prepare for the building of similar biospheres in space, which will likely house the first human settlements outside this planet.

In September 1991, Biosphere II became the subject of controversy. Have interested students search for magazine and newspaper articles to find out why. You might want to divide the class into two groups to debate the following topic: Biosphere II—Science or Scam?

GAZETTE
BIOSPHERE II:
A WORLD UNDER GLASS

In the dry foothills of Arizona's Santa Catalina mountains, a privately funded group of scientists has designed and developed a glass-enclosed "terrarium" that contains models of biomes found on Earth. This world in miniature, Biosphere II (the scientists refer to our Earth as Biosphere I), is 1.27 hectares in area, or a little larger than two football fields. It houses some 3800 species of plants as well as fishes, goats, hummingbirds, pigs, moths, bats, and—since early 1991—8 human beings.

The human inhabitants of Biosphere II (who are fondly called Biospherans) will remain sealed in their artificial world for two years. Their goals are: to enhance human understanding of the complex interactions among Earth's living and nonliving things, to develop methods for improved recycling, and to investigate means of establishing self-contained, self-sustaining settlements in outer space. The project is a cooperative effort that has involved many scientists from different fields.

Under its glass dome, Biosphere II is divided into several parts. In one corner stands a five-story building complex that contains apartments as well as research, recreational, and health facilities. Next to the building complex is a farm that is approximately the size of an ice-hockey rink. At the farm, grains, garden vegetables, and tropical fruits are grown in soil enriched with manure, compost, and earthworms. Livestock and freshwater fishes are also raised on the farm.

TEACHING STRATEGY:
ADVENTURE

FOCUS/MOTIVATION

Show students photographs or slides of NASA interpretations of space colonies. Ask:

• **What must a space colony provide to support living things?** (Food, energy, water, recreational space, and so on.)

• **Which of these factors can you observe in the illustrations of space colonies?** (Answers will vary, depending on the illustrations used, but most illustrations include plants, animals, living space, and so on.)

• **How can scientists construct a "space colony" on the Earth?** (By building an enclosed system and seeing if it can support living things over a long period of time.)

Point out that that is just what people who constructed Biosphere II did. Now have students read the Adventures in Science article.

CONTENT DEVELOPMENT

Point out that Biosphere II obviously does not contain every type of ecosystem found on the Earth, but that it does have representative ecosystems from all major biomes.

• **Why would it be impossible to construct a biosphere that contained an example of all Earth ecosystems?** (The biosphere would be enormous and cost far too much money. In fact, most scientists would assert that to do so would mean to construct a

SCIENCE, TECHNOLOGY & SOCIETY

▲ From the top of Biosphere II's mountain, you can see the marshes, (top left), ocean (center left), savanna (top right), and rain forest and its stream (bottom).

Alongside the farm and building complex, the remaining environments lie in a carefully planned sequence. Next to the farm is the model rain-forest biome. The glass dome above the rain forest soars 26 meters above the forest floor (about the height of a seven-story building) to house a mountain, a forest, a pond, and 300 species of plants. The rain-forest plants were selected by Dr. Ghillean Prance, director of the Kew Royal Botanic Gardens in London, England. From this model, scientists hope to learn ways to rebuild damaged rain forests.

Water from the rain forest flows down the miniature mountain and collects in a stream that runs through the next model biome, the savanna. This model is the joint effort of Dr. Tony Burgess, an ecologist and botanist who runs the U.S. Geological Survey's Sonoran desert lab, and Dr. Peter Warshall, a biologist and anthropologist. The savanna contains microbes, insects, and hummingbirds as well as species of grasses from Africa, Australia, and South America.

Next, the stream runs into a small freshwater marsh then ends its jour-

▲ The eight Biospherans have an enormous responsibility: caring for an entire world.

ney in a saltwater marsh. Dr. Walter Adey, a marine biologist at the Smithsonian Institute, designed these marshes in addition to the lagoon, coral reef, and ocean. The marine habitats are homes for fishes, shellfish, corals, and sea plants.

Beyond the miniature sea is Biosphere II's final model biome—a cool, foggy desert designed after Mexico's Baja California. Dr. Burgess and Dr. Warshall (who also designed the savanna) chose the 300 plant species and animals for this area, where cacti and mesquite bushes share space with kangaroo rats, insects, and even scorpions.

Biosphere II works as a self-contained unit. Plants take human and animal wastes and turn them into the oxygen and food needed for animal life. Air is purified by pumping it through the farm's soil, where microorganisms strip it of pollutants. Water is purified through the interactions of plants, fishes, and microorganisms in the farm's fish tanks. (Drinking water is further purified through evaporation and condensation.) Human waste is treated to kill harmful microorganisms, then flows into the marshland, where microorganisms and water hyacinths break it down and purify it.

In spite of all this careful planning, the scientists working on the project admit that there are many uncertainties in Biosphere II. So beneath Biosphere II lie pipes and pumps and fans designed to cool and filter the air, store water, recycle wastes, and move the structure's air. Biosphere II also has a power plant to provide the project with electricity.

Despite its uncertainties, Biosphere II offers scientists a unique research opportunity. In Biosphere II they are discovering ways to improve the Earth's environments as well as ways for humans to survive far from it in outer space.

GAZETTE ■ 129

new planet exactly like the Earth.)

Discuss the various ecosystems that were constructed in Biosphere II. Have students describe the kinds of plants and animals they would expect to find in each of the ecosystems in Biosphere II.

FOCUS/MOTIVATION

Show students an enclosed aquarium or terrarium. Ask:

• **How does this model simulate Biosphere II?** (Although it is much smaller and contains only one ecosystem, it too must pro-

vide all the substances that living things need to survive and maintain life.)

INDEPENDENT PRACTICE

▶ *Activity Book*

After students have read the Science Gazette article, you may want to hand out the reading skills worksheet based on the article in the *Activity Book.*

Additional Questions and Topic Suggestions

1. According to the article, what are the main ecosystems that are maintained within Biosphere II? (Small farm, rain forest, miniature mountain, savanna, freshwater marsh, saltwater marsh, desert, and ocean.)

2. Why are the scientists committed to spending at least two years within Biosphere II? (The interactions among organisms within any ecosystem, not to mention a biosphere with many ecosystems, are very complex. In order to fully understand the interactions within the biosphere on a long-term basis, the scientists must stay in the biosphere for at least two years. In fact, it would take many more years to get a fully accurate study and accounting of the interactions and problems that arise within Biosphere II.)

Critical Thinking Questions

1. How does Biosphere II compare to the biosphere we call planet Earth? (It is a simulation of many of the ecosystems on planet Earth. However, the Earth is far more complex and has many more ecosystems than could possibly be built within an enclosed biosphere.)

2. How can the knowledge gained through Biosphere II help space scientists plan colonies in outer space? (First, scientists will gain a better understanding of what must be put into a biosphere to maintain life. Through Biosphere II, they will not only learn what they did right, but also what they did wrong. Second, scientists will gain a better understanding of the social interactions that occur among people who are forced to live together in a closed system for long periods of time. Third, because building a space biosphere will be extremely expensive, money, time, and perhaps lives will be saved by experimenting on Earth prior to trying to build a biosphere in space.)

3. If given the opportunity, would you volunteer to live in Biosphere II? What about an actual colony in space? (Accept all answers. Some students will be thrilled with the idea; others will be very negative.)

G ■ 129

CONSERVATIONISTS
TO THE RESCUE?

Background Information

During the last several decades, concern about environmental issues has reached an all-time high, both in the United States and abroad. An important aspect of environmental protection is conservation, particularly the preservation of endangered species.

Endangered species are those species that face the threat of extinction. They need human help and protection to survive. The idea of conservation has always carried with it the implication of equal care and protection for *all* species. But with species disappearing at an ever-increasing rate and over a thousand plants and animals on the current endangered list, conservation efforts will not be able to save them all. And conservationists may be forced by limited time and resources to make choices.

Who could formulate guidelines for making such difficult decisions? One participant might be the International Union for Conservation of Nature and Natural Resources. Established by the United Nations in 1948, the IUCN publishes information on endangered species in its *Red Data Book*. In 1961, the IUCN set up the World Wildlife Fund, which raises money for conservation programs.

TEACHING STRATEGY:
ISSUE

FOCUS/MOTIVATION

Display two pictures of wild animals, perhaps of a lion and a rhinoceros. Tell students:

Suppose the lion and the rhinoceros are endangered species; that is, their numbers have been reduced to a point where, without careful management and protection, they could become extinct, or disappear forever.

Stimulate a class discussion by asking questions such as:

Conservationists
to the Rescue?

Bathed in early morning light, a herd of large, dark brown sambar deer grazes on a grassy hillside at the edge of a forest in southern Asia. Suddenly, one of the deer raises its head in alarm and sniffs the air. Soon the entire herd is wary and watchful–ready to flee in an instant.

The reason for their alarm quickly becomes obvious. Emerging from the woods a mere 225 meters away, a tiger strides up the hillside. The big cat's powerful muscles ripple as it moves. For a moment, the tiger stops and turns its head toward the deer. Then it continues on its way. This morning, at least, the tiger is not hungry. The deer are left to graze in peace.

Tigers are a vanishing species. They have disappeared from many parts of Asia where they were once common. In an effort to save them, conservation groups such as the World Wildlife Fund have raised millions of dollars. This money is used to support research into tiger behavior and to establish preserves in the wild where the cats are protected.

To some extent, the effort has been successful. India now has 11 preserves for tigers. In some of these protected areas, the cat population is increasing once more. Conservationists are hopeful that tigers can continue to live in the wild.

But not everyone wants tigers living in the wild. In areas near some of India's preserves, tigers have killed both animals and people. Some Indians living near preserves oppose the government's attempts to save the tiger.

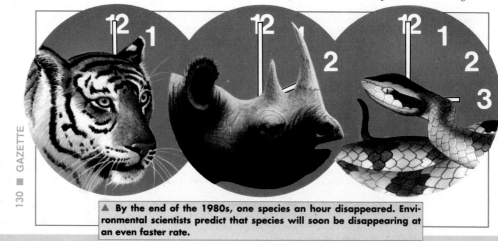

▲ By the end of the 1980s, one species an hour disappeared. Environmental scientists predict that species will soon be disappearing at an even faster rate.

• **Do you think these animals are worth saving?**
• **What if you could save only one?**
• **How would you decide which one to save?**
• **Would it be a difficult decision to make? Why?**

CONTENT DEVELOPMENT

Explain to students that in less affluent countries people struggle to find fuel, food, and clothing. Land that could be set aside for animal preserves may be desperately needed to grow crops. Basic survival comes before concern for endangered species.

• **Why are some Indians not sympathetic to the plight of the tiger in their country?** (They see the tiger as a threat to them, their livestock, and their livelihood.)
• **Why might it be difficult to convince the Indians of the need to protect the tiger?** (The tiger's future would be less important to them than their own future.)

They feel the tiger is not an endangered species that should be saved, but a dangerous threat that should be removed.

A FIGHT TO THE FINISH

Each year, more plants and animals become endangered. As conservationists work to save them, questions often arise about whether all species of living things should be saved. And if not all, which ones should be saved?

The answers are not simple. Some situations involve a conflict between the needs of humans and the needs of wildlife. Other situations require a decision about which species are worth time, effort, and money. For example, should developers be prevented from building in the Pine Barrens forest of New Jersey if the construction endangers a type of moth that lives there? Or is it worth thousands of dollars to save a kind of sparrow that lives only in a small part of Florida near Cape Canaveral?

FACING THE FACTS

To do their job, conservationists have to face tough questions like these. Some leading conservationists are very practical about the issues. Norman Meyers, for example, is a well-known environmental scientist. He notes that each hour another species, counting insects and other invertebrates (animals without backbones), disappears.

"Sad to say," Meyers writes, "the question is not how to save *all* these species; we just do not have the resources to rescue more than a small fraction."

Meyers suggests that first the value of each species be determined. The decision would be based on economics, the environment, and the survival of people. Then, the most valuable species should receive help first.

For example, in the African country of Kenya, lions are a big tourist attraction. Tourism brings lots of money to the country. Therefore, lions may be worth saving.

Additional Questions and Topic Suggestions

1. In recent decades there have been many battles between conservationists trying to protect a particular species and citizens and industries trying to protect jobs and livelihoods. Two of the most publicized instances are the debates over the fates of the snail darter in Tennessee and the spotted owl in Oregon and Washington. Research these or other examples of controversies that focus on the survival of a species versus the economic survival of humans. Can you think of any possible solutions to the problem?

2. The article points out that tourism brings money to Kenya. Visit a travel agency and the library and collect information on safaris and other tours that feature wildlife as attractions. Find out what the tours do to help preserve the wildlife they depend on and what the countries visited actually gain from tourism. Why would tourism be of help to only certain species?

REINFORCEMENT/RETEACHING

Ask students to imagine what it would be like to live in a country where food and land are scarce. Ask them if they would be willing to share their food and land with wild animals who could also be a threat to their lives.

CONTENT DEVELOPMENT

Point out to students that it has generally been the aim of conservationists to work to save all species. But in recent years it has become increasingly clear that there simply isn't enough money or time to save all species. This has placed conservationists and others in the unenviable position of having to choose which species to save.

• **How could the needs of humans decide the fate of a species?** (Where the survival of humans were at stake, the species would probably lose out.)

• **According to the article, what factors might be used to determine if a species should be helped?** (Economics, the environment, and the survival of people.)

• **Why is it difficult to assess the value of any species?** (Often not much is known about the species; it could be very valuable and we just don't know it yet. Also, because species are all parts of intricate ecosystems, their loss will change the ecosystems in ways we can't begin to imagine but that could potentially endanger our own survival.)

Class Debate

Have students work in teams to debate the following statement.

The International Union for the Conservation of Nature and Natural Resources (IUCN) should establish a set of criteria to be used to determine which species should be helped.

▶ This California condor is one of many species of animals that is threatened with extinction.

A tropical plant called the periwinkle is the source of two drugs used to treat cancer. And the venom of the Malayan pit viper, a cousin of the rattlesnake, is used to stop blood clots that cause heart attacks. In Meyers' view, the periwinkle and the pit viper should be among the first to receive help.

THE UNKNOWN FACTOR

It is clearly to our advantage to invest time and money in preserving useful species of plants and animals. The trouble is, there are probably thousands of species that could be very valuable to people—only no one yet knows it!

Are we wiping out species that hold secrets that would help us cure cancer and AIDS, feed a hungry world, or solve the energy crisis? Scientists and conservationists Paul and Anne Ehrlich of Stanford University think we might be. And they also see a further complication. When species disappear, the ecosystems, or environments, to which they belong are changed or even destroyed. All life on the Earth depends on ecosystems. Ecosystems provide important services such as the maintenance of soils and the control of crop pests and transmitters of human disease. As the Ehrlichs write, "Humanity has no way of replacing these free services should they be lost...and civilization cannot persist without them."

The Ehrlichs cite yet another reason for saving as many species as possible—"plain old-fashioned compassion." For many conservationists, stopping the extinction of species is a moral issue.

CONCERN AROUND THE WORLD

The International Union for the Conservation of Nature and Natural Resources (IUCN) is a worldwide group associated with the United Nations. The IUCN's position is that we are "morally obliged to our descendants and to other creatures" to act wisely when it comes to conserving plants and animals.

Most conservationists would agree that each time a species vanishes, the world is a bit poorer. Consider just the sheer beauty of many of the endangered plants and animals. The main reason for saving tigers and condors, for example, is that they are among the Earth's most magnificent creatures.

Perhaps sadly, people tend to feel more concern for species that are pretty or striking than for those that are plain. The black rhinoceros of Africa and the Higgin's eye mussel of rivers of the Midwest are both in danger. The world knows about the threat to the rhinoceros. But few people know about the Higgin's eye, even though it is closer to extinction than the rhino.

How can conservationists decide which endangered species to help or, at least, to help first? Norman Meyers has an interesting approach. When many people are injured in a big disaster, physicians often first treat victims who are badly hurt but who will recover if treated promptly. Meyers suggests that the same approach be used for species in danger. First help those species that are in the greatest danger and that have a good chance of surviving extinction. Still, says Meyers, it will not be easy to decide which species to aid and which to ignore. Making these decisions, he adds, "will cause us many a sleepless night."

ISSUE (continued)

ENRICHMENT

Point out that some conservationists feel we have a moral obligation to save species. Ask students what that means. Encourage them to discuss moral obligation as a reason for action. If necessary, bring up the idea of right and proper conduct, duty to the future, and responsibility for our actions.

INDEPENDENT PRACTICE

▶ *Activity Book*

After students have read the Science Gazette article, you may want to hand out the reading skills worksheet based on the article in the *Activity Book*.

What Became of Africa's Animals?

he sun is not yet up. In the kitchen of a comfortable home on the outskirts of a medium-sized city, a man is brewing coffee. Looking at a calendar, he checks the date—January 24, 2050. Although it is still cool outside, the man wears short pants and a short-sleeved shirt. He expects another scorching day here in East Africa.

Just as dawn breaks the man jumps into a vehicle and drives away from the city. On each side of the road sprawl rich farms with vast, neatly cultivated fields of crops. Within 20 minutes, he pulls up to a gate, where a guard greets him. His workday has begun. This man is a game warden at a large national park and wildlife sanctuary.

At the same time every morning, the war-den makes the rounds to see how the wild animals in the park are doing. The road over which he drives is paved with blacktop. The warden wonders how it must have been back in the 1990s, when wardens drove battered cars over roads that were nothing more than dirt tracks.

At that time, the park was far away from any farms and cities. All around it stretched grassy plains. Wild animals wandered freely inside and outside the park. In 2010, how-ever, the land near the park was set aside for farming. The population of the country had grown so large that all the fertile land was needed to produce food. Only the parks were left wild. "At least," the warden thinks to himself, "my country saved the parks." In a country nearby, the need for food had

GAZETTE ■ 133

Background Information

Most experts agree that African nations must strike a balance between conserva-tion and economic development. Africa is presently the only continent on the Earth in which food production has not risen faster than population growth. The im-porting of foodstuffs is a serious drain on the economies of small developing na-tions. In addition, mineral and energy re-sources that could boost the African econ-omy continue to remain unexploited. These resources must be developed if African nations are to become sufficient-ly industrialized.

Although the situation presented in this article is quite appealing, arriving at such an ideal state of compromise will not be easy. Simply taking land from the animals and giving it to farmers or industrialists will not necessarily result in a stronger econ-omy; the redistributed land must be man-aged properly. Without careful planning, Africa could lose its animals and the growth potential of its available land.

A major problem today is that Africa's developing nations lack the technologi-cal personnel and institutional organiza-tion needed to manage redistributed land and direct industrial development. Con-servation organizations in Western na-tions that want to aid the Africans might do well to consider this need. Perhaps the best way to ensure that preservation of Africa's wildlife is for highly developed nations to provide Third World countries with managers and training programs that will enable them to use their land wisely.

Additional Questions and Topic Suggestions

1. South America faces problems similar to those of Africa, as many tropical rain forests must give way to the needs of people and industry. Learn more about the situation in South America, then report your findings to the class.

2. Do you think that the situation presented in this article is the way Africa will be in the year 2050? Write a story of your own in which you present a different outcome for the issue of people versus wildlife.

3. Find out more about the preservation of wildlife in the national parks of the United States. You may wish to join with other students in preparing a classroom display about our national parks.

been so great that even the national parks were turned into farms.

As the warden reaches the park's western boundary, he stops to check the condition of a high wire fence that encloses it. The fence was built 20 years earlier to stop animals from wandering off park property onto farmland. Elephants, buffaloes. antelopes, and zebras were eating the farmers' crops. Lions were killing livestock and threatening people. When the farmers complained, the fence was put up.

The fence was not strong enough to stop the elephants, however. They broke through the fence and kept destroying crops. In the end, there was only one solution to the problem. The elephants had to go. Most were killed, but some young ones were caught and shipped to a special park far away from both farms and cities. It is one of the few parks that are big enough to contain such large, far-roaming animals. Only these parks still have elephants and, for that matter, lions. Even with fences separating them, people do not want to live next door to animals as dan-

gerous as lions. So lions are permitted only in the most distant parks.

KEEPING ANIMALS ALIVE

Back in his vehicle, the warden drives through a broad valley. On all sides are antelopes and zebras, even a few buffaloes. The warden stops at a large concrete drinking tub. He switches on a pump and watches the tub fill with water. It is the dry season in East Africa, and the natural watering holes in the park have dried up. Water must be pumped out of the ground for the animals to drink. Before the fence went up, they could leave the park during the dry season to drink at rivers out on the plains. But the animals no longer have that freedom, so the warden must provide water for them.

As the warden continues his rounds, he meets two of his park rangers. They are counting the number of wildebeests, a type of antelope, in a herd. Years ago, more than a million wildebeests visited the park each year in the wet season. When the parkland

FUTURE (continued)

CONTENT DEVELOPMENT

• **Do you get the impression from the article that this African nation is better off economically than it was in the 1980s? Why or why not?** (Yes. Near the beginning of the article, the warden describes the rich farms that he passes on either side of the road. Also, the warden's own home sounds like a comfortable suburban home not unlike one found in the United States.)

• **Do you get the impression that this nation is more industralized than it was in the 1980s? Explain.** (Yes. The growth of cities and suburban areas usually implies a certain level of industrialization, or at least economic progress. Also, the building of modern roads leading into the city implies economic progress and industrialization.)

Discuss with students the arrangements that must be made if animal preserves are to exist side by side with farmland. Point

▶ **Wildebeests travel the African countryside in search of green grass to eat. During the dry seasons, the wildebeests must be able to leave an area with dried grass for an area with moist grass. If the human population continues to grow, however, the wildebeests will be unable to roam great distances. What will the consequences be?**

dried out and the grass turned brown in the dry season, the wildebeests would leave. They would travel to an area 160 kilometers away to find water and green grass to eat. But that area was finally taken over by farms and villages. Because they no longer had a place to go in the dry season, most of the wildebeests died. The government's conservation department rounded up the rest of the wildebeests and drove them back to the park. They can survive in the park because of the drinking tubs. But the small amount of grass left on the land during the dry season can support few wildebeests.

So the number of wildebeests must be kept below 20,000 or they will starve. That is why

the rangers keep count. Once the herd grows larger than 20,000, the warden and his rangers have to kill some of the older animals to keep the size of the herd down. The meat is given to the farmers living just outside the park.

The warden looks over the wildebeest herd with pride. True, it is not nearly as impressive as the herds that used to roam 40 to 50 years ago, he thinks. But still people have a chance to see the animals. The warden remembers how, on a trip to the United States, he visited a national park in the west-

ern part of that country. He saw shaggy American bison walking around in the park. Two centuries had passed since the bison wandered freely far and wide, but in the parks they had been preserved. It is the same with his country's wildebeests.

TWILIGHT THOUGHTS

Late in the day, the warden pauses at a rocky hillside. For a moment, he glimpses a flash of yellow fur with black spots. Then it is gone. "A leopard," he whispers to himself. It has been a year since he has seen one, although he knows that at least six leopards inhabit the park.

Leopards, unlike lions, are meat eaters that seem able to survive near large numbers of people. Leopards move about mostly at night and are loners. Lions are active partly in daylight and live in groups. It takes the meat of many large animals, such as wildebeests and zebras, to feed a group of lions. But a leopard can live very well on smaller prey, such as baboons.

Driving home, the warden thinks about how wonderful it is to be able to see leopards prowl and zebras roam. He cannot help thinking that if his country had fewer people, there could be more wildlife parks. "But," he reminds himself, "we've done our best."

GAZETTE ■ 135

out that high wire fences are needed to keep animals from roaming onto nearby farmland. Also emphasize that not all wild animals in Africa would be able to adjust to life in a national park.

• **Which animals might not survive the kind of arrangements described in the article?** (Elephants and wildebeests; possibly lions.)

• **Why?** (Elephants would probably break down even the strongest fences, so they would not be allowed to live near farms. Lions also would probably not be allowed

near farms because people would be afraid to live near such dangerous animals. The wildebeests would have trouble adapting to living in the park year-round because there is not enough food and water available during the dry season.)

INDEPENDENT PRACTICE
▶ *Activity Book*

After students have read the Science Gazette article, you may want to hand out the reading skills worksheet based on the article in the *Activity Book.*

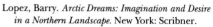

For Further Reading

If you have been intrigued by the concepts examined in this textbook, you may also be interested in the ways fellow thinkers—novelists, poets, essayists, as well as scientists—have imaginatively explored the same ideas.

Chapter 1: Interactions Among Living Things

Attenborough, David. *The Trials of Life.* Boston, MA: Little, Brown.

Defoe, Daniel. *Robinson Crusoe.* New York: Penguin.

London, Jack. *Call of the Wild.* New York: Macmillan.

Chapter 2: Cycles in Nature

Adams, Richard. *Watership Down.* New York: Avon.

Burton, Jane, and Kim Taylor. *Nightwatch.* New York: Facts on File.

Kipling, Rudyard. *The Jungle Book.* New York: Penguin.

Chapter 3: Exploring Earth's Biomes

Carson, Rachel. *The Edge of the Sea.* New York: Signet.

George, Jean C. *Julie of the Wolves.* New York: Harper & Row Junior Books.

George, Jean C. *My Side of the Mountain.* New York: Dutton.

Lopez, Barry. *Arctic Dreams: Imagination and Desire in a Northern Landscape.* New York: Scribner.

Perry, Donald. *Life Above the Jungle Floor: A Biologist Explores a Strange and Hidden Treetop World.* New York: Simon and Schuster.

Chapter 4: Wildlife Conservation

Henry, Marguerite. *Mustang, Wild Spirit of the West.* New York: Macmillan.

Lasky, Kathryn. *Home Free.* New York: Macmillan.

Mowat, Farley. *Never Cry Wolf.* New York: Bantam Books.

Activity Bank

Welcome to the Activity Bank! This is an exciting and enjoyable part of your science textbook. By using the Activity Bank you will have the chance to make a variety of interesting and different observations about science. The best thing about the Activity Bank is that you and your classmates will become the detectives, and as with any investigation you will have to sort through information to find the truth. There will be many twists and turns along the way, some surprises and disappointments too. So always remember to keep an open mind, ask lots of questions, and have fun learning about science.

Activity Bank

COOPERATIVE LEARNING

Hands-on science activities, such as the ones in the Activity Bank, lend themselves well to cooperative learning techniques. The first step in setting up activities for cooperative learning is to divide the class into small groups of about 4 to 6 students. Next, assign roles to each member of the group. Possible roles include Principal Investigator, Materials Manager, Recorder/Reporter, Maintenance Director. The Principal Investigator directs all operations associated with the group activity, including checking the assignment, giving instructions to the group, making sure that the proper procedure is being followed, performing or delegating the steps of the activity, and asking questions of the teacher on behalf of the group. The Materials Manager obtains and dispenses all materials and equipment and is the only member of the group allowed to move around the classroom without special permission during the activity. The Recorder, or Reporter, collects information, certifies and records results, and reports results to the class. The Maintenance Director is responsible for cleanup and has the authority to assign other members of the group to assist. The Maintenance Director is also in charge of group safety.

For more information about specific roles and cooperative learning in general, refer to the article "Cooperative Learning and Science—The Perfect Match" on pages 70–75 in the *Teacher's Desk Reference*.

ESL/LEP STRATEGY

Activities such as the ones in the Activity Bank can be extremely helpful in teaching science concepts to LEP students—the direct observation of scientific phenomena and the deliberate manipulation of variables can transcend language barriers.

Some strategies for helping LEP students as they develop their English-language skills are listed below. Your school's English-to-Speakers-of-Other-Languages (ESOL) teacher will probably be able to make other concrete suggestions to fit the specific needs of the LEP students in your classroom.

• Assign a "buddy" who is proficient in English to each LEP student. The buddy need not be able to speak the LEP student's native language, but such ability can be helpful. (**Note:** *Instruct multilingual buddies to use the native language only when necessary, such as defining difficult terms or concepts. Students learn English, as all other languages, by using it.*) The buddy's job is to provide encouragement and assistance to the LEP student. Select buddies on the basis of personality as well as proficiency in science and English. If possible, match buddies and LEP students so that the LEP students can help their buddies in another academic area, such as math.

• If possible, do not put LEP students of the same nationality in a cooperative learning group.

• Have artistic students draw diagrams of each step of an activity for the LEP students.

You can read more about teaching science to LEP students in the article "Creating a Positive Learning Environment for Students with Limited English Proficiency," which is found on pages 86–87 in the *Teacher's Desk Reference*.

Activity Bank

GARBAGE IN THE GARDEN

BEFORE THE ACTIVITY

1. Divide the class into groups of three to six students per group.
2. Gather all materials at least one day prior to the activity.

PRE-ACTIVITY DISCUSSION

Make sure that students understand the activity procedure by asking questions such as the following.

• **How is the soda bottle prepared for this activity?** (The top is cut off and holes are punched into the bottom and sides.)
• **How is the bottle used?** (It is used as a container for the materials that will eventually decompose into compost.)
• **What do you put inside the soda bottle?** (Grass clippings, weeds, leaves, topsoil, vegetable and fruit scraps.)
• **Why do you think it is important to cut the materials that go into the bottle into small pieces?** (Answers will vary. Students may suggest that this gives decay bacteria a larger surface area on which to grow.)
• **What sort of information should you include in the data table in which you record your observations?** (Possible answers: Date on which observations were made, date on which water was added to the bottle, observations of the change in height, appearance, temperature, and/or odor of the bottle's contents. Have students come to a consensus on the design of the data table that they will be using and sketch it on the chalkboard.)

TEACHING STRATEGY

1. You may wish to cut off the tops of the soda bottles before this activity. The easiest way to remove the top of a plastic soda bottle is with a single-edged razor blade.
2. Decomposition in a compost pile generates some heat. Heat build-up is extremely unlikely to become a problem in students' miniature compost piles. (In fact, compost formation may be slow due to lack of heat build-up.) However, if any bottles are observed to be hot (not just slightly warm), smell as if they are burning, or start to smolder, add some cool wa-

More and more people are starting to put garbage in their gardens. You might think this practice would endanger health, smell bad, and damage the garden. But if it is done properly, it is safe, free of unpleasant odors, and beneficial to plant growth. Thanks to the action of helpful bacteria (which are often assisted by burrowing creatures such as worms), the garbage breaks down to form a dark-colored, nutrient-rich substance called compost.

In this activity you will explore the process of making compost.

Materials

2-L clear plastic soda bottle	weeds and leaves
small nail or push pin	uncooked vegetables and fruit scraps
scissors	china marker
topsoil	cheesecloth
150 mL beaker	rubber band
scraps of paper	plastic fork
grass clippings	foam meat tray

Procedure

1. Carefully poke holes in the sides and bottom of the soda bottle with the nail. Use the accompanying diagram as a

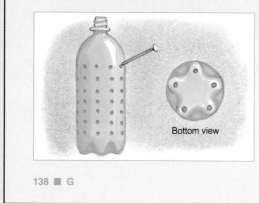

Bottom view

guide. **CAUTION:** *Be very careful and take your time.* Take turns making the holes—there are many to make.

2. Using the nail, poke a large hole near the top of the bottle at the point where the sides become vertical and the plastic thins out. Starting at this hole, carefully cut off the top of the bottle with the scissors. **CAUTION:** *Be careful when working with sharp objects.*

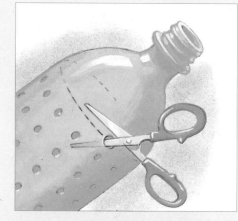

3. Label your bottle with the names of the people in your group and the date. Then put the bottle on the meat tray.
4. Fill the bottle about one-third full with grass clippings. Add 100 mL of soil, then 20 mL of water. The contents of the bottle should be moist but not soaking wet. If the contents are still dry, add a little more water.
5. With the scissors, cut the paper, leaves, weeds, and vegetable and fruit scraps into pieces no larger than 1 cm across. Fill the bottle about one-half full with the cut-up materials.

ter, then dump the contents onto old newspaper to help dissipate the heat. Add some topsoil to the contents before restoring them to the bottle, and instruct students to check the bottle daily for further heat problems.

3. If time or space is a problem, compost can be made from grass clippings, bits of weeds and leaves, and fruit and vegetable scraps in about a month in warm weather. Stuff a garbage bag with these materials and put the bag in a warm place outside. Mix the contents of the bag once or twice a week.

DISCOVERY STRATEGIES

Discuss how the activity relates to the chapter ideas by asking questions similar to the following.

• **What are decomposers? Why are decomposers important?** (Decomposers are organisms that break down the complex chemical compounds in dead plants and animals, forming simpler compounds that they release into the environment. With-

6. Use the plastic fork to mix the contents of the bottle well. If any materials fall onto the meat tray, lift the bottle, remove the tray, and dump the tray's contents into the bottle. Then put the tray back under the bottle.

7. Make a mark on the outside of the bottle to indicate the height of the contents. Cover the bottle with a piece of cheesecloth. Secure the cheesecloth with the rubber band. Then place the bottle in a warm location.

8. Twice a week, observe the contents of the bottle. Touch the sides of the bottle and note whether the bottle feels warm or cool to the touch. **CAUTION:** *If the bottle feels hot, notify your teacher immediately.*

9. After you have made your observations, add some water if the contents are dry. Once a week, mix the contents with the fork and mark their height on the side of the bottle. Write the date next to the new mark. Make sure you replace the cheesecloth when you have finished making your observations. **Note:** *If the contents start to smell bad, like rotten eggs or vinegar, mix the contents every time you make your observations.*

(continued)

G ■ 139

out decomposers, the raw materials needed by producers would be "locked up" in the form of dead plants and animals.)

Tell students that researchers have found recognizable hot dogs and readable newspapers several decades old in sanitary landfills.

• **What can you infer from this about decay and decomposers in a typical sanitary landfill?** (Little decay takes place; decomposers cannot go to work on materials that are buried deep inside a sanitary landfill.)

• **Many towns, especially in the Northeast where landfill space is scarce, no longer allow people to throw grass clippings, autumn leaves, and other yard waste into the regular garbage. Why do you think the towns have these rules?** (Because yard wastes are easily composted, it does not make sense to allow them to take up badly needed landfill space.)

• **How do you think towns with these rules deal with yard wastes?** (Accept all logical answers. Most collect yard wastes separately for composting or have a special place in the town dump where residents take their yard wastes.)

• **Why is composting important to organic gardeners, and to gardeners in general?** (Composting allows gardeners to make natural, chemical-free "fertilizer" for the garden from waste materials.)

OBSERVATIONS

1. The pieces became smaller and darker in color. Gradually, it became harder to distinguish among the various components of the mixture. Students may notice that the smell of the bottle's contents improves over time.

2. Answers will vary.

3. It went down.

4. Answers will vary. It usually takes two to three months.

5. Black or dark brown, fairly homogeneous, crumbly, and somewhat sweet-smelling.

ANALYSIS AND CONCLUSIONS

1. The action of decomposer bacteria broke down the materials.

2. To let air in.

3. The desirable bacteria need oxygen or are not harmed by it; undesirable bacteria are slowed down or killed by oxygen.

4. The materials in the center and bottom of the pile do not get enough air and become a place where the undesirable decay bacteria can live.

5. Answers will vary. Students should recognize that bacteria are necessary for decay to occur.

6. The materials in compost have been broken down by decomposer bacteria so that the nutrients that were once locked up in the materials are available for use by plants.

7. Composting, like other forms of recycling, removes materials from the waste stream so that they do not end up in a landfill. This helps to save space for materials that have to be disposed of in a landfill.

8. Students' plans should be reasonable and well thought out.

GOING FURTHER

Student experiments will vary, but should include a control.

Observations

1. How did the contents of the bottle change over time?

2. What kind of fruit and vegetable scraps did you add to the bottle? Which kinds of scraps decomposed the fastest? The slowest?

3. How did the level of the bottle's contents change over time?

4. How long did it take for the contents of the bottle to finish decomposing?

5. What does your "finished" compost look like?

Analysis and Conclusions

1. Why did the materials in the bottle change?

2. Why do you think you had to put holes in the bottle and cover the bottle with cheesecloth?

3. Some decomposer bacteria use oxygen, a substance that makes up about 21 percent of the air you breathe. Others do not use oxygen, but are not harmed by it. Still others are slowed down or even killed by oxygen. What can you infer about decomposer bacteria and making compost?

4. If the materials in a compost heap are not mixed regularly, it may start to smell bad. Explain why this might occur.

5. Predict what would have happened if the bottle and the materials in it had been sterilized. Would your results have been the same?

6. Compost improves the texture of garden soil, making it easier for plants to grow in it. It also acts like fertilizer. Explain why compost adds nutrients to the soil.

7. Landfills—commonly known as garbage dumps—are running out of space. In some parts of the country, little space is available for making new landfills. And people desperately need landfill space to dispose of garbage. How might making compost solve part of the landfill crisis?

8. Imagine that you and the members of your group have just been selected as part of a special task force. Your job is to devise a plan that will reduce by 90 percent the amount of yard waste that is ending up in the local landfill. Keep in mind the needs, attitudes, and abilities of the different kinds of people in your community as you work on the plan.

Going Further

Design an experiment to test how the formation of compost is affected by one of the following factors: light, heat, moisture, air.

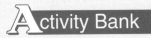

ON YOUR MARK, GET SET, GROW!

In every environment, the supply of resources is limited. In fact, some resources are so limited that there is not enough to go around. Because of this, organisms must compete with one another for the scarce resources. Competition can occur between species and within a species. How do different degrees of competition affect the growth and survival of organisms? Find out in this activity.

What Do You Do?

1. Obtain four clean half-gallon milk cartons, dried beans, soil, scissors, and a large plastic or foil tray.

2. Using the scissors, cut off the side that has the opened spout on each of the milk cartons. With the pointed tip of the scissors, poke three or four holes in the opposite side.

3. Fill each carton about two-thirds full of moist soil. Using your finger to make the planting holes, plant beans 3 cm deep and 8 cm apart in the first carton. Plant beans 3 cm deep and 5 cm apart in the second carton, 3 cm apart in the third carton, and 1 cm apart in the fourth carton.

4. Place the cartons side by side on the tray. Put the tray in a sunny spot.

5. Water the soil regularly so that it remains moist, but not soaking wet. Observe the cartons daily. Record your observations.

What Did You Learn?

1. Did the seeds sprout at the same time? Did the seedlings grow at the same rate and in the same way? Describe how the seedlings grew.

2. Did the seedlings in some cartons grow better than the seedlings in other cartons? Why do you think this was the case?

3. Compare your results with those of your classmates. Did you obtain similar results? Why do you think this was the case?

4. What are some possible sources of error in this activity?

5. Using what you learned in this activity, explain why gardeners have to thin out seedlings.

6. Weeding makes gardens look nicer. But is there any other reason for weeding? Explain.

7. What effect(s) do you think fertilizer would have on the space needs of bean seedlings?

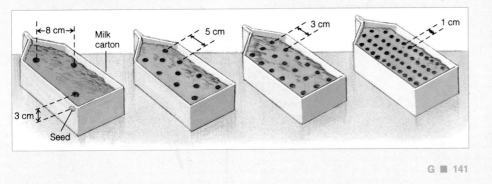

G ■ 141

Activity Bank

ON YOUR MARK, GET SET, GROW!

BEFORE THE ACTIVITY

1. Divide the class into groups of three to six students per group.
2. Gather all materials at least one day prior to the activity.

PRE-ACTIVITY DISCUSSION

Have students read the activity procedure.

• **What is the variable in this experiment?** (The spacing of the seeds.)

• **What are some factors in this experiment that have to be controlled, or kept the same, for each carton of seeds?** (All factors that might affect the growth of the seeds—except for the experimental variable—need to be controlled. These factors include type of seed used, size of planting holes, amount of soil, light, temperature, and water.)

DISCOVERY STRATEGIES

Discuss how the activity relates to the chapter ideas by asking questions similar to the following.

• **What resources are the seeds competing for?** (Accept all logical answers.)

• **What sorts of adaptations might be useful to a plant that has to compete for space?** (Allow students to be creative in their suggestions.)

WHAT DID YOU LEARN?

1. Students will probably observe that the seeds sprout at the same time but grow at different rates and in different ways. The seedlings that had a lot of space grew bushy and full, whereas the crowded seedlings were spindly and their leaves were not as large. Students may observe that in the fourth, most crowded carton, some of the seedlings were eventually crowded out by their neighbors and died.

2. Students will probably observe that the less crowded seedlings grew better than the more crowded ones. The less crowded seedlings did not have to compete so much for nutrients, water, and sunlight. In the least crowded container, there might even have been sufficient resources for each seedling to thrive. In contrast, each seedling in the crowded cartons had to share the resources in the carton with many other seedlings and thus was not able to get all the resources it needed to grow well or even to survive. As a result, the growth of the crowded seedlings was stunted.

3. Answers will vary.

4. Answers will vary. Possible answer: differing amounts of sunlight, water, or warmth; seeds that did not germinate for reasons other than crowding.

5. To make sure that the plants are not too crowded and that each plant will have the space and associated resources it needs.

6. Yes. The weeds compete with desirable plants, such as flowers or vegetables. Removing the weeds reduces competition.

7. Accept all logical answers. Possible answer: It might reduce the amount of space needed by an individual plant. Design an experiment to test this idea. Student designs will vary, but should include an experimental group that receives fertilizer and a control group that does not.

Activity Bank

BEFORE THE ACTIVITY

1. Divide the class into groups of three to six students per group.
2. Gather all materials at least one day prior to the activity.

PRE-ACTIVITY DISCUSSION

• **How many degrees are in a circle?** (360)

Have a student volunteer come to the front of the class. Have the volunteer face the class, then turn his or her back on the class.

• **How many degrees did** [person's name] **turn?** (180)

Have the volunteer make a quarter-turn to the right or left.

• **How many degrees did** [person's name] **turn?** (90)

Have the volunteer make several more turns in various multiples of 45° to make sure the class understands the concept.

TEACHING STRATEGY

This activity can also be performed individually, and makes a good homework or extra-credit assignment.

DISCOVERY STRATEGIES

Discuss how the activity relates to the chapter ideas by asking questions similar to the following.

• **What are some examples of natural cycles in time?** (Accept all logical answers. Possible answers include the seasons of the year, life cycles, and circadian rhythms.)

• **What natural cycle did we study in this activity?** (Phases of the moon.)

• **Why are the biological rhythms of many ocean organisms in harmony with the phases of the moon?** (The phases of the moon are a result of the position of the moon and sun relative to Earth, and the position of the moon and sun determines the height of the tides. It is advantageous for ocean organisms that are affected by the height of the tides to be in harmony with the tidal cycles. Being in harmony with the tidal cycles also makes these organisms in harmony with the phases of the moon. The biological rhythms of nocturnal organisms may be directly linked to

---

Did you ever notice that the moon looks different at different times of the month? One night, it's just a sliver of light. Ten nights later, it's a big round ball of light. And over the course of the next fourteen nights, it gradually shrinks until there seems to be no moon at all!

The moon goes through its endless cycle of growing and shrinking because it revolves around the Earth, which in turn revolves around the sun. The relative positions of the Earth, moon, and sun determine how much of the moon's surface reflects light back to the Earth. How? Find out in this activity.

What Do I Need?

10–15 cm ball of Styrofoam or yarn
knitting needle or dowel about 30 cm long and 0.5 cm in diameter
room with lamp

What Do I Do?

1. Carefully stick the point of the knitting needle into the ball. The ball represents the moon.

Knitting needle

Styrofoam ball

2. Turn on the lamp. The lamp represents the sun. Turn off any other lights in the room and close the shades if it is still daytime.

---

3. Stand in the middle of the room, facing the lamp. You represent an observer on Earth. Hold the knitting needle at arm's length in front of you. How much of the part of the "moon" facing you is illuminated by the lamp? How much is in darkness? Record your observations and make a sketch to show what the moon looks like.

4. Turn your body 45° to the left. (A complete circle is 360°; an "about-face" is 180°.) Keep your arm and the ball you are holding in the same position. Record your observations and make a sketch of the moon.

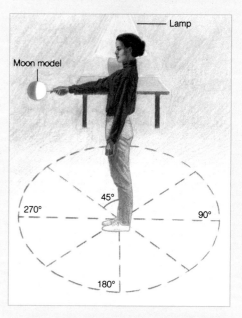

Lamp
Moon model
270°
45°
90°
180°

5. Repeat step 4 six more times. One final turn of 45° should bring you back to where you started.

---

the phases of the moon if they are affected by light intensity.)

WHAT DO I DO?

Check student drawings for accuracy.
3. None of the visible face of the "moon" is illuminated; all of it is in darkness.

WHAT DID I LEARN?

1. Eight
2. The moon is directly between Earth and the sun.

3. During the lowest high tide (neap tides), the moon looks like half a circle. At 270° (first quarter), the right-hand half of the moon is illuminated. At 90° (last quarter), the left-hand half of the moon is illuminated.
4. The highest high tides (spring tides), occur during the new and full moons.
5. The spawning of the grunion and the hatching of the grunion eggs are associated with the highest high tides. The spawning of the red crab and the mating and spawning of the worms (palolo

What Did I Learn?

1. During a lunar cycle, the moon appears to change shape. These shapes are known as phases. In this activity you modeled all of the phases. How many phases are there?

2. The phase in which the moon is not visible in the sky is called the new moon. Describe the position of the Earth, sun, and moon during the new moon.

3. When the moon and the sun are at right angles to one another (270° and 90° in the circle), the high tides are at their lowest. Describe how the moon appears during these lowest high tides.

4. When the sun, moon, and Earth are in a straight line, the high tides are at their highest. Describe the appearance of the moon during the highest high tides.

5. Review page G51. What biological events are associated with the highest high tides? With the lowest high tides?

6. Why is it critical for the biological clocks in grunion to be in harmony with the phases of the moon? (*Hint:* You may find it helpful to review pages G45 and G51.)

7. Prepare a brief illustrated report or a poster to share your findings with your classmates.

worms) are associated with the lowest high tides.

6. The phases of the moon are linked to the tides. If the grunion laid their eggs before the highest high tide, the waves—which reach higher on the beach as the new and full moons approach—would wash the eggs away. If the grunion laid their eggs too long after the highest high tide, then the eggs would not have time to complete their development before the waves washed them out of the sand.

7. Student projects should reflect an understanding of the concepts developed in this activity.

Activity Bank

A SAUCEPAN SIMULATION OF A CYCLE

BEFORE THE ACTIVITY

1. Divide the class into groups of three to six students per group.

2. Gather all materials at least one day prior to the activity.

PRE-ACTIVITY DISCUSSION

Review the processes of the water cycle by asking questions such as the following.

• **What is evaporation?** (The process in which water from the surface of a body of water absorbs enough energy—usually from sunlight—to change into the vapor phase and escape into the air.)

• **What process in the water cycle follows evaporation? What happens in this process?** (Condensation. Water vapor, upon contacting a cool surface, loses heat energy and changes into liquid droplets.)

• **What process follows condensation? What happens in this process?** (Precipitation. Water droplets in the air coalesce, become to large and heavy to remain suspended in the air, and fall to the ground.)

• **What happens to liquid water on the surface of the Earth?** (It may soak into the ground, flow into bodies of water, and/or be taken up by living things.)

• **What happens to the water that is taken up by living things?** (It is eventually released back into the environment in the form of liquid or vapor, through processes such as excretion, respiration, transpiration, and guttation.)

DISCOVERY STRATEGIES

Relate the processes of the water cycle to other natural phenomena by asking questions such as the following.

• **Evaporation and boiling both involve the change of a liquid into a gas. In evaporation, molecules located at the surface of the liquid "jump" into the air when they obtain sufficient energy. In boiling, molecules in the interior of the liquid obtain enough energy to escape into the air. Why do you think boiling, rather than evaporation, was used to change water from a liquid to a gas in step 4?** (Evapo-

The processes in the water cycle continuously move water between the Earth's surface and the atmosphere. In this activity you will observe the basic processes that form the water cycle: condensation, evaporation, and precipitation.

Materials

- 2 same-sized jars (such as those used for baby food), one of which has a lid
- 2 same-sized flat containers such as pie pans
- measuring cup or 250-mL beaker
- medium-sized saucepan (about 2.5 L, or 2 qt)
- hot plate or stove
- small saucepan with long heat-proof handle (about 1.5 L, or 1 qt)
- ice
- oven mitt or heat-proof glove

Procedure

1. Measure 100 mL of water into each jar and each flat container. Securely cover the appropriate jar with its lid. Put the jars and one of the flat containers in a sunny place. Put the other flat container in a dark closet.

2. Let the jars and the containers stand for about a day, then examine them. Use the measuring cup to measure the amount of water in the jars and containers. Record your observations.

3. Fill the large saucepan about one-fourth full with water. Put the pan on the hot plate. Turn on the hot plate and bring the water in the pan to a boil. **CAUTION:** *Be careful when working with a heat source.* Record your observations.

4. Fill the small saucepan with ice cubes. Put on the oven mitt. Grasp the handle of the small saucepan with your covered hand. Hold the small saucepan so that the main part of the pan, but not the handle, is over the boiling water in the large saucepan. **CAUTION:** *Do not put your hand or any other part of your body directly above boiling water. Steam can cause bad burns.*

5. Watch what happens to the bottom of the small saucepan. Record your observations.

6. Turn off the hot plate and clean up after your equipment has cooled off.

Small saucepan

Ice cubes

Oven mitt

Large saucepan

Boiling water

Hot plate

ration would have taken too long.)

• **Under certain weather conditions, the windshield of a car fogs up, making it hard for the driver to see out. Why do you think windshields fog up?** (Warm, moist air inside the car comes in contact with the cold glass of the windshield, and water condenses out of the air onto the glass.)

• **Using what you know about the water cycle and any observations you may have made of windshield fogging, explain how each of the following actions affect the** fogging. Why do they have this effect?

a. turning on the air conditioner

b. redirecting the flow of air in the car so that it blows on the windshield

c. turning up the temperature of the car and/or turning on the heater

d. switching the air intake to circulate

e. switching the air intake to vent

f. increasing the fan speed

g. winding down the windows

(Accept all logical answers.)

Observations

1. What happened to the water in the jars and flat containers?
2. Describe what you observed about the boiling water.
3. What happened to the bottom of the small saucepan?

Analysis and Conclusions

1. What water-cycle process caused the results in step 2?
2. Using the results from step 2, compare the amount of water in the two jars, in the two flat containers, and in the open jar and the flat container that were in the sunny place. What can you conclude about evaporation from these results?
3. Identify the water-cycle processes that you observed in step 5. Explain your answer.
4. Compare your results with those of your classmates. Are they similar or different? Explain why.

5. On a hot, sticky summer day, you notice water collecting on the outside of your glass of ice water. One of your friends says that the hot weather has caused the pores in the glass to open up so that the water leaks out. You suspect that the water got on the outside of the glass another way. What is your hypothesis? How might you go about testing your hypothesis?
6. Cold air can hold less water than warm air. The loss of enough heat energy causes water vapor to condense into liquid water. Use this information to explain the following events.
   a. Steam condenses on a pan that contains ice.
   b. Dew forms on grass during the night.
   c. Morning fog disappears as the day gets warmer.

   How do these events relate to the water cycle?

OBSERVATIONS

1. Probable answer: The water disappeared from the flat container that was left in the sun. A small amount of water disappeared from the flat container in the closet and from the uncovered jar. No water disappeared from the covered jar.
2. Bubbles form at the bottom of the water and rise to the surface, where they burst. A cloud of steam forms about the water.
3. The bottom of the pan became cloudy with a film of water. The droplets making up the film grew larger as they flowed together and as new water was added by the steam. When the drops were large enough, they fell down into the boiling water.

ANALYSIS AND CONCLUSIONS

1. Evaporation.
2. Possible answer: Because no water was lost from the covered jar and some water was lost from the uncovered jar, we can conclude that the surface of a liquid must be exposed to the air for evaporation to occur; molecules of the liquid need to have a place to escape. Because the flat container in the closet had more water in it than the flat container that was put in a sunny place, we can conclude that evaporation is speeded up by sunlight. (Students may reason that energy from sunlight may be transferred to the molecules at the surface of the liquid, "giving them a boost" that enables them to escape into the air.) Because the flat container lost more water than the jar, we can conclude that the larger the surface area, the faster the rate of evaporation. (Students may also infer that molecules escape from the surface of an evaporating liquid.)
3. Condensation and precipitation. Steam changed to liquid water when it touched the cool surface of the pan, and condensation is the process in which water changes from a vapor to a liquid. The water droplets that condensed on the pan grew larger and fell down into the boiling water, and precipitation is the process in which water droplets fall back to Earth.
4. Answers will vary. The results from the evaporation experiments may vary greatly, due to factors such as the shape of the jars and flat containers, relative humidity, and amount of air circulation.
5. Students will probably hypothesize that the water on the outside of the glass got there when water vapor in the air condensed upon contact with the cold glass. Possible experiments include filling the glass with soda and seeing if soda appears on the outside of the glass, and checking the glass for pores under the microscope.
6. a. Some of the heat energy of the steam's water molecules is lost when the steam comes in contact with the surface of the cold pan, so the steam condenses to form water droplets. b. As the air cools during the night, it often becomes saturated. If the air temperature is equal to the dew point temperature (temperature at which the air is saturated) water vapor in the air condenses onto surfaces such as those of grass blades. c. The condensed water molecules that form fog (which is actually a stratus cloud formed close to the ground) gain heat energy and change from liquid water to water vapor. Events *a* and *b* involve condensation, and event *c* involves evaporation.

Activity Bank

TAKE IT WITH A GRAIN OF SALT

BEFORE THE ACTIVITY

1. Divide the class into groups of three to six students per group.
2. Gather all materials at least one day prior to the activity. You might want to have students bring materials from home.

PRE-ACTIVITY DISCUSSION

Have students read the entire activity procedure.

• **What materials do you need for this activity?** (Two drinking glasses or jars, Epsom salts, spoon, saucer or jar lid, yarn or string, thread or dental floss, pencil).

• **What is the first thing you do in this activity?** (Assign cooperative-learning roles to each member of the group. If cooperative-learning groups have already been established, students should take up their previously arranged-for roles.)

• **Summarize what you do after that.** (Dissolve Epsom salts in water in glasses, set up yarn and saucer, set up thread and pencil.)

TEACHING STRATEGY

This activity can also be individually. As such, it makes a good homework or extra-credit assignment.

DISCOVERY STRATEGIES

Discuss how the activity relates to the chapter ideas by asking questions similar to the following.

• **Why is it important for ecologists to understand the water cycle?** (Accept all logical answers. Students should recognize that the water cycle involves the living part of an ecosystem as well as the non-living part.)

• **Why is important for geologists (scientists who study rocks and the Earth) to understand the water cycle?** (The water cycle is closely linked with the formation and destruction of rocks and with forces of weathering and erosion, which shape Earth's surface.)

• **The cycles of materials through the environment form a link between earth science and life science. What are some ways in which earth science and life science are linked?** (Accept all logical answers.

Have you ever seen pictures of the stone spikes, columns, and other strange formations inside a cave? These unusual and often beautiful rock formations, like the "castles" of salts in Mono Lake (shown on page G37), are byproducts of the water cycle. Discover what the water cycle has to do with rocks in this activity.

What You Need

2 small (about 235 mL) drinking glasses or jars
Epsom salts
spoon
saucer or jar lid
30 cm of yarn or heavy cotton string
20 cm of thread or dental floss
pencil

What You Do

1. Assign roles to each member of the group. Possible roles include: Recorder (the person who records observations and coordinates the group's presentation of results), Materials Manager (the person who obtains all materials and coordinates cleanup), Principal Investigator (the person who reads instructions to the group, makes sure that the proper procedure is being followed, and asks questions of the teacher on behalf of the group), and Specialists (people who perform specific tasks such as preparing the glasses of solution, setting up the yarn part of the experiment, or setting up the thread part of the experiment). Your group may divide up the tasks differently, and individuals may have more than one role, depending on the size of your group.

2. Fill the glasses about three-fourths full with water. Add Epsom salts to the water a teaspoon at a time and stir. Keep adding Epsom salts to the water until no more will dissolve.

3. Place the glasses so that the saucer is between them. Then place the ends of the yarn in the glasses, as shown in the accompanying illustration. Note that the center of the yarn is lower than the ends and hangs over the saucer without touching it.

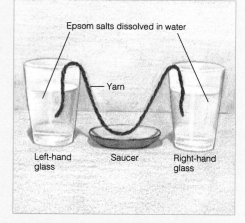

Epsom salts dissolved in water

Yarn

Left-hand glass

Saucer

Right-hand glass

4. Tie a knot in one end of the piece of thread. Tie the other end of the thread around the pencil. Adjust the length of the dangling part of the thread so that knot will hang about 1 cm above the bottom of the left-hand glass when you rest the pencil across the top of the glass.

5. Moisten the knot with water and dip it in the Epsom salts. Then rest the pencil

One possible answer is that fossils found in rocks give scientists information about dinosaurs and other organisms that lived long ago.)

WHAT DID YOU LEARN?

1. To catch the water that drips from the center of the piece of string.

2. The water level in the glasses went down. Students will probably observe colorless crystals forming on the sides and bottom of the glasses. This occurred because the water evaporated. As the water evaporated, it left behind dissolved Epsom salts, which formed the crystals.

3. A large cluster of colorless crystals should form on the knot. Additional crystals should form along the thread and on the bottom and sides of the left-hand glass. The right-hand glass will also have crystals on its bottom and sides.

4. A structure of Epsom salts that looks like a stalactite should form in the center of the yarn. A pile of Epsom salts that resembles a stalagmite should be growing from the middle of the saucer. The point

across the top of the left-hand glass. Make sure that the knotted thread is submerged.

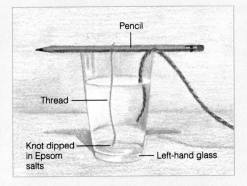

Pencil

Thread

Knot dipped in Epsom salts

Left-hand glass

6. Observe the glasses, saucer, yarn, and thread daily. Record your observations.

1. What do you think is the purpose of the saucer?

2. What happened to the glasses? Why do you think this occurred?

3. What happened to the thread?

4. What happened to the yarn? What happened to the saucer?

5. How do you think stone or rust "icicles" form in caves and on the undersides of bridges?

6. What process of the water cycle did you observe in this activity? Explain.

7. How might the process you observed be used to obtain chemicals dissolved in water?

8. What does the water cycle have to do with rocks?

of the "stalagmite" should be directly below the point of the "stalactite."

5. Water dissolves minerals in the rock above the cave or in the concrete or steel that makes up the bridge. Gravity pulls the water downward, to the roof of the cave or the underside of the bridge. As the dripping water evaporates, the minerals it carries are deposited.

6. Evaporation, because that is the process by which liquid water turns to water vapor. As the water evaporates, the dissolved substances in it are left behind.

7. Evaporation removes the water and leaves dissolved minerals behind.

8. Some rocks are formed when water containing dissolved substances evaporates, leaving the minerals behind.

Activity Bank

CUTTING DOWN THE RAIN

BEFORE THE ACTIVITY

1. Divide the class into groups of three to six students per group.
2. Gather all materials at least one day prior to the activity.

PRE-ACTIVITY DISCUSSION

Have students read the entire laboratory procedure.

• **What materials do you need for this activity?** (Plant, sandwich bags, twist ties, scissors.)

• **Why is it important to choose two branches that are as similar as possible?** (Students should realize that there should be only one variable—the one being tested—in a scientific experiment. This concept is often easiest for students to understand when phrased in terms of equality and fairness.)

DISCOVERY STRATEGIES

Discuss how the activity relates to the chapter ideas by asking questions similar to the following.

• **How do plants fit into the water cycle?** (Plants take in liquid water through their roots and release water vapor through their leaves.)

• **How might plants contribute to the humidity of the tropical rain forest?** (Possible answer: Plants release much water vapor through their leaves as a result of transpiration.)

• **In this activity, you constructed a model to examine the effects of deforestation, or forest destruction. Do you think this model is a valid one? Why or why not? How might you go about finding out whether this model is a reasonable one?** (Accept all logical, well-thought-out answers. Students who do not like this model might point out that water might enter the air due to evaporation on bare ground, or think that grasses and other small plants can take over the task of putting water into the air after trees have been cut down. Although this model is rather artificial, it does illustrate a proven phenomenon—widespread destruction of forest is strongly correlated with decreased precipitation.)

Of all Earth's biomes, tropical rain forests probably get the most media coverage. Unfortunately, this is because tropical rain forests are in great danger—they are being cut or burned down at an alarmingly fast rate. Many wonderful animals and plants will disappear with the forests. In addition, the loss of the forests may change the climate of the tropics. How? Find out in this activity.

What Do I Do?

1. Obtain a medium-sized plant with several branches, two plastic sandwich bags, two twist ties, and a pair of scissors.

2. Select two branches that are as similar as possible in size and number of leaves.

3. Cover one of the branches with a plastic bag. Secure the bag with the twist tie. Be careful not to break or damage the branch while putting on the bag. This branch represents an intact tropical rain forest.

4. Using the scissors, snip off all the leaves on the other branch. Then cover the branch as in step 3. This branch represents an area in which the tropical rain forest has been cut down.

5. Put the plant in a sunny spot. Observe the plant the next day.

What Did I Learn?

1. Describe what you observed. Where do you think the water came from?

2. What can you infer about the amounts of water put into the air by intact forests and by cleared areas?

3. How do plants fit into the water cycle? (*Hint:* If you have trouble answering this question, review Section 2–2.)

4. Explain why the destruction of forests might lead to change in rainfall.

5. Why should people who live in other biomes be concerned about what is going on in the tropical rain forests?

WHAT DID I LEARN?

1. There is water on the inside of the bag surrounding the undamaged branch and no water on the inside of the bag surrounding the leafless branch. Water came from inside the leaves (through transpiration).

2. Forests put much more water into the air than cleared areas. If students have already studied plants, you might wish to briefly review the concept of transpiration.

3. Plants take up liquid water from the soil and release it as water vapor from their leaves.

4. It reduces the rate at which water vapor enters the air, which in turn slows down the water cycle. Less water vapor means fewer clouds, which means less precipitation.

5. Student answers will vary, but should include the concept that all the living and nonliving things on Earth are ultimately connected to one another.

GRANDEUR IN THE GRASS

The most noticeable grasslands animals are undoubtedly the large grass-eaters, such as the bison of the North American prairie, kangaroos of the Australian outback, zebras of the African savanna, saiga antelope of the Asian steppe, and rhea (an ostrichlike bird) of the South American pampas. However, grasslands teem with smaller, less noticeable organisms. Take a closer look at grasslands by doing this activity.

Materials

terrarium case or aquarium with a tightly-fitting fine screen cover
coarse gravel
activated charcoal
sand
potting soil
notebook and pencil
plastic bags and jars with covers for collecting organisms
plants and animals collected from a grassy field

Procedure

1. Put a layer of gravel 3 cm deep in the terrarium. Add some more gravel to the back of the terrarium to make one or two low hills. Sprinkle a little activated charcoal on the gravel.

2. Mix three parts of potting soil to one part of sand. Spread the sandy soil about 7 cm deep over the gravel, following the hills and valleys in the gravel.

3. Obtain the proper permission to collect organisms from a grassy field. Before you start collecting, look around. What kinds of plants do you see? What kinds of animals? Record your observations in your notebook in the form of drawings and written notes.

4. Collect grasses and a few other small plants from a grassy field. Be sure to include the roots and some of the soil around the roots. Put the plants in a plastic bag to protect them from drying out.

5. Catch a few small animals, such as insects, earthworms, and one or two spiders. Use the jars to hold your animals. **Note:** *Earthworms must be kept cool and moist, so make sure you put damp soil or moist paper towels in the jar with the earthworms.* Make sure that there are air holes in the covers of the jars and that the jars are covered securely.

6. Plant the plants you have collected in the terrarium. Water the plants. Then carefully transfer your animals from the jars into the terrarium.

7. Keep the terrarium in a sunny place. Water the plants every few days with a fine stream of water. Make sure that spiders and other insect-eaters have enough to eat. Observe the terrarium daily and record your observations in your notebook. Remember to record any changes you make in the terrarium, such as watering or adding new insects.

(continued)

Activity Bank

GRANDEUR IN THE GRASS

BEFORE THE ACTIVITY

1. Divide the class into groups of three to six students per group.
2. Gather all materials at least one day prior to the activity.

PRE-ACTIVITY DISCUSSION

• **What are the main characteristics of a grasslands biome?** (Dominant form of plant life is grasses; receives less precipitation than a forest but more than a desert.)
• **Where are grasslands biomes found?** (North America, central Asia, South America, Australia. You may want to point out that grasslands are generally found in the interiors of continents and then describe the effects of mountain ranges on rainfall.)

• **What kind of large animals would you expect to find in an African savanna?** (Possible answers: zebras, lions, giraffes, antelope, ostriches) **In a North American prairie?** (Possible answers: bison, pronghorn antelope, prairie dogs, coyotes.)

DISCOVERY STRATEGIES

Discuss how the activity relates to the chapter ideas by asking questions similar to the following.
• **What types of small animals live in grasslands?** (Answers will vary, depending on what students found in the grassy field.)
• **Why is it important to record observations in as much detail as possible?** (Answers will vary. Students should recognize that careful and detailed records minimize the chances of something important being missed.)
• **Although some are much better than others, most field biologists can draw. Why do you think this is so?** (Drawing is a useful skill for most biologists, and tends to improve with practice.)

PROCEDURE

You may wish to check the observations recorded in student notebooks.

OBSERVATIONS AND CONCLUSIONS

1. Student drawings will vary.
2. Student answers will vary. Possible changes include the growth of plants, disappearance of insects due to being eaten by the spider, and new types of insects appearing in the terrarium because of hidden eggs or pupae hatching or because they were hiding on the plants and were not noticed earlier.
3. Answers will vary, but should include descriptions of feeding relationships and the places where organisms live.
4. Answers will vary.
5. Student posters should accurately reflect what they have learned in this activity.

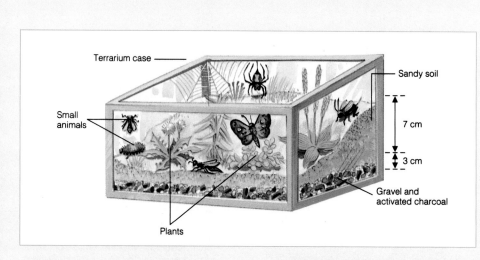

Labels: Terrarium case, Sandy soil, 7 cm, 3 cm, Small animals, Gravel and activated charcoal, Plants

Observations and Conclusions

1. Make a labeled drawing of your terrarium that shows what kinds of plants and animals it contains.

2. How does your terrarium change over time? Why do you think these changes occur?

3. How do the living and nonliving things in the terrarium interact with one another? How are they dependent on one another?

4. Compare your terrarium with those prepared by other groups in your class. How are they similar? How are they different? How can these similarities and differences be explained?

5. Prepare a poster to share what you have learned about smaller grasslands organisms.

PAPER ROUTE

A simple, yet effective conservation measure is recycling. In recycling, wastes such as scrap paper, old cans, empty plastic soda bottles, and broken glass jars are used as the raw materials for making new items. For example, old aluminum beverage cans are melted down to produce metal that is used for foil wrap, new beverage cans, and other useful products. In this activity you will try your hand at recycling old newspapers, junk mail, scraps of cloth and thread, and other odds and ends.

Materials

scrap paper (from sources such as newspapers, magazines, junk mail, notebook paper, and construction paper)
small amount of scraps of fabric and thread (optional)
scissors (optional)
1000-mL (1-L) beaker
hot water
laundry starch
dishpan, about 30 × 34 × 13 cm
egg beater
wood frame, about 25 × 30 cm
4 push pins
piece of window screen, about 25 × 30 cm
rolling pin
blotting paper

Procedure

1. Tear the paper into pieces less than 5 cm across. If you have fabric, rip or cut it into pieces less than 1 cm across. If you have thread, cut it into pieces less than 5 cm long. Put the pieces in the beaker. When the beaker is full, dump the pieces into the dishpan. Prepare about 1500 mL of pieces.

2. Add 6 L hot water and 360 mL starch to the dishpan.

3. Taking turns, use the eggbeater to beat the mixture in the dishpan until it is about the consistency of pancake batter or white glue. The beaten mixture is called pulp.

4. Attach the screen to the frame with the push pins, as shown in the illustration on page G152.

5. Slide the frame, screen-side up, into the pulp. Wriggle the frame a little so that bits of pulp are distributed evenly across the screen. Lift the screen straight up from the pan and let the water drip into the pan. Repeat this procedure two or three more times, or until the screen is completely covered by a layer of pulp several millimeters thick.

6. Unpin the screen. Carefully put the screen and the wet sheet of pulp on a piece of blotting paper. Cover the screen and sheet of pulp with another piece of blotting paper.

7. Firmly roll the rolling pin over the blotting paper to press the excess water from the pulp sheet.

8. Flip the "sandwich" of blotting paper over. Carefully remove the top piece of blotting paper and the piece of screen to reveal the piece of recycled paper that you have made.

9. Allow the recycled paper to dry. Then peel it off the bottom piece of blotting paper.

(continued)

---

egg beater to mix the bits of paper, hot water, and starch in the dishpan until the mixture is the consistency of pancake batter.)
• **How do you collect pulp onto the frame?** (Slide the frame into the pulp at an angle, wriggle the frame in the pan so that the bits of pulp are distributed evenly on the screen, then lift the frame straight up out of the pan.)
• **What do you do with the sheet of pulp on the frame?** (Unpin the screen and put the screen with its wet sheet of pulp on blotting paper. Cover the pulp sheet with another piece of blotting paper, then press the blotting-paper "sandwich" with a rolling pin. Flip the "sandwich" over, remove the top sheet of blotting paper and the screen, and allow the pulp sheet to dry.)

TEACHING STRATEGY

1. If you do not use a standard sized dishpan for this activity, you may need to adjust the sizes of the frame and screen.
2. You may wish to involve parents by having students build the wood frame at home. One of the simplest, if not the cheapest, methods of constructing the frame is to use precut needlework stretcher bars, which are generally available at craft stores. Two packages costing about $2–$3 each are needed to make one frame.
3. Have students save up appropriate materials prior to this activity. Art and home economics teachers will often be able to supply scraps for this activity. For best results, fabric scraps should be used sparingly—just enough to add some color.

DISCOVERY STRATEGIES

Discuss how the activity relates to the chapter ideas by asking questions similar to the following.
• **Why is recycling important?** (Accept all logical answers. Students should recognize that recycling helps to conserve resources.)
• **What are some other substances that can be recycled? How are they recycled?** (Answers will vary. Possible answers: Some plastics items can be shredded and then melted down. The melted-down plastic can be used to make new plastic items. Used engine oil can be re-refined to make fresh oil.)

Activity Bank

PAPER ROUTE

BEFORE THE ACTIVITY

1. Divide the class into groups of three to six students per group.
2. Gather all materials at least one day prior to the activity. See notes in the Teaching Strategy for suggestions.

PRE-ACTIVITY DISCUSSION

Have students read the entire activity procedure.
• **What materials do you need for this activity?** (Scrap paper, beaker, hot water, starch, dishpan, egg beater, frame, push pins, screen, rolling pin, blotting paper. Scissors and scraps of fabric and thread are optional.)
• **What do you do with the scrap paper?** (Tear it into small pieces and put the pieces in the beaker.)
• **How do you make the pulp?** (Use the

• **What is the difference between recycling and reusing?** (Accept all logical answers. In general, recycling involves processing materials in some way.)

• **What are some things that can or should be reused?** (Answers will vary. Encourage students to be creative. Possible answers: Grocery bags can be reused as grocery bags. Milk cartons can be reused as plant pots. Cans can be reused as pencil jars. Potato-chip cans can be reused for homemade cookies. Juice and soda bottles can be reused for chilling water in the refrigerator.)

OBSERVATIONS AND CONCLUSIONS

1. Answers will vary depending on the materials used. The paper is usually grayish with flecks of color and is rather rough in texture. The paper is said to be recycled because waste materials were used to make it.

2. Answers will vary. Differences in the types of materials making up the paper or in the relative proportions of the materials can have an enormous effect on the appearance of the finished product.

3. Answers will vary. Students should realize that there are many more steps involved in the commercial manufacture of recycled paper. For example, the pulp is bleached, processed so that it extremely smooth, pressed thin by machines, and trimmed. In addition, the pulp probably does not contain anything except paper, and is probably not 100 percent post-consumer waste.

4. Answers will vary. Students will probably think of ways in which their paper can be used for decoration.

5. Answers will vary. Student answers should reflect an understanding of the need to conserve raw materials and to minimize solid waste.

Observations and Conclusions

1. Describe the paper you made. Why is the paper said to be recycled?

2. Compare your sheet of paper to those made by your classmates. How do they differ? What do you think caused these differences?

3. How is your paper different from commercially made recycled paper? What do you think causes these differences?

4. What are some possible uses for the paper you made?

5. In your own words, explain why recycling is important.

Appendix A

The metric system of measurement is used by scientists throughout the world. It is based on units of ten. Each unit is ten times larger or ten times smaller than the next unit. The most commonly used units of the metric system are given below. After you have finished reading about the metric system, try to put it to use. How tall are you in metrics? What is your mass? What is your normal body temperature in degrees Celsius?

Commonly Used Metric Units

Length   The distance from one point to another

meter (m)   A meter is slightly longer than a yard.
1 meter = 1000 millimeters (mm)
1 meter = 100 centimeters (cm)
1000 meters = 1 kilometer (km)

Volume   The amount of space an object takes up

liter (L)   A liter is slightly more than a quart.
1 liter = 1000 milliliters (mL)

Mass   The amount of matter in an object

gram (g)   A gram has a mass equal to about one paper clip.
1000 grams = 1 kilogram (kg)

Temperature   The measure of hotness or coldness

degrees
Celsius (°C)   0°C = freezing point of water
100°C = boiling point of water

Metric–English Equivalents

2.54 centimeters (cm) = 1 inch (in.)
1 meter (m) = 39.37 inches (in.)
1 kilometer (km) = 0.62 miles (mi)
1 liter (L) = 1.06 quarts (qt)
250 milliliters (mL) = 1 cup (c)
1 kilogram (kg) = 2.2 pounds (lb)
28.3 grams (g) = 1 ounce (oz)
°C = 5/9 x (°F - 32)

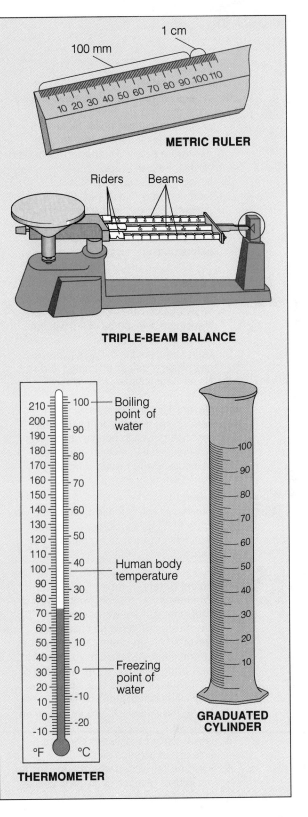

METRIC RULER

TRIPLE-BEAM BALANCE

Riders   Beams

THERMOMETER

Boiling point of water

Human body temperature

Freezing point of water

GRADUATED CYLINDER

Glassware Safety

1. Whenever you see this symbol, you will know that you are working with glassware that can easily be broken. Take particular care to handle such glassware safely. And never use broken or chipped glassware.
2. Never heat glassware that is not thoroughly dry. Never pick up any glassware unless you are sure it is not hot. If it is hot, use heat-resistant gloves.
3. Always clean glassware thoroughly before putting it away.

Fire Safety

1. Whenever you see this symbol, you will know that you are working with fire. Never use any source of fire without wearing safety goggles.
2. Never heat anything—particularly chemicals—unless instructed to do so.
3. Never heat anything in a closed container.
4. Never reach across a flame.
5. Always use a clamp, tongs, or heat-resistant gloves to handle hot objects.
6. Always maintain a clean work area, particularly when using a flame.

Heat Safety

Whenever you see this symbol, you will know that you should put on heat-resistant gloves to avoid burning your hands.

Chemical Safety

1. Whenever you see this symbol, you will know that you are working with chemicals that could be hazardous.
2. Never smell any chemical directly from its container. Always use your hand to waft some of the odors from the top of the container toward your nose—and only when instructed to do so.
3. Never mix chemicals unless instructed to do so.
4. Never touch or taste any chemical unless instructed to do so.
5. Keep all lids closed when chemicals are not in use. Dispose of all chemicals as instructed by your teacher.

6. Immediately rinse with water any chemicals, particularly acids, that get on your skin and clothes. Then notify your teacher.

Eye and Face Safety

1. Whenever you see this symbol, you will know that you are performing an experiment in which you must take precautions to protect your eyes and face by wearing safety goggles.
2. When you are heating a test tube or bottle, always point it away from you and others. Chemicals can splash or boil out of a heated test tube.

Sharp Instrument Safety

1. Whenever you see this symbol, you will know that you are working with a sharp instrument.
2. Always use single-edged razors; double-edged razors are too dangerous.
3. Handle any sharp instrument with extreme care. Never cut any material toward you; always cut away from you.
4. Immediately notify your teacher if your skin is cut.

Electrical Safety

1. Whenever you see this symbol, you will know that you are using electricity in the laboratory.
2. Never use long extension cords to plug in any electrical device. Do not plug too many appliances into one socket or you may overload the socket and cause a fire.
3. Never touch an electrical appliance or outlet with wet hands.

Animal Safety

1. Whenever you see this symbol, you will know that you are working with live animals.
2. Do not cause pain, discomfort, or injury to an animal.
3. Follow your teacher's directions when handling animals. Wash your hands thoroughly after handling animals or their cages.

One of the first things a scientist learns is that working in the laboratory can be an exciting experience. But the laboratory can also be quite dangerous if proper safety rules are not followed at all times. To prepare yourself for a safe year in the laboratory, read over the following safety rules. Then read them a second time. Make sure you understand each rule. If you do not, ask your teacher to explain any rules you are unsure of.

Dress Code

1. Many materials in the laboratory can cause eye injury. To protect yourself from possible injury, wear safety goggles whenever you are working with chemicals, burners, or any substance that might get into your eyes. Never wear contact lenses in the laboratory.

2. Wear a laboratory apron or coat whenever you are working with chemicals or heated substances.

3. Tie back long hair to keep it away from any chemicals, burners and candles, or other laboratory equipment.

4. Remove or tie back any article of clothing or jewelry that can hang down and touch chemicals and flames.

General Safety Rules

5. Read all directions for an experiment several times. Follow the directions exactly as they are written. If you are in doubt about any part of the experiment, ask your teacher for assistance.

6. Never perform activities that are not authorized by your teacher. Obtain permission before "experimenting" on your own.

7. Never handle any equipment unless you have specific permission.

8. Take extreme care not to spill any material in the laboratory. If a spill occurs, immediately ask your teacher about the proper cleanup procedure. Never simply pour chemicals or other substances into the sink or trash container.

9. Never eat in the laboratory.

10. Wash your hands before and after each experiment.

First Aid

11. Immediately report all accidents, no matter how minor, to your teacher.

12. Learn what to do in case of specific accidents, such as getting acid in your eyes or on your skin. (Rinse acids from your body with lots of water.)

13. Become aware of the location of the first-aid kit. But your teacher should administer any required first aid due to injury. Or your teacher may send you to the school nurse or call a physician.

14. Know where and how to report an accident or fire. Find out the location of the fire extinguisher, phone, and fire alarm. Keep a list of important phone numbers—such as the fire department and the school nurse—near the phone. Immediately report any fires to your teacher.

Heating and Fire Safety

15. Again, never use a heat source, such as a candle or burner, without wearing safety goggles.

16. Never heat a chemical you are not instructed to heat. A chemical that is harmless when cool may be dangerous when heated.

17. Maintain a clean work area and keep all materials away from flames.

18. Never reach across a flame.

19. Make sure you know how to light a Bunsen burner. (Your teacher will demonstrate the proper procedure for lighting a burner.) If the flame leaps out of a burner toward you, immediately turn the gas off. Do not touch the burner. It may be hot. And never leave a lighted burner unattended!

20. When heating a test tube or bottle, always point it away from you and others. Chemicals can splash or boil out of a heated test tube.

21. Never heat a liquid in a closed container. The expanding gases produced may blow the container apart, injuring you or others.

22. Before picking up a container that has been heated, first hold the back of your hand near it. If you can feel the heat on the back of your hand, the container may be too hot to handle. Use a clamp or tongs when handling hot containers.

Using Chemicals Safely

23. Never mix chemicals for the "fun of it." You might produce a dangerous, possibly explosive substance.

24. Never touch, taste, or smell a chemical unless you are instructed by your teacher to do so. Many chemicals are poisonous. If you are instructed to note the fumes in an experiment, gently wave your hand over the opening of a container and direct the fumes toward your nose. Do not inhale the fumes directly from the container.

25. Use only those chemicals needed in the activity. Keep all lids closed when a chemical is not being used. Notify your teacher whenever chemicals are spilled.

26. Dispose of all chemicals as instructed by your teacher. To avoid contamination, never return chemicals to their original containers.

27. Be extra careful when working with acids or bases. Pour such chemicals over the sink, not over your workbench.

28. When diluting an acid, pour the acid into water. Never pour water into an acid.

29. Immediately rinse with water any acids that get on your skin or clothing. Then notify your teacher of any acid spill.

Using Glassware Safely

30. Never force glass tubing into a rubber stopper. A turning motion and lubricant will be helpful when inserting glass tubing into rubber stoppers or rubber tubing. Your teacher will demonstrate the proper way to insert glass tubing.

31. Never heat glassware that is not thoroughly dry. Use a wire screen to protect glassware from any flame.

32. Keep in mind that hot glassware will not appear hot. Never pick up glassware without first checking to see if it is hot. See #22.

33. If you are instructed to cut glass tubing, fire-polish the ends immediately to remove sharp edges.

34. Never use broken or chipped glassware. If glassware breaks, notify your teacher and dispose of the glassware in the proper trash container.

35. Never eat or drink from laboratory glassware. Thoroughly clean glassware before putting it away.

Using Sharp Instruments

36. Handle scalpels or razor blades with extreme care. Never cut material toward you; cut away from you.

37. Immediately notify your teacher if you cut your skin when working in the laboratory.

Animal Safety

38. No experiments that will cause pain, discomfort, or harm to mammals, birds, reptiles, fishes, and amphibians should be done in the classroom or at home.

39. Animals should be handled only if necessary. If an animal is excited or frightened, pregnant, feeding, or with its young, special handling is required.

40. Your teacher will instruct you as to how to handle each animal species that may be brought into the classroom.

41. Clean your hands thoroughly after handling animals or the cage containing animals.

End-of-Experiment Rules

42. After an experiment has been completed, clean up your work area and return all equipment to its proper place.

43. Wash your hands after every experiment.

44. Turn off all burners before leaving the laboratory. Check that the gas line leading to the burner is off as well.

Glossary

Pronunciation Key

When difficult names or terms first appear in the text, they are respelled to aid pronunciation. A syllable in SMALL CAPITAL LETTERS receives the most stress. The key below lists the letters used for respelling. It includes examples of words using each sound and shows how the words would be respelled.

Symbol	Example	Respelling
a	hat	(hat)
ay	pay, late	(pay), (layt)
ah	star, hot	(stahr), (haht)
ai	air, dare	(air), (dair)
aw	law, all	(law), (awl)
eh	met	(meht)
ee	bee, eat	(bee), (eet)
er	learn, sir, fur	(lern), (ser), (fer)
ih	fit	(fiht)
igh	mile, sigh	(mighl), (sigh)
oh	no	(noh)
oi	soil, boy	(soil), (boi)
oo	root, rule	(root), (rool)
or	born, door	(born), (dor)
ow	plow, out	(plow), (owt)

Symbol	Example	Respelling
u	put, book	(put), (buk)
uh	fun	(fuhn)
yoo	few, use	(fyoo), (yooz)
ch	chill, reach	(chihl), (reech)
g	go, dig	(goh), (dihg)
j	jet, gently, bridge	(jeht), (JEHNT-lee), (brihj)
k	kite, cup	(kight), (kuhp)
ks	mix	(mihks)
kw	quick	(kwihk)
ng	bring	(brihng)
s	say, cent	(say), (sehnt)
sh	she, crash	(shee), (krash)
th	three	(three)
y	yet, onion	(yeht), (UHN-yuhn)
z	zip, always	(zihp), (AWL-wayz)
zh	treasure	(TREH-zher)

biogeography: the study of where plants and animals live throughout the world

biological clock: an internal timer that keeps track of a cycle of time and helps an organism stay in step with rhythmic cycles of change in the environment

biome: a division based on climate, plants, and animals; an environment that has a characteristic type of climax community

canopy: the layer of a forest biome that consists of the tops of trees; the "roof" of a forest

captive breeding: the practice of getting animals in zoos to have offspring

carbon cycle: the cyclical series of processes in which carbon moves through the living and non-living parts of the environment

climax community: the stable community that is the final stage of succession

commensalism: a form of symbiosis in which one organism benefits and the other is not harmed

community: the living part of an ecosystem

competition: the type of interaction in which organisms struggle with one another to obtain resources

conifer: a plant, usually an evergreen tree, that produces its seeds in cones

consumer: an organism that cannot make its own food

decomposer: an organism that breaks down the bodies of dead organisms into simpler substances

deforestation: the destruction of forests

desertification (dih-zert-uh-fih-KAY-shuhn): the process in which desertlike conditions are created where there had been none in the recent past

dispersal: the movement of living things from one place to others; spreading out

diurnal (digh-ER-nuhl): active during the day

ecological succession: the process in which the community in a particular place is gradually replaced by another community

ecology: the study of the relationships and interactions of living things with one another and with their environment

ecosystem: a unit consisting of all the living and nonliving things in a given area that interact with one another

endangered: in danger of becoming extinct

environment: all the living and nonliving things with which an organism may interact

estivation: a summer resting state

estuary (EHS-tyoo-air-ee): an environment found at the boundary between fresh water and salt water that contains a mixture of fresh water and salt water

exotic species: a species that is not native to a place

extinct: no longer in existence; used to describe subspecies, species, and so on, in which there are no living individuals

food chain: a representation of a series of events in which food energy and matter are transferred from one organism to another

food web: a diagram that consists of many overlapping food chains

freshwater biome: the biome that consists of the Earth's bodies of fresh water, such as lakes, ponds, streams, and rivers

habitat: the place in which an organism lives and obtains the resources it needs to survive

hibernation: a winter resting state

host: an organism that provides a home for another organism; in parasitism, the organism that is harmed by the parasite

marine biome: the ocean biome

migration: the movement of organisms from one place to another in response to periodic environmental changes; usually refers to cyclical movements

mutualism: a form of symbiosis in which both organisms benefit

niche (NIHCH): an organism's role in an ecosystem, which includes everything the organism does and everything the organism needs in its environment

nitrogen cycle: the cyclical series of processes in which nitrogen moves from the nonliving parts of the environment to living things and back again

nocturnal (nahk-TER-nuhl): active during the night

oxygen cycle: the cyclical series of processes in which oxygen moves through the living and nonliving parts of the environment

parasite: an organism that lives on or inside the body of a host organism and harms the host

parasitism: a form of symbiosis in which one organism benefits and the other is harmed

permafrost: the layer of permanently frozen soil in the tundra

phytoplankton: microscopic producers (organisms that can make their own food) that live near the surface of the ocean and other bodies of water

population: a group of organisms of the same species living together in the same area

predator: an organism that kills and eats another organism

prey: an organism that is eaten by a predator

producer: an organism that is able to make its own food by using a source of energy to turn simple raw materials into food

symbiosis (sihm-bigh-OH-sihs; plural: symbioses): a close relationship between two organisms in which one organism lives near, on, or even inside another organism and in which at least one organism benefits

taiga: the northernmost coniferous forest biome

water cycle: the cyclical series of processes in which water moves through the living and nonliving parts of the environment

wildlife conservation: the intelligent management of living resources so that they provide the greatest possible benefit for the longest possible time

Index